# Portraits de femmes

# DU MÊME AUTEUR

## Aux Éditions Gallimard

*Femmes*, roman, 1983 (Folio n° 1620).

*Portrait du Joueur*, roman, 1985 (Folio n° 1786).

*Théorie des Exceptions*, 1986 (Folio essais n° 28).

*Paradis II*, roman, 1986 (Folio n° 2759).

*Le Cœur Absolu*, roman, 1987 (Folio n° 2013).

*Les Folies Françaises*, roman, 1988 (Folio n° 2201).

*Le lys d'or*, roman, 1989 (Folio n° 2279).

*La Fête à Venise*, roman, 1991 (Folio n° 2463).

*Improvisations*, essai, 1991 (Folio essais n° 165).

*Le rire de Rome*, entretiens avec Frans De Haes, 1992 (« L'Infini »).

*Le Secret*, roman, 1993 (Folio n° 2687).

*La Guerre du Goût*, essai, 1994 (Folio n° 2880).

*Sade contre l'être suprême* précédé de *Sade dans le temps* (Quai Voltaire, 1989), 1996.

*Studio*, roman, 1997 (Folio n° 3168).

*Passion fixe*, roman, 2000 (Folio n° 3566).

*Éloge de l'infini*, essai, 2001 (Folio n° 3806).

*Liberté du XVIIIᵉ*, essai, 2002 (Folio 2 € n° 3756).

*L'Étoile des amants*, roman, 2002 (Folio n° 4120).

*Poker*, entretiens avec la revue *Ligne de Risque*, 2005, (« L'infini »).

*Une vie divine*, roman, 2006 (Folio n° 4533).

*Les Voyageurs du Temps*, roman, 2009 (Folio n° 5182).

*Discours Parfait*, essai, 2010 (Folio n° 5344).

*Trésor d'Amour*, roman, 2011 (Folio n° 5485).

*Fugues*, essai, 2012.

*(Suite en fin d'ouvrage)*

Philippe Sollers

# Portraits de femmes

Flammarion

ISBN : 978-2-0812-5493-0

*Pour Stanzi*

« Amour ne tourmente que ces gens-là qui prétendent lui rogner les ailes ou l'enchaîner quand il lui a plu de venir voler à eux. Comme c'est un enfant, et plein de caprices, il leur arrache les yeux, le foie et le cœur. Mais ceux qui accueillent sa venue avec allégresse, et qui le flattent et le laissent s'envoler quand il lui plaît, et quand il revient l'acceptent volontiers, ceux-là sont toujours certains de ses faveurs et de ses caresses, et de triompher sous son empire. »

Nicolas Machiavel

*Lettre du 10 juin 1514*

On ne naît pas homme, on le devient, la plupart du temps à ses dépens. C'est un long chemin dangereux qui, le plus souvent, ne mène nulle part. On vous montre des directions, on vous les impose, c'est fou ce que le mot « homme » engendre comme bruit de valeurs. Il faut ceci, il faut cela, tenez-vous droit et marchez au pas, tu seras un homme, mon fils, comme moi j'ai été fils pour pouvoir commander des fils. Tables de la loi, catéchisme en bois, formules toutes faites, la plus sinistre étant un mannequin en képi, devant un cercueil décoré, faisant état de sa tristesse, mais aussi de sa « fierté » à l'égard d'un soldat « qui n'est pas mort pour rien, les armes à la main ».

Tableaux d'honneur, champs d'honneur, monuments aux morts, mémorials, sacrifices, bénédictions, exemples à suivre, « le vrai tombeau des morts est le cœur des vivants », transmissions, initiations, commémorations, cendres. La voie est tracée, il faut se courber, faire du sport, de la gymnastique, se pencher sur des livres, et encore des livres, que vous n'avez pas plus envie de lire que de courir à n'en plus finir. Quand tout un système s'effondre, comme aujourd'hui, ce fameux homme n'est plus qu'un délinquant précoce, un terroriste cinglé, un trader scotché jour et nuit à son ordinateur. S'il n'a pas déjà divorcé deux ou trois fois, il rentre chez lui, subit la mauvaise humeur de sa femme, les demandes tapageuses et absurdes de ses enfants, les voix hallucinées de la télévision, l'affairement autour du Net, la société, quoi, qui vit chez lui comme chez elle. Il essaye de dormir un peu, la tête pleine de chiffres ou de chèques à faire. Il a un travail, celui-là, encore heureux, il n'est pas chômeur, sans-papiers, ou sans domicile fixe. Il peut même faire partie d'une minorité influente, et croire peser (mais si peu !) dans les décisions du marché. C'est l'homme, enfin, ou ce qu'il en reste, dans la mondialisation en cours. De plus en plus de femmes se reconnaîtront d'ailleurs dans ce portrait rapide.

Supposons un réfractaire de naissance. Très tôt, il va être conscient d'un trucage massif. Sa famille est un montage hasardeux, son pays une fable, l'école une prison de futurs cadavres, l'armée une comédie pénible, la religion, quelle qu'elle soit, un opium de mauvaise qualité. Ce qu'il entend augmente ses doutes, la publicité incessante lui donne

la nausée, les massacres organisés achèvent de l'édi-
fier sur le règne d'une stupidité profonde. Plus on
lui demande de faire l'homme, plus il a envie de
faire le contraire. L'église homosexuelle essaye de
l'approcher, mais non, rien à faire, les ensembles,
même latéraux, ne sont pas pour lui. S'occupera-
t-il d'argent ? Non. De politique ? Non plus. De la
foire aux images ? Pas davantage, sauf, peut-être,
comme moyen de survie au pays des fous et des
folles. Il n'est donc pas « humaniste », cet homme ?
Comme l'a dit quelqu'un, il n'aura pas la stupidité
de se déclarer antihumaniste. Il est donc athée ? Eh
non, le rôle est ingrat, et réclame des convictions.
Mais alors, Dieu, la foi, la vérité, l'avenir de
l'humanité, la science ? La science, pourquoi pas,
les mathématiques passant en premier.

Cet enfant, pourtant, promis à sa carrière
d'« homme », a vite repéré une fissure dans ce beau
programme mortel. Quelque chose lui fait signe
dans un angle du faux décor. Cet angle a un nom :
*femmes*. Il note de plus en plus que, même si elles
disent le contraire (avec, parfois, un fanatisme
d'homme), *elles n'y croient pas*. Écoutez, c'est un
secret, n'allez pas le crier sur les toits. N'attendez
pas qu'elles approuvent le moins du monde votre
découverte. Servez-vous-en si vous en êtes capable,
en restant un enfant, mais n'avouez jamais. Vous
voyez que la reine est nue, mais silence. Vous êtes

sur un terrain explosif, fantastique, au cœur de la comédie humaine et divine. Retenez-vous, cachez-vous, mettez les masques qu'il faut, vous approcherez peu à peu du but : savoir ce qui se trame vraiment sous l'étiquette immémoriale « homme ».

Vous avez une mère, des sœurs, des tantes : commencez par elles, en les entraînant de votre côté. Vous évitez tout conflit avec les pères, les frères ou les oncles, vous évitez de même les affrontements avec les éducateurs ou les professeurs. Vous n'aurez pas à écrire un jour l'enfance d'un chef, mais celle d'un déserteur. En un mot, vous n'êtes pas *recrutable*. Apprenez à discerner vos alliées et vos ennemies dans le continent féminin. N'oubliez pas : elles sont *doubles*, les ennemies peuvent, à l'improviste, devenir des alliées (et même les meilleures), les alliées peuvent se transformer en ennemies (les pires). Scrutez, écoutez, devinez. Cette mégère veut être apprivoisée, cette dévote vous regarde avec un drôle d'air, cette mélancolique s'éclaire en vous rencontrant, cette femme savante adore les frivolités, cette précieuse ridicule est perdue pour vous à jamais. Vous avez un grand maître pour jouer sur le théâtre du monde : Molière. L'amour est médecin, vous serez médecin dans cette région agitée et sombre. Des femmes-médecins vous aideront. Commencez tout de suite : vous êtes le garçon imprévu, rêveur, dissipé, renfermé, exubérant, « terrible », énigmatique. Aucune punition ne vous fait peur. Ils vont dans le mur, vous sautez par-dessus le mur. La vie est courte, vous décidez d'en avoir plusieurs.

Ma mère est la plus jeune de trois sœurs. Je lui dois beaucoup, en positif comme en négatif. Positif : beauté, désinvolture, rires fréquents, autonomie, et, surtout, deux yeux de différentes couleurs, le droit très brun, l'autre plus clair, doré, insondable. J'ai passé beaucoup de temps à fixer ses yeux, et à me demander si elle avait conscience d'être deux en une. Personne ne semblait remarquer que cette chouette pouvait être simultanément un bon ou un mauvais œil. Ajoutez à cela une peau de soie, très mangeable, et vous avez le côté ensoleillé du tableau.

Négatif : autoritarisme, espionnage en douce, crises de colère fréquentes. Par chance, elle aime le confort, donc la tranquillité, donc son canapé avec sa belle lampe jaune, dans lequel (non, ce n'est pas possible !) *elle lit*. Elle ne fait pas semblant, elle lit vraiment. Se rappelle-t-elle ce qu'elle lit ? C'est moins sûr, elle n'est pas programmée pour ça, mais pour s'entourer d'elle-même à travers les mots. Enfant, je n'ai aucune idée de ce « Proust » dont elle fait grand cas. Est-ce un modèle d'homme ? Peu probable.

Cela dit, maman est souvent malade, et moi aussi. Vous comprenez pourquoi, c'est un dialogue. Heureusement, je suis son dernier enfant, un garçon après deux filles, *enfin*. Elle a 30 ans quand je nais, c'est une bourgeoise décalée, éclairée, aimant peu Bordeaux malgré l'art d'y vivre, elle est née à Paris (tiens, la voilà petite fille, très chic, debout sur une table, dans le parc de Vincennes). Avec elle, au moins, c'est clair : les « hommes » n'ont aucune importance, ils sont nécessaires, utiles, ennuyeux, payeurs, lourds. Pas de dépression, pourtant, aucune mélancolie affichée, une imagination fantasque, la vengeance par le rire. Une femme de beaucoup d'esprit, donc, « à la française », dons d'imitation décapants, causticité, cruauté. Maman, tu m'ennuies souvent, mais je t'adore. J'aime ton cou, ta gorge, ton nez, tes oreilles, tes yeux de fée ou de sorcière. Tu sens bon.

On s'aime, on se méfie l'un de l'autre, mais, sans toi, je ne serais pas sorti de mes maladies, j'aurais végété dans des hôpitaux militaires dont tu m'as tiré, par ton obstination, lors de la guerre d'Algérie, et la maison de l'île de Ré, rasée par les Allemands pendant la guerre, n'aurait probablement pas été

18

reconstruite (elle gênait leurs batteries côtières).
Je te revois là, vivante et jeune, pas du tout fantôme, assise près de l'eau sur le banc de bois blanc, sous le pin parasol. J'entends ta voix, disant plus tard à ma femme « Ma petite Julia ! » ou à mon fils, descendant du train à La Rochelle : « Mon trésor ! »

J'ai dû prendre, à la fin, la décision d'interrompre ta vie. Je te téléphonais deux fois par jour, j'ai tenu ta main, en plein été, à Bordeaux, et j'ai senti ton cœur passer dans le mien. Dans une de nos dernières conversations, je n'ai rien trouvé de mieux à te dire que « Je te prends avec moi avec la pensée. » Tu m'as répondu : « C'est énorme. » Et puis, un matin, le téléphone a sonné dans le vide. J'ai demandé au médecin si tu étais partie sans souffrance. J'entends sa réponse, claire et terrible : « Sans souffrance apparente. » Un peu plus tôt, il m'avait dit : « Ne répondez jamais aux questions qu'on ne vous pose pas. » À l'une de mes sœurs (pas à moi), tu as murmuré : « C'est dur de mourir. » Depuis quelque temps tu répétais souvent : « Rien ne m'est plus, plus rien ne m'est. » Je protestais. Et toi : « Ce qui m'embête, c'est la peine que tu vas avoir. » Je l'ai eue. Je l'ai toujours.

J'ai remarqué, au cimetière, que, chez nous, on mourait au mois d'août. Quand tu as disparu, il y a longtemps qu'on était ruinés, maisons et jardins effacés, meubles sauvés de justesse. Tu ne regrettais

19

rien, tu plaisantais. Après tout, tu avais fait de l'escrime très jeune, à cause de ton père, et tu avais conduit ta voiture très tôt et jusque très tard.

J'ai vécu ce charme discret de la bourgeoisie, qui a été emporté par le raz-de-marée du temps. Matins des femmes qui, une fois l'homme parti à son bureau, paressent pendant des heures, écoutent la radio, traînent en chemise de nuit ou en peignoir. Ces filles (mes sœurs) sont élevées pour ne jamais travailler, et ne travailleront jamais, sauf dans le mariage à enfants. C'est très condamnable, mais ça m'arrange, le désordre me plaît. On fait à peine attention à moi, preuve, à mes yeux, que je suis d'une espèce différente. Dans les jeux, je compte pour du beurre, et voilà.

Ce genre de paradis, pas du tout artificiel, a un prix mortel : le cancer. Premier cancer du sein pour ma mère (on l'opère), elle s'en tire, elle sera rejointe, beaucoup plus tard, par son explosion soudaine. Deuxième cancer, radical celui-là, pour sa sœur aînée, Laure. Quel personnage, celle-là.

Elle habite la maison symétrique d'à côté, deux frères ayant épousé deux sœurs (j'ai donc tout de suite, deux pères et deux mères), tout cela rassemblé dans un grand jardin. Laure est, sans conteste, l'autorité du clan, détestée par la sœur des frères, restée célibataire, qui vit dans un autre coin du jardin, dans une « chartreuse » avec pigeonnier, le grand style, quoi. Elle s'appelle Maxie, c'est la plus mystérieuse.

Laure, c'est la beauté stricte, l'élégance et l'intelligence, la tragédie aussi, c'était fatal. Elle domine ma mère, c'est ma deuxième mère, angélique et sévère. Elles ont fait installer un téléphone d'une maison à l'autre, ce qui leur permet de s'appeler vingt fois par jour, pour un oui ou un non. Laure a un mari opaque et silencieux, alors que le mari de Marcelle (mon père) est timide et plutôt musical. Mais enfin, c'est entendu : Laure règne, et, bien qu'elle ait un fils plus âgé que moi (mon « parrain »), elle m'a repéré, elle sait que je ne marche pas droit, que je devine des choses, que je passe trop de temps dans les buissons et les arbres, bref que je prépare une évasion. Ça l'intéresse, elle me surveille l'air de rien, mais regard perçant.

J'ai compris qu'elle est malheureuse, Laure, qu'elle étouffe, s'ennuie, se transforme en forteresse imprenable. Elle a, dans sa chambre, un crucifix en ivoire, réputé, je ne sais pourquoi, « janséniste ». C'est bien la seule qui semble croire à sa religion. Oui, c'est ça, elle est de Port-Royal, elle méprise ces bourgeois matérialistes très peu catholiques, et ce clergé si indulgent et si compromis. Son écrivain n'est pas Proust (comme pour ma frivole de mère, qui lit aussi Colette), mais Dostoïevski. Elle

21

m'embête avec ses silences de glace, mais, au fond, elle m'encourage. Pas de crucifix chez Marcelle (qui n'aime pas les curés), pas de Dieu chez Laure, qui s'en tient à la représentation de son propre martyre par l'exhibition de celui du pauvre Jésus-Christ.

Elle aime son petit Blaise Pascal (c'est moi) qui ne semble pas vouloir rentrer dans les ordres (pas mal) ni faire des affaires (très bien). Je suis peut-être révolté et impur, mais pur. Ce monde est poussière, mensonge, illusion, ordure, son mari, comme la plupart des maris, est un porc. Elle appelle la mort de toutes ses forces, elle est ravissante, la mort vient.

On est en août, le jardin éclate de fleurs. Elle rentre d'une séance de photos chez un professionnel de Bordeaux, *on fait des photos avant qu'elle meure*. Elle est très lasse, elle ne se plaint pas, elle a tout compris de leurs intentions. Elle se couche, elle ne se relèvera pas, je l'entends vaguement mourir depuis les escaliers, c'est la désolation de la désolation pour sa sœur plus jeune. Voilà une martyre qui donne raison au mot terrible de Picasso, « les femmes sont des machines à souffrir ». Ce Picasso est un criminel conscient, il a le droit de dire des choses de ce genre. Mais Laure *accuse*, elle ne se plaint pas. Elle les gifle de néant, je l'admire. En même temps, soyons francs : je suis débarrassé d'un témoin gênant.

Je rêve quelquefois d'elle. Elle apparaît toujours dans un halo bleu sombre, distante mais consolatrice. J'ai quand même réussi à la séduire du temps de mes maladies infantiles (asthme, otites à répétition). J'ai de la fièvre, et je prétends qu'une seule personne peut me soulager, elle. Je la demande, je la redemande, ma mère est jalouse (c'est aussi le but recherché). Laure vient, elle s'assoit au bord de mon lit, je lui tends mon bras droit comme pour une prise de sang, elle me caresse doucement la *saignée* du bras jusqu'au pouls. Elle prend ma fièvre sur elle, mon cœur de vampire bat pour elle. C'est délicieux, et ça me fait un bien fou. On se tait dans la pénombre, on ne se regarde pas, vous avez compris. Au bout de cinq ou six fois, elle ne vient plus, c'est trop clair. Voilà de l'érotisme torride, ou je ne connais pas la musique.

Après la mort de Laure, la sœur des frères triomphe, et maman va être marginalisée. Les hommes ne comprennent rien, c'est leur faiblesse, mais aussi leur force. Ils suivent le programme, fixé, semble-t-il, de toute éternité. On se marie, on fait des enfants, on travaille, on a ses petites manies, on paye, on joue la comédie. Les femmes, elles, s'ennuient.

Pauvre charmante Laure, si belle, si *pointue*, au pays des mirages. Pauvres femmes de tous les temps, d'ailleurs, obligées, sauf exception, de jouer dans ce mauvais film.

Maxie, mon autre tante, m'a repéré, elle aussi. Pas vraiment jolie, mais enveloppée, elle est tordue de refoulement, mais en même temps rumine de mauvaises pensées que je n'ai aucun mal à déchiffrer. Elle est intéressante et bizarre. Sans doute, elle est devenue ce qu'on appelle une « vieille fille » vouée au souvenir de son père mort, mais sa supposée dévotion et sa chasteté sont des golfes d'ombre. Elle m'invite souvent chez elle (c'est à cent mètres en traversant le jardin), sa chartreuse est froide, genre musée et odeur cirée. Elle a fait du piano, il est là, je pianote. Il faut dire que sa bibliothèque classique est impressionnante (mais elle ne lit rien). D'où viennent ces œuvres complètes et reliées de Fénelon, de Chateaubriand, de Hugo, du Tasse? Pourquoi ces rangées de Jules Verne, et surtout ce dictionnaire Larousse, grand format, cuir rouge, que j'ai récupéré pour finir? Mystère.

Maxie est bien avec le curé du lieu, elle l'invite une fois par semaine à prendre le thé sous les arbres. Elle a ses amies, des retraitées du corps, en train de devenir, plus vite qu'elle, de vieilles toupies. Elle n'est vraiment pas mal, oblique, sournoise, et la mort de Laure vient de la rajeunir d'un coup. Elle a l'air sérieux, mais regarde beaucoup en dessous. Elle tient peut-être, avec moi, sa vengeance contre ma mère. Elle sait comment m'exciter en tout bien tout honneur. Enfin, je ne rêve pas : ces promenades du soir dans le jardin, bras dessus, bras dessous, ce coude de mon bras droit, à travers son chemisier, contre son sein gauche… Il est bien là, ce sein, même si on feint de ne pas le sentir. Et son déshabillé de soie bleue après sa

toilette ? Et sa salle de bains, qui en sait plus long
qu'elle sur ses pensées furtives, non dites, inconfes-
sables, juste un peu de feu aux joues, avec son
regard noir, ravi de se retrouver en miroir ?

Non, je ne rêve pas, elle regarde le bas de mon pyjama, quand, pour une raison ou une autre, je viens dormir chez elle. On est seuls, chacun dans une chambre, mais ce bas de pyjama l'échauffe. Quelle grandiose hypocrite ! Elle voudrait savoir et elle ne veut surtout pas savoir. J'ai 13 ans, je suis mince et blond, très mignon, vous n'en doutez pas. Un soir, je suis dans mon lit, chez elle, avec un livre que je ne lis pas, elle est déjà couchée dans sa chambre bleue de vierge, et (non, je ne rêve pas !) au bout d'une heure (elle doit faire semblant de lire un truc, mais quoi ?), je l'entends dire de loin : « Tu ne veux pas venir lire dans mon lit avec moi ? » Imbécile, crétin triple nouille, il fallait y aller, et vite ! Je m'entends répondre piteusement « Je vais dormir. » Quel idiot, quel *lâche* !

Qu'est-ce qui se serait passé ? Mais rien, bien sûr, c'est-à-dire plein de choses dans ce rien. De la chaleur, des mots entrecoupés, du faux sommeil.

L'aurais-je touchée ? Peut-être, rien que pour entendre « Non, non, il ne faut pas. » Me serais-je caressé en douce ? C'est plus que probable. Aurais-je fini par regagner mon lit ? Sans doute. Mais le lendemain, quel matin, quelle après-midi, quel soir ! Rien ne se serait vraiment passé, mais quel événement du passé !

Pas la peine d'insister : le groupe humain où je me trouve fonctionne à l'inceste, le suggère à chaque instant pour mieux l'interdire, mais avec une telle intensité qu'on n'entend que lui à chaque tournant. J'ai l'oreille qu'il faut pour cette révélation, tragique pour eux, féerique pour moi. Ici un peu de flûte enchantée, le reste est silence.

Silence, comme est silencieux ce couple de pigeons que j'observe, posé sur une branche d'acacia. Ils se bécotent sans arrêt, tantôt l'un, tantôt l'autre, c'est une idylle en plein ciel, un signal pour l'observateur. Ce dernier se souvient brusquement des fables qu'il apprenait par cœur dans son royaume :

> « *Amants, heureux amants, voulez-vous voyager,*
> *Que ce soit aux rives prochaines,*
> *Soyez-vous l'un à l'autre un monde toujours beau,*
> *Toujours divers, toujours nouveau,*
> *Tenez-vous lieu de tout, tenez pour rien le reste.* »

La Fontaine, Molière, ce jeune garçon va se souvenir de ce rythme.

Eugenia (prononcez Éhourénia) arrive à Bordeaux, venant du Pays basque espagnol. Elle a 30 ans, j'en ai 15. C'est une très belle femme brune, chaleureuse, ironique, qui a déjà pas mal vécu, notamment dans la clandestinité, à cause de ses opinions politiques. Elle trouve chez nous une couverture de femme de ménage en attendant mieux. Eugénie, génie : coup de foudre pour moi, surprise pour elle. Elle est anarchiste, elle ne voit pas d'objection au passage à l'acte. Chaque fois que je lis un article parlant de « mon dépucelage par une bonne espagnole », ou, tout aussi vulgaire, d'« amours ancillaires », j'ai une petite nausée de fond, et je plains la personne qui a utilisé, une fois de plus, ce cliché grossier et réactionnaire.

On s'est aimés follement un peu partout : à Bordeaux, à Saint-Jean-de-Luz, à Saint-Sébastien, et, plus tard, à Paris. Peu de paroles (mais je parle couramment l'espagnol grâce à elle, et, surtout, son argot sexuel), beaucoup de gestes précis. On ne s'est pas fait prendre une seule fois, ce qui relève d'un professionnalisme inné. Souvent seuls, en plus, à la campagne, pendant l'été, comme sur ce perron, le soir, en silence, sous le grand marronnier voleur de moineaux, incessants frissons dans les feuilles.

Là, c'est Baudelaire, et son « vert paradis des amours enfantines » :

> « *Les courses, les chansons, les baisers, les bouquets,*
> *Les violons vibrant derrière les collines,*
> *Avec les brocs de vin, le soir, dans les bosquets.* »

C'est-à-dire les cinq sens à la fois, *enfin*, en acte.

Pas de poésie sans femmes *spéciales*, pas de femmes spéciales sans poésie. Dans le même mouvement, musique et peinture. Oubliez des tonnes de romans coincés, oubliez Proust, la jalousie et la société dans son ensemble, oubliez Dostoïevski et ses possédés, oubliez aussi le côté morbide de Baudelaire. Mais quand ce dernier chante l'amour sensuel, *c'est ça*. On n'a pas fait mieux, et on ne fera jamais mieux.

> « *Des femmes dont l'œil par sa franchise étonne.* »

> « *Bizarre déité, brune comme les nuits,*
> *[…]*
> *Sorcière au flanc d'ébène, enfant des noirs minuits.* »

> « *Que les soleils sont beaux dans les chaudes soirées,*
> *Que l'espace est profond, que le cœur est puissant.* »

> « *Mère des souvenirs, maîtresse des maîtresses.* »

> « *Et tout semblait lui servir de bordure.* »

« *Tu fais l'effet d'un beau vaisseau qui prend le large,*
*Chargé de toile, et va roulant,*
*Suivant un rythme doux, et paresseux, et lent.* »

« *Ta tête, ton geste, ton air,*
*Sont beaux comme un beau paysage,*
*Le rire joue en ton visage,*
*Comme un vent frais dans un ciel clair.* »

Comment faire mieux, en effet, que *Le Vin des amants* et son « délire parallèle » ?

« *Aujourd'hui l'espace est splendide !*
*Sans mors, sans éperon, sans bride,*
*Partons à cheval sur le vin,*
*Pour un ciel féerique et divin !*
*[…]*
*Mollement balancés sur l'aile*
*Du tourbillon intelligent,*
*Dans un délire parallèle,*

*Ma sœur, côte à côte nageant,*
*Nous fuirons sans repos ni trêves*
*Vers le paradis de mes rêves !* »

Vous avez bien lu « ma sœur ». « Mon enfant, ma sœur… »

Et voilà : cette jeune femme n'avait pas l'air d'une déesse, mais c'en était une, ouvrant pour moi la Nature à elle-même. En espagnol, on appelle ça le « *cante jondo* », le chant profond. Vous pouvez encore trouver de vieux enregistrements de *La Niña de los peines*, la fille aux peignes, des merveilles de flamenco. On a beaucoup écouté cette musique ensemble, Eugenia et moi, dans les quartiers populaires de Bordeaux, et, plus tard, dans un cabaret spécialisé de Paris, *Le Catalan*. Il fallait voir ces Andalouses danser :

> *« Tes nobles jambes, sous les volants qu'elles chassent,*
> *Tourmentent les désirs obscurs et les agacent,*
> *Comme deux sorcières qui font*
> *Tourner un philtre noir dans un vase profond. »*

Eugenia, le matin, poursuivie un peu partout dans les chambres (non, ne me dites pas que vous avez fait l'amour sur les lits de vos parents et de vos sœurs !), Eugenia l'après-midi, rendez-vous dans les greniers ou les caves, Eugenia la nuit, à pas de loup vers son lit. Déesse, fée, sorcière, peu importe. L'essentiel est le « tourbillon intelligent », le « délire parallèle ».

Je ne sais pas où elle est passée, mon Eugenia, quelque part en Argentine, d'après les dernières nouvelles que j'ai eues d'elle. Beaucoup de Basques, on le sait, finissent ainsi, en Amérique du Sud. J'ai connu d'autres femmes basques : elles sont courageuses, discrètes, fières, obstinées, tenaces, la langue qu'elles parlent vient d'on ne sait où, elle est saccadée et abrupte, leurs danses traditionnelles sont réglées par un rituel compliqué. Sous la violence, quelle douceur. De 15 à 20 ans, voilà mes *études*.

Ce que je veux dire est très simple : une femme est faite, ou non, pour vous confronter à la vérité physique, à son abîme, à son sillage, à ses éclosions. Le corps libre et antisocial d'Eugenia acceptait le mien. C'est rare. L'une veut vous *sortir*, vous faire voyager, une autre veut vous épouser, une troisième espère un enfant, une quatrième veut vous utiliser dans le marché d'animation culturelle, et je ne parle pas de toutes celles qui veulent absolument écrire, trois romans, dix recueils de poèmes, idéalisations, préciosités, romantisations. Celle-là, au contraire, a envie de moins s'ennuyer, aime la poésie vécue, les caresses, le repos, le sommeil, les fleurs, l'océan, les arbres. Les autres s'agitent, elle nage. En tant qu'« homme », vous avez gagné, si, en plus de l'autorité souple qu'elle vous reconnaît, vous la faites rire, et si vous devenez son frère, son partenaire de jeu, et, subrepticement, son enfant. Faites-vous aimer comme un enfant, espèce d'homme. De là, viennent, parfois, des liens indéfectibles.

Les amoureux partagent leur enfance, c'est-à-dire les désirs avant qu'ils soient des désirs. C'est pourquoi l'expression « coup de foudre » est si juste. Rien d'orageux, pourtant, éclair et tonnerre dans un ciel très bleu, éclair provenant du calme. J'ai assisté à ce phénomène, un jour, dans une île grecque. Ça n'a pas de nom, c'est inouï, vous pouvez mettre le nom divin sur l'éclair, mais vous l'effacez du même coup. Voici maintenant venir une femme qui a précisément écrit un livre qui s'appelle *Les Éclairs*.

Mon premier roman, *Une curieuse solitude*, est dédié à E S M, c'est-à-dire à Eugenia San Miguel. Que vient faire le plus grand des anges dans cette apparition féminine (et dans le surnom qu'elle garde pour moi : « l'ange ») ? C'était un ange, oui, un démon si l'on veut, mais ce qui me frappe le plus, maintenant, c'est sa gentillesse. Son sourire indulgent me poursuit.

Mon premier livre est un succès, une rencontre est aménagée par mon éditeur avec une femme dont j'ai à peine entendu parler, membre du « jury Femina », ce qui, à mes yeux, est le comble du ridicule. Stupeur : c'est Dominique, la plus belle femme que j'ai jamais rencontrée (photo), mélodieuse et rieuse. Coup de foudre immédiat de ma part. Elle vit à la campagne, dans les environs de Paris, elle a 45 ans, elle en paraît 35 (photo), j'en ai 22. Aucun doute : c'est une déesse à séduire.

Elle est née à Bruxelles, a été mariée deux fois (une fille), mais je comprends peu à peu que son ascendance est hollandaise et juive polonaise. Pas très grande, yeux très bleus, gorge généreuse, rire cascadant, *le rire*. Elle est encore en grand deuil d'un second mari, dessinateur et sculpteur, elle dessine elle-même très bien (elle voit mieux que moi la peinture). Avertissement : un de ses livres s'appelle *Artémis*, qui n'est pas une déesse tranquille. Elle aime les chiens, un chien-loup d'abord, un boxer ensuite. Sauvagerie ? Oui, en un sens, et on le démontrera tous les deux par une attitude antisociale constante.

J'insiste, elle se fait prier, et me voici, tout en gardant ma chambre d'étudiant, dans une grande maison entourée d'un parc, avec cette beauté, autre sorcière, autre fée, magie, enchantements, trains de rêves. Elle m'étonne beaucoup avec ses rêves (« c'est comme s'ils étaient écrits en direct, je les recopie »). Elle écrit chaque matin, pendant trois ou quatre heures. Son boxer, Caramel, est jaloux de moi.

Son histoire de Femina ne dure pas longtemps, elle est trop personnelle, trop indépendante. Elle critique les goûts vieillots et conventionnels de ses partenaires, un minable petit complot est organisé, elle est virée. Tant mieux, liberté totale. J'ai une voiture, je l'emmène à Bordeaux, on s'embrasse dans les garages des maisons qui n'ont pas encore été rasées après la faillite de mon industriel de père, elle couche dans le lit de l'une de mes sœurs.

Je l'emmène ensuite dans l'île, elle nage très bien, elle est toute bronzée, elle semble heureuse. Tout de suite un accord de fond : la musique. Silence, écriture, amour, lecture, écriture, musique. J'achète sans cesse des disques (discothèque en vinyles, trésor classique), musique. Elle voit mieux les tableaux de l'intérieur, elle écrit sur Breughel, Bosch, Van Dyck, Van Eyck, je connais mieux la musique. Cadeau contre cadeau : tu regardes le moindre détail de couleur, j'entends le dessous des notes. Là encore, clandestinité immédiate, évitement des clichés sociaux (femme plus âgée-jeune homme, *Chéri* de Colette, etc.). Comme je suis très en avance sur mon âge (merci Eugenia), je conduis vite et elle me suit.

Direction l'Espagne, suite dans les idées. On arrive dans le grand Barcelone d'autrefois, la ville qui ne dort pas, sauf, et encore, entre 5h et 6h du matin. L'hôtel s'appelle *L'Oriente*, sur la *Rambla de las flores*. Il est frais, couloirs blanchis à la chaux, le « Gaspacho » est excellent. Dominique découvre la « Sangria », et, le soir, au *Caracoles*, à côté de la Plaza Real, les *gambas a la plancha*. Le matin, on va parfois dans les environs, à Sitges, se baigner longtemps. Il fait très chaud, le sable brûle. La sieste est amoureuse, et plutôt agitée, si j'en crois le désordre des draps.

À cinq heures de l'après-midi, il y a corrida à la *Monumental*. Foule, le grand Dominguin officie, et, une autre fois, Ordóñez. Que les opposants aux courses de taureaux me pardonnent (ou pas), j'ai vu ces génies risquer leur vie. On rentre en marchant beaucoup, Dominique porte de petites robes légères, elle est très regardée, c'est normal. Ensuite, dîner, glaces, cigare pour moi, flux des passants et passantes, incessants, incessantes, jamais vu ça ailleurs.

Mais pas de blague, il faut écrire. On monte le matin à Montjuich, en haut de la ville, vue sur le port, jardin tropical, et là, chacun à une table, un peu loin l'un de l'autre, on écrit (surtout elle) pendant deux ou trois heures. Elle a son cahier, j'ai mes carnets. L'expression qu'elle répétera sans cesse, jour après jour, à Paris, à Venise, est « j'ai fait ma page ». Le mot *page* a une intensité sacrée. Stylo, encre bleue (je lui remplis son stylo), belle écriture ronde, pratiquement sans ratures, entrée du médium, corps bien droit, visage tourné de temps en temps vers les feuillages, ou, à Venise, vers l'eau de la Giudecca. Disons les choses : c'est elle qui m'a appris une discipline stricte, la traversée de la vie et des apparences au bout des mots. Sans elle, j'aurais certainement eu tendance à me disperser, et à attendre. Or la vérité n'attend pas, le papier est là.

Voici maintenant le bel appartement de Dominique, au cinquième étage, plein sud, dans le 7e arrondissement de Paris. Lumière « hollandaise », luxe dépouillé à la Vermeer, ordre, calme, beauté, fraîcheur de l'acajou, miroirs, loggia à l'étage, dont la fenêtre donne, au loin, sur les toits du musée d'Orsay. Retrait, travail, sommeil, rires, musique. Pas de temps à perdre avec qui que ce soit. Dîners en tête à tête, avec une bouteille de margaux, ou dans de petits restaurants, dans le dix-septième, pour ne rencontrer personne. Longues marches, les soirs d'été, au bord de la Seine. On a rendez-vous, pour la nuit, deux fois par semaine. Sinon, téléphone et passages en fin d'après-midi.

Je me revois, fin 1964, à Venise, achevant un livre, *Drame*, qui sera dédié « A D », c'est-à-dire à Dominique, mais aussi A D : *Anno Domini*. Venise incognito, pendant plus de 30 ans, printemps et automnes, c'est elle, encore elle, toujours elle. Je lui dédie aussi, plus clairement, un *Dictionnaire amoureux de Venise*, de la façon suivante : « À la Grande Petite Jolie Belle Beauté » (G P J B B). Dans ses livres (*Trente ans d'amour fou*, *Journal amoureux*, et les autres), elle m'appelle « Jim », clin d'œil à Joyce et à sa devise : « Le silence, l'exil, la ruse. »

Une fois Venise parcourue en tous sens, pendant 6 ou 7 ans, avec ses trésors d'églises, l'emploi du temps est invariable : réveil pour moi à 6h (c'est devenu automatique), petit déjeuner dans la chambre aux trois fenêtres sur l'eau, autre café et journaux en bas, sur le ponton, écriture jusqu'à midi, elle dehors près de l'eau, moi en haut, volets entrebâillés. Déjeuner léger à *La Riviera*, du côté de la gare maritime, sieste jusqu'à 16h. Dominique va se promener avec un livre, elle a fait *sa page* le matin, moi je dois continuer mes lignes. Dîner à 20h, après un passage rapide à l'église des Gesuati, deux cierges allumés en l'honneur du plafond de Tiepolo, *La Gloire de saint Dominique*. Nous sommes des saints un peu particuliers. Dîner, donc, sur les Zattere, friture de poissons et chianti, longue marche jusqu'à la Salute et retour, moment silencieux sur un banc rouge de la place San Agnese. Le clocher sonne, montée dans la chambre, sommeil.

Écrire, marcher, dormir, et encore écrire et encore dormir. Les soleils couchants, à Venise, ciel rouge, eau mercurielle, mâts flambants de lumière dorée, mouettes inlassables, passage des paquebots et des remorqueurs, sont indescriptibles. Monteverdi et Vivaldi en parlent très bien, c'est le *Gloria*, la gloire. C'était comme ça au commencement, et maintenant, et toujours, et dans les siècles des siècles, amen.

Ne nous dérangez pas, on est très forts, mais aussi très fragiles. Prendre tout Venise *pour soi* est une activité à plein temps, et la belle Dominique est une virtuose de la liberté calme du temps. Je la regarde, là, avec ses pendants d'oreille (elle en a une vingtaine, tous différents les uns des autres, *ça lui va*). D'où vient-elle ? Elle a quelque chose d'indonésien, comme si ses ancêtres hollandais étaient passés par Java, Sumatra, par là, mais l'énigme juive polonaise reste entière. Vous allez me dire que je n'aime que des étrangères, tiens, oui, c'est curieux. La poésie, avec les Françaises, ne va pas de soi, sauf exception. Encore Baudelaire, dont Dominique peut réciter des poèmes par cœur : « Tu fais l'effet d'un beau vaisseau qui prend le large... » « Entends la douce nuit qui marche... ». Voix ronde, diction parfaite (venant de sa mère, Esther, professeur dans cette dimension). Le rire, la voix, le corps qui s'enveloppe dans le rire et la voix, la marche accordée au partenaire (très important), les mots sans cesse en éveil (et pour cause), l'humour désinvolte et cruel, l'œil qui voit.

Jalousie ? Bien sûr, comme elles font toutes, mais pas pour mes embardées physiques (elle sait, depuis l'Espagne, qu'il y en a). Silence là-dessus de part et d'autre, antennes, en revanche, sur ce qui risquerait d'arriver *si*. Il y aura un *si*, qui, en plus de plusieurs vies parallèles mouvantes, m'obligera à une stabilité, d'ailleurs compliquée, de double vie.

La question consiste à ne pas inquiéter, alerter, blesser. Je n'ai jamais compris ce que signifiait la fidélité sexuelle, et je trouve lumineuse la distinction sartrienne entre amours nécessaires et amours contingentes. Dans les amours nécessaires, la fidélité de base est un roc intellectuel ou sensible. On n'abandonne rien, on ne renie rien, on est une mémoire devenue vivante, on se tait, on évacue la psychologie inutile. La Société, on le sait, veut des amours perturbées pour mieux contrôler ses membres. Tous les romans en vivent, malheur à celui ou à celle qui ne vend pas son trouble ou sa névrose. *Il faut du malheur*, veuillez vous conformer à cette injonction du marché. Les gens heureux n'ont pas d'histoire, ils se marient, se remarient, font beaucoup d'enfants, etc. Racontez-nous plutôt vos angoisses, vos embarras, vos échecs. N'espérez pas la moindre indulgence pour votre organisation quasi militaire de la vraie vie selon vous. Vision péniblement masculine, vous dira une opinion se croyant féminine. Vous voilà reclassé « homme », alors que vous n'en connaissez pas un comme vous.

Aucune importance : l'opinion (ou le milieu littéraire) est à mille lieues d'imaginer votre vie, à la fois dépensière et ascétique, une existence réglée comme celle d'un peintre ou d'un musicien. Même aveuglement sur la nature profonde de vos relations avec vos partenaires « nécessaires ». La police veut que le « nécessaire » soit fiché, et le « contingent » surveillé. Si vous n'allez pas chercher vous-même la Loi et la police, elles vous fichent la paix. Vous êtes la *lettre volée* elle-même, bien en évidence, celle que la police, qui la cherche là où elle n'est pas, ne voit pas. Céline a raison : « Les hommes torchent les lois, les femmes font l'opinion. » Si vous avez la chance de tomber sur une femme qui se fout de l'opinion, vous avez décroché un trésor. Des tensions, oui, quelques nuages, des crispations vite dissipées, rien de grave. Elle est de votre côté, pour le meilleur et pour le pire. Vous êtes son amant, son mari, son frère, son fils, son père, son enfant. Elle est *fière de vous*, ses raisons ne regardent qu'elle, et elles sont très bonnes.

Ce comportement antispectaculaire et anti-people, surtout lorsque l'un des protagonistes s'occupe, stratégiquement, du spectacle, énerve beaucoup les professionnels des apparences. Ils voudraient en savoir plus, annuler vos livres, vous entraîner dans leur bruit. En 2000, Bernard Pivot, dans une de ses émissions, a cru nous piéger, Dominique et moi, en nous invitant ensemble, elle pour *Journal amoureux*, moi pour *Passion fixe*. Il était très content de son petit scoop. Il y a eu un peu d'agitation autour, et puis c'est retombé, lisez les livres.

Dominique, sans aucun artifice, est restée très belle jusqu'à la fin de sa vie. Elle a continué, chaque jour, à écrire « sa page », et à tenir son journal. Cette discipline explique sa forme, rêves racontés compris. Lorsque nous étions séparés, on s'écrivait chaque jour, et ces lettres seront sans doute publiées, les siennes, avec le temps, étant de plus en plus inspirées et fermes. Je la revois sans cesse à Venise, où son ombre plane en pleine lumière heureuse. Je l'ai accompagnée jusqu'au bout de façon déchirante. Je vis sous sa protection de fée, et, si je lui demande de me faire signe, sa réponse est simple : écris, et je serai là. Et elle est là.

Dans un de ses plus beaux livres, *Les Éclairs*, elle dit ceci :

« Le jour de ma disparition ne pourra jamais être considéré comme une prise de la mort sur moi, mais comme une saisie de moi sur la mort. À ce moment-là, je serai tranquille, sachant avoir écarté tous les rideaux, longé tous les corridors, monté et descendu tous les escaliers, enfoncé toutes les portes, toutes les fenêtres, mangé à toutes les tables, dormi dans tous les lits, sur tous les prés, les sables, noirci tous les cahiers, sachant l'avoir aimé, lui, avant de découvrir la seule issue qui permette, enfin, le premier geste et le premier pas. »

Un autre de ses livres, tout aussi beau, s'appelle *La Voyageuse*.

Tout cela pour dire que les amoureux sont seuls au monde, puisqu'ils sont un monde à eux seuls. L'amour isolé et libéré, contrairement au côté grégaire de l'enfer, *lieu où l'on n'aime pas*. Magie quotidienne, donc, où le temps, grâce à l'autre, *surgit*, et ne passe pas. Dans un de ses cahiers, vers la fin, je trouve mon écriture, avec cette citation de Spinoza qu'elle m'avait demandé de lui recopier : « Nous sentons et nous expérimentons que nous sommes éternels. » Elle est soulignée trois fois.

J'ai prié le prêtre de Saint-Thomas-d'Aquin, à Paris, de répéter cette phrase lors de la bénédiction religieuse. Il a lu aussi, sur mon conseil, le prologue de l'Évangile de Jean : « Au commencement était le Verbe. » Je le récite, moi, intérieurement au présent : « Au commencement *est* le Verbe. »

Il y a un silence de l'amour, profond, complice, animal, musical. Le sourire de ravissement de Dominique, apparemment très absente, en écoutant Bach, par exemple. Dans les dernières semaines, elle parvenait encore à chanter avec moi l'air de Chérubin dans *Les Noces de Figaro*, tant de fois fredonné ensemble à Venise, en passant sous une glycine bleue du côté de San Trovaso :

> *« Mon cœur soupire*
> *La nuit, le jour,*
> *Qui peut me dire*
> *Si c'est d'amour… »*

À l'hôpital de l'Hôtel-Dieu, le son des cloches de Notre-Dame était pour elle un enchantement, et l'un de ses derniers plaisirs (« la Nature me manque ») aura été le vol des mouettes au-dessus de Paris.

Elle oubliait beaucoup de choses. Je l'entends me dire, de sa belle voix ronde : « Petit cœur qui se souvient de tout. » Je suis dans le couloir, je vais partir, elle est dans son lit médicalisé, elle dort, je reviens vers elle, je l'embrasse. Elle ouvre les yeux et me serre vivement la main : « Au revoir, petit chéri ! » Oui, c'est ça : tout un océan vivant de mémoire. « Au revoir, petit cœur ! » « Au revoir, petit chéri ! »

Puisque nous venons de côtoyer la maladie et la mort, je ne dirai jamais assez mon admiration pour les femmes de soins, pour leur générosité, leur simplicité, leur courage. Comment remercier toutes les infirmières noires et leur détachement, leur savoir-faire énergique et doux, leur gaieté ? Je dis « Mafily », par exemple, et je salue son imposante présence. Mais il y a aussi des femmes-médecins exceptionnelles, comme l'étonnante et charmante Monique H., qui a été longtemps près de Dominique, et, à travers d'innombrables dérangements, jusqu'à la fin. La médecine poussée à ce point est admirable, une des seules choses vraiment admirables dans un monde de bruit et de douleur. Merci encore, chère Monique, pour ce plant de cèdre libanais que vous m'avez offert, et qui va grandir, dans un jardin, pour de longues années après ma propre disparition. C'est le début de *L'Éclaircie*, cette histoire de cèdre, et vous y avez fait allusion de cette façon.

Quand je téléphonais le matin, pour prendre des nouvelles de Dominique, une des gardes présentes, Christine, par exemple (merci, merci), disait à haute voix en lui passant l'appareil : « Domi, c'est votre amoureux. » Un amoureux très singulier, et, décidément, très fidèle.

Domi, en musique, donne l'air suivant :
DO MI LA DO RÉ
LA SI FA SI LA MI.

Domi l'adorée, la si facile amie, s'est fait aimer dans des tas d'endroits sinistres, comme cette clinique du sombre 19e arrondissement. Une nuit, laissant là son déambulateur, elle a essayé de s'échapper, et on l'a retrouvée trois étages plus bas, au pied de l'escalier. Cela lui a valu une grande amitié avec une infirmière tchétchène, qui lui a téléphoné régulièrement pendant au moins trois mois. Des Africaines entrent dans sa chambre, elles sourient en me tendant un plateau-repas. Je reste là, un long moment, en silence. Le jour tombe, je baisse un peu le store, je diminue la climatisation. « Au revoir, petit chéri ! » C'est la nuit.

Maintenant, trois souvenirs en rafale.
Je suis enfermé dans l'hôpital Villemin, à Paris, pendant la guerre d'Algérie. J'essaye de me faire réformer (je n'y arriverai que trois mois plus tard, après un dur séjour dans des hôpitaux militaires de l'Est). Je retrouve Dominique dans le seul endroit

désert, la chapelle. Elle dans son manteau d'astrakan, moi en pyjama bleu marine en toile écrue, on s'embrasse dans ce lieu hautement désaffecté, preuve que le Saint-Esprit existe. Même sensation plus qu'étrange dans le parc de Versailles, du côté du petit Trianon. J'ai perdu 20 kilos après une grève de la faim, je m'appuie sur une canne, Dominique me soutient, je suis enfin réformé (grâce à Malraux) pour « terrain schizoïde aigu », ce qui me permet d'entrevoir Marie-Antoinette avec ses moutons, dans l'ombre.

Une des dernières sorties joyeuses de Dominique a lieu pour la publication du *Larousse illustré* où son nom vient d'apparaître. On va chercher le volume ensemble (champagne). La notice qui la concerne gratifie son œuvre d'« une grande exigence formelle ». Elle est nettement plus chaleureuse que la mienne, je feins d'être jaloux, on rit.

L'événement le plus mystérieux : on est à Venise et un concert va être donné en hommage à Jean-Paul II. C'est peu après l'attentat, on imagine le déploiement de sécurité. On est en train de dîner, quand je dis à Dominique : « Allons au concert – Mais on n'a pas d'invitation ! – On verra. » Elle est très élégante, comme toujours, alors que j'ai sur le dos une vieille veste Mao ramenée de Chine. Là, de nouveau, Saint-Esprit : on passe tous les barrages de l'armée et de la police, on est invisibles, on arrive sur le perron de *La Fenice*, un employé s'approche, et je lui demande de me laisser entrer « comme si Stendhal le lui demandait ». Ce Sésame invraisemblable opère, et il nous installe dans la loge impériale. Le concert est désastreux (une symphonie de Mahler), le pape, en bas, dans l'allée centrale, s'ennuie ferme, et tapote sa cuisse droite avec un éventail.

Ce récit est rigoureusement exact. J'aurais pu avoir un revolver sur moi (aucune vérification d'identité, aucune fouille), et abattre tranquillement Sa Sainteté depuis notre loge. À ce moment-là, ma veste Mao aurait probablement attiré l'attention des services de sécurité. Mais nous voici déjà, bras dessus, bras dessous, ni vus ni connus, sur les quais de Venise, et le nom de « Stendhal » résonne au loin comme un rire d'opéra.

J'ai dédié trois livres à trois femmes aussi différentes que possible, Eugenia, Dominique, et voici Julia. Son prénom est écrit en cyrillique au début de *Nombres*. Là encore, coup de foudre, ce qui signifie dans un très grand calme : ah, il va falloir beaucoup de temps pour ce cas.

Un corps apparaît avec son passé (il faut apprendre son passé comme une langue étrangère), mais aussi, parfois, d'où le côté « foudre », avec son futur. Dans ce futur certain, mais imprévisible, il y a vous. Vous étiez là ce jour-là, quelqu'un passe, vous êtes embarqué pour un voyage dont vous ne connaissez ni la destination ni les escales. Seule évidence : c'est du long cours, comme les grandes navigations d'autrefois.

Julia a 25 ans, je viens d'en avoir 30. Elle arrive de Sofia, en Bulgarie, avec une bourse d'étudiante. Elle est très belle (photo), brune aux yeux noirs, voix mélodieuse, français parfait. Elle vient m'interroger, dans le petit bureau de la revue *Tel Quel*, sur les mouvements d'avant-garde en littérature. Je m'attends à des connaissances minimales de sa part, à une écoute polie et mécanique (l'Université), mais pas du tout, elle me cite d'emblée les surréalistes, me demande ce que je pense des formalistes russes et des futuristes. Pas un mot de « communisme » ni de responsabilité sociale de l'écrivain. Il y en a pourtant une : le langage. On ne transforme pas la société si on ne change pas son langage. Vœu pieux, parfaitement idéaliste, puisque la société n'est là que pour méconnaître la façon dont elle parle (la preuve : aujourd'hui).

La littérature et l'art, seuls lieux de liberté par rapport à la société, surtout après les désastres totalitaires ? D'accord, d'accord. Mais il faut approfondir. Je l'invite à dîner, on va à *La Coupole*, la conversation se poursuit, on ne s'est plus quittés depuis.

Il lui est impossible de rentrer dans son pays d'origine. Son père est un croyant orthodoxe suspect, elle aurait voulu faire des études d'astrophysique, mais la littérature l'emporte, elle peut venir en France grâce à la politique de De Gaulle, lequel, par ailleurs, vient de reconnaître la Chine, via Malraux. Le « rideau de fer » est toujours là, le

« mur de Berlin » aussi, ça n'en finira jamais, même si les craquements de l'Empire s'annoncent. J'étonne toujours quand je dis que mon « maoïsme » de jeunesse aura été une conséquence de la politique gaulliste, c'est pourtant vrai, l'ennemi principal ayant été l'ex-URSS, et les États-Unis, avant leur déroute asiatique, suivie de l'effacement du rêve Kennedy.

Enfin, bon, que faire ? On vit comme des étudiants, Julia tombe malade, je suis obligé de remuer ciel et terre pour lui obtenir une chambre à l'hôpital Cochin (son passeport est communiste), elle ne peut plus habiter des chambres chez l'habitant (ah, celle du quai Louis-Blériot !), il faut faire vite. Comme elle s'est fait remarquer par ses connaissances et son intelligence (séminaires divers, dont celui de Barthes, qui écrira sur elle un très beau texte, *L'Étrangère*), on lui propose des postes dans l'université américaine. Mais non, voyons, la France. Alors, avec les Français, ce sera la guerre ? Eh bien, la guerre.

On se marie donc discrètement à la mairie du 5e arrondissement. Deux témoins, et sa sœur, venue à Paris depuis le Conservatoire de Moscou (elle est violoniste). Pas d'alliances, fou rire mal retenu pendant le discours du maire, pas de photos. On va déjeuner à *La Bûcherie*, un de nos rendez-vous, à côté de la librairie *Shakespeare and Co°*, et là, hasard objectif surréaliste, on tombe sur Aragon en tête à tête avec Elsa Triolet. Après qu'il m'a couvert de fleurs pour mon premier livre, j'ai vu Aragon plusieurs fois, ou plutôt j'ai assisté, chez lui, à d'interminables lectures emphatiques, par lui-même, de ses poèmes. Je n'ai aucune sympathie pour Elsa Triolet, qui est venue une fois, dans le bureau d'Aragon, m'apporter un de ses livres, avec la dédicace suivante : « Pour Philippe Sollers, maternellement. » *Maternellement* ! Au diable !

Aragon n'a aucune idée de la jeune femme qui m'accompagne, et qui est, depuis quelques minutes, ma femme. Le culte religieux communiste pour le couple Aragon-Elsa a été tel que l'équation : jeune écrivain français + femme venue de l'Est ne pouvait être causée et recomposée que sur ce modèle. On a donc entendu ce disque cent fois, soit comme proposition d'appropriation (communiste), soit comme condamnation (bourgeoise). Eh non, que voulez-vous, ce n'est pas du tout la même histoire. On vit une autre vie, un autre roman.

On s'est ainsi aimés, Julia et moi, à Paris, Saint-Sébastien, New York, Pékin, Shanghai, Washington, Londres, et surtout dans ma maison de l'île de Ré, dont elle est devenue, en l'embellissant, la reine. Ah, cet été brûlant de 1967 ! Comme ces jeunes mariés sont bizarres ! Ils n'arrêtent pas de se baigner, de jouer au tennis, de lire, d'écrire, de faire l'amour, de dormir. Qu'est-ce qu'ils lisent, y compris sur le sable ? Les philosophes (surtout Nietzsche) et, splendide découverte, les gros livres encyclopédiques de Joseph Needham, *Science and Civilisation in China*. La Chine ? Ah oui, la Chine. Julia fait une licence de chinois, j'en apprendrai un bout pendant deux ans, histoire de mieux comprendre Laozi, Zhuangzi. Il y a un drôle de type, là-bas, Mao, qui vient de mettre en scène une baignade ahurissante, suivi par des milliers de drapeaux rouges dans le Yangtsé. Un grand criminel ? Sans doute, sans doute, mais comme les Russes et les Américains ne sont pas contents, on verra.

On se lève tôt. Julia travaille beaucoup, je n'ai jamais vu quelqu'un travailler autant. Elle parle couramment l'anglais et le russe, est très forte en grec et en latin, presque pas d'accent en français, juste une touche de charme. Elle est drôle, passionnée, infatigable, nos discussions durent encore, et, comme elle est toujours aussi belle, c'est de la musique de pensée dans les fleurs. Elle peut s'illustrer en linguistique avec des innovations majeures, étonner Jakobson, Lévi-Strauss, Benveniste, Barthes, Lacan, devenir une psychanalyste reconnue et une universitaire internationale. C'est maintenant une star en Angleterre, aux États-Unis, au Japon, en Norvège (prix Holberg, l'équivalent du Nobel pour les sciences humaines). Il n'y a que les Français qui, logiques, décident le plus souvent de l'ignorer dans leurs pénibles palmarès récurrents des « intellectuels ».

Cette Byzantine agace et énerve les Hexagonaux. Ils et elles sont jaloux, et d'ailleurs comment peut-elle tolérer un mari aussi imprévisible qu'incontrôlable ? Ce Sollers a non seulement trahi sa classe mais sa patrie en n'épousant pas une Française. C'était un beau parti, il le paiera cher. Il y a tous les livres de Julia, mais l'un d'eux me touche particulièrement, un volume de vulgarisation très enlevé, *Le Langage, cet inconnu*, signé Julia Joyaux, et republié plus tard, en poche, sous le nom de Julia Kristeva. Elle s'appelle tantôt Julia Kristeva, tantôt Julia Joyaux, Madame Joyaux, femme de Philippe Joyaux, dit lui-même Philippe Sollers. Il n'y a pas de « Julia Sollers », comme il a fallu, un jour, le rappeler à Lacan, surpris d'avoir commis cette faute.

De temps en temps, une étudiante américaine vient sonner à la porte de mon studio, et me demande, avec distance et méfiance, si je suis « Monsieur Kristeva ». Quand j'habite chez Julia, à New York, je suis en effet « Monsieur Kristeva », ce qui ne me dérange pas, au contraire. Je profite de mon incognito d'écrivain français inconnu, ma littérature étant « *too French* » et absolument censurée par l'université puritaine américaine. Inutile de s'expliquer là-dessus, et d'ailleurs les différents appartements de Julia sont très agréables.

Julia s'amuse : elle écrit un très bon roman sur notre jeunesse agitée, *Les Samouraïs,* un polar épatant, *Meurtre à Byzance*, une grande biographie théâtrale et lyrique de sainte Thérèse d'Avila, et puis, côté sérieux, *Le Génie féminin*, trois volumes sur Hannah Arendt, Mélanie Klein, Colette. Son plus beau livre est sans doute *Le Temps sensible*, sur Proust. Le plus audacieux : *La Révolution du langage poétique* (Lautréamont, Mallarmé). Céline apparaît dans *Pouvoirs de l'horreur*, et *Soleil noir, dépression et mélancolie* est un modèle d'analyse clinique. Tous ces volumes sont traduits un peu partout, et, récemment (bonjour le temps !), en chinois.

Dans ses cours et ses conférences, en français ou en anglais, Julia est claire, documentée, passionnée. Ses étudiants l'adorent, ses patients et ses patientes la respectent, tandis que le clergé psychanalytique et universitaire m'en veut beaucoup. Bien entendu, comme pour Dominique, les prétendants, parfois très connus, ont été multiples. Comme c'est curieux : je viens d'oublier leurs noms.

L'amour dure trois ans, dit-on, ou même moins, et c'est vérifiable quand il ne s'agit pas d'amour. En réalité, l'amour dure toujours, il faut simplement mieux définir ce *toujours*. D'une façon ou d'une autre, visible ou invisible, vous sacralisez quelqu'un dans son existence entière, sa respiration et sa mort. L'amour, s'il a lieu, est plus fort que la mort. Dans l'amour, quoi qu'il arrive, même aux confins de l'horreur ou de la démence, vous touchez du doigt la défaite de la mort.

C'est pourquoi chaque moment est important, et la durée sans temps mort. Vous êtes le peintre et le musicien de ces femmes, elles deviennent des personnages centraux de vos romans, elles peuvent prendre d'autres formes, d'autres figures, elles sont parfois rejointes par celles dont on ne peut pas dire le nom. Ce moment où l'une ou l'autre sort des vagues est unique, ce foulard est unique, ce fou rire aussi. La poudre du temps leur appartient. En peinture, c'est l'année où Picasso comprend que seul un violon « cubiste » peut représenter son grand amour, Eva. En musique, c'est Monteverdi qui les rassemble toutes pour une assomption fastueuse (la Vierge Marie, à Venise, en vaut dix mille). Dans les siècles des siècles, c'est maintenant, c'est toujours.

Mais c'est aussi bien Don Giovanni et son catalogue, où Mozart, pourtant très amoureux de sa petite Stanzi, vous révèle son éventail de passions possibles. Rien ne lui échappe dans les rues de Vienne ou de Prague, il note, il note, ce sont chaque fois des antidotes à la Reine de la Nuit. Les femmes sont des Muses, et si elles sont toxiques ou grotesques, elles n'en sont pas moins inspiratrices d'un aspect fondamental du réel. En voici une qui pleure, c'est beau. En voilà une autre qui rit ou qui dort, c'est encore plus beau. Tous ces accents, toutes ces couleurs sont à mettre en madrigaux, en quatuors, en tableaux. *Les Flûtes de Pan*, de Picasso, en sont une démonstration vivante. Une femme arrive, elle refait de lui un enfant curieux de ses sœurs, il pousse la démonstration jusqu'à l'absurde, dieu et le diable sont enfin unis, et d'ailleurs, dans cette nouvelle Grèce, il n'y a que des déesses plus ou moins favorables et des multitudes de dieux.

La merveilleuse et géniale Cecilia Bartoli a raison de dire que Mozart est le seul musicien à avoir saisi toutes les variations de la substance féminine, colère, effusion, drôlerie, dissimulation, sublime, charme vénéneux, souffrance, pseudo-innocence, défi, douceur. Elle-même rêve d'interpréter le rôle de Don Giovanni. C'est dans ses cordes. Qui ne l'a pas vue chanter n'a rien vu. J'ai eu la chance de la voir répéter et tenir la salle du Grand Théâtre de Bordeaux, après quoi, à la surprise générale, elle m'a fait dîner publiquement à sa droite. Dans la même salle, j'allais, à 12 ans, assister aux « matinées classiques », notamment aux *Fausses Confidences* de Marivaux. Bonjour le temps ! Grandiose Cecilia, d'une gaieté étourdissante, ressuscitant Vivaldi, bouleversant Haendel ou Mozart.

Julia, enceinte, était le jardin lui-même et tous les oiseaux à la fois. Je lui faisais écouter du Haydn, musicien cellulaire des fibres. Notre fils, David, aime beaucoup Haydn et Mozart (il connaît la vie de ce dernier par cœur, et a mis, comme indicatif de son portable, le début de la 40e Symphonie en sol mineur). Il a eu de grandes difficultés de santé, et, là encore, surprise de voir Julia dépenser toutes ses forces pour sa survie et l'amélioration de sa vie. Les femmes et les enfants, grand chapitre. Que vient faire un homme dans cette dimension ? J'ai trouvé : de la ponctuation.

David : un enfant courageux, fort, fragile, ultra-sensible. Il sait qu'au fond je suis comme lui : très fragile. Il ne me dérange jamais, et si j'ai droit, de temps en temps, à « mon charmant papa », tout va. Que de terreurs on a vécues à cause de lui, surtout Julia, dans des hôpitaux où il était transporté de jour ou de nuit. J'ai gardé un cadeau de lui, puisque je fume trop : une boîte de *Ricola*, « Cassis sans sucres, avec édulcorants, bienfaisant, adoucissant, rafraîchissant, bonbons aux plantes, mélange de 13 plantes des montagnes suisses, don de la nature. » Ça vaut bien les dizaines ou les centaines d'avions ou de petites voitures que je lui ai offerts ici ou là, sans parler des trains électriques, puis, avec le temps, des ordinateurs de plus en plus perfectionnés (je ne sais pas m'en servir), et des portables (jamais assez).

Mais le plus important n'est pas là : il peut vous réciter impeccablement quatre ou cinq fables de La Fontaine, du Baudelaire non stop, ou bien *El Desdichado* de Nerval (« le prince d'Aquitaine à la tour abolie »), bref le cœur de sa langue natale :

> *« J'aime le jeu, l'amour, les livres, la musique,*
> *La ville et la campagne, enfin tout, il n'est rien*
> *Qui ne me soit souverain bien,*
> *Jusqu'au sombre plaisir d'un cœur mélancolique. »*

La Fontaine insiste beaucoup sur la relation entre « rien » et « tout » (« Tenez-vous lieu de tout,

66

tenez pour rien le reste »). La double négation, dans « Il n'est rien qui ne me soit souverain bien », est une trouvaille fabuleuse, reprise par Voltaire dans « Le Paradis terrestre est où je suis ». Cette vision du monde est en passe d'être de plus en plus interdite.

David apparaît, sous le nom de Jeff, dans *Le Secret* (sa mère, Julia, s'appelle Judith dans le même livre). Une chanson pour lui, enfant : *Le Temps des cerises*. Oui, il doit *revenir* ce temps révolutionnaire, comme doivent revenir sans fin les gais rossignols, le merle moqueur, et aussi les belles avec leur folie en tête. Je siffle assez bien. David me dit : « Parle aux oiseaux ! » Le plus drôle, c'est que j'y arrive. Même sa mère, incrédule et athée notoire, est obligée de le reconnaître pendant une minute, pas plus.

L'enfance est un royaume dont les femmes ont la clé. Elles l'égarent, on la retrouve, on revisite leur enfance avec elles, ça peut durer une nuit, trois jours, des années. Beaucoup d'entre elles ont été ravagées par leurs mères qui ont projeté sur elles leurs échecs, leur ressentiment, leur *androphobie* aggravée, transmise par leurs propres mères. Ou alors, ce sont des pères humiliés, mauvaise affaire, mais pas meilleure lorsqu'ils sont écrasants, intrusifs, séducteurs pénibles. C'est plombé.

Pourtant, il y a des minorités, dispersées un peu partout dans les foules. Ce sont elles qui appellent, parfois sans le savoir. L'appel est souriant, silencieux, réservé, oblique. C'est une proposition algébrique et géométrique, un appel d'air. Déchiffrez-moi, vous êtes peut-être la racine carrée de mon équation. Les mots ont tout de suite un autre sens, les ambiguïtés se propagent, la pudeur domine. C'est aujourd'hui, ou plus tard, ou jamais. Il y a beaucoup de jamais, c'était un moment quand même. C'est sans aucune insistance qu'on vous demande ou pas d'insister. Ou plutôt : on vous demande de demander sans rien demander. Débrouillez-vous, trouvez l'atmosphère. De toute façon, si quelque chose doit se passer, elles l'auront décidé elles-mêmes. Elles se racontent ce qu'elles veulent, mais elles ne cèdent qu'à elles-mêmes. « Tiens, je n'aurais jamais cru ça de moi, et pourtant c'est moi. »

Vous gardez vos femmes pivotales, vous laissez venir ce que le roman veut de vous. Impossible de le nier, il veut quelque chose. D'abord vous surprendre, vous réveiller dans un angle, vous rappeler votre précarité, votre nullité, votre néant toujours refoulé. Il faut répondre, pas forcément pour un bien, mais le mal fait partie du jeu, il informe. À partir de *Femmes*, livre plus « public », je décide de faire le tour de la question. J'ai mes notes de terrain, me voilà encyclopédiste, ou, du moins, chimiste. Je vais proposer mon classement des événements et des éléments. C'est le moment. L'exergue de Faulkner annonce la couleur : « Né mâle et célibataire dès son plus jeune âge. Possède sa propre machine à écrire, et sait s'en servir. »

Je lis le prière d'insérer de l'époque (1983) : « Accélération du temps, coulisses de la société... tourbillon des rapports de forces, falsification incessante de l'information… décor en mutation, filmé à travers l'écran féminin qui, comme toujours, mais plus que jamais, dit la vérité comique ou tragique des passagers se croyant acteurs… irréalisation endiablée de tout… »

Bien vu il y a trente ans, ou pas ?

J'ai donc avec moi, à Venise, des carnets de bord tenus depuis plus de dix ans, scènes ou portraits multiples d'une époque de mutation très agitée. Le livre est très cru, et je m'étonne encore, en le relisant, d'avoir osé ces peintures. Les personnages féminins sont tantôt négatifs (montée d'un féminisme agressif), tantôt positifs (femmes indépendantes et libres). Je garde un souvenir ému d'une Anglaise, Cyd, dont le modèle, dans la vie, était irlandaise. Elle m'a beaucoup aidé à New York, quand je m'ennuyais là-bas, en butant sur l'incroyable névrose puritaine des Américaines. Une autre pensée particulière pour Ysia, la diplomate chinoise du roman, dont personne, comme c'est étrange, ne m'a jamais parlé. Le narrateur de ce livre voyage beaucoup, aux États-Unis, en Italie, en Israël, sans parler de ses activités à Paris, et c'est, chaque fois, l'occasion d'aventures acides ou heureuses.

Le livre a été un succès, mais, bizarrement, la critique s'est fixée sur les personnages masculins, assez reconnaissables, en passant complètement sous silence les héroïnes du récit, et elles sont nombreuses, souvent facilement identifiables. Qui se cache, ou plutôt se montre, dans ces militantes d'un nouveau pouvoir, Kate, Bernadette ? Qui est cette responsable politique que j'appelle Flora ? Ou cette écrivaine très folle, Elissa ? À qui correspond celle que j'appelle « La Présidente » ? Ce n'est pas à moi de donner les noms, d'autant plus que les « clés », dans un roman, sont toujours multiples, mais on trouvera difficilement, dans un livre de la fin du 20e siècle (et même du début du suivant), autant de renseignements, sur la transformation de la substance féminine, pour le pire ou pour le meilleur, à travers le temps.

Même question sur les changements des rapports entre les sexes. Ce n'est pas au journalisme de répondre, ni à la sociologie, ni à la décomposition philosophique, mais bien au roman. Le roman interroge ce que personne ne veut savoir concrètement. J'ouvre de gros romans ennuyeux anglo-saxons, vantés par une presse unanime, et je bute sur de vieilles histoires familiales sur fond de dépression historique. Quelque chose est *retombé*, on ne s'amuse plus, la gratuité s'est évaporée, sale temps pour la liberté.

Ne pas donner les noms, bien sûr, et rendre non identifiables les femmes qui prennent des risques dans leur vie sociale ou privée : souci éthique élémentaire. Si je dis que, dans *Portrait du Joueur*, la jeune femme avec qui je visite le CERN (bonjour les particules élémentaires !), et qui s'appelle Joan, a bel et bien existé, quelle importance ? Je la revois, ravissante et bizarre, en écrivant ces lignes (bonjour le boson !). Et quelle importance si, en pure perte, j'insiste sur le personnage scandaleux de Sophie, dans le même livre, en affirmant, ce que personne n'est prêt à accepter, que ses lettres pornographiques sont authentiques ? Même question pour *Le Cœur Absolu*, roman où les femmes affluent en tous sens, un vrai carnaval. N'empêche, Sophie est, de loin, le personnage le plus étonnant de tous mes livres.

Je dis donc tranquillement que l'expérience véridique d'un homme avec des femmes est peu souhaitée, réprouvée, déniée, et qu'il y a là, de plus en plus sensible, un tabou que le marché surveille. Pauvre Cyd, pauvre Ysia, pauvre Sophie, pauvre Louise avec son clavecin à Venise ! Pauvre Liv, pauvre Sigrid, pauvre Deborah ! Vous êtes là, pourtant, en toutes lettres, vous respirez clandestinement à Paris, Milan, Barcelone, New York. On a dû se tromper, vous êtes de purs fantasmes, je ne vous ai jamais touchées, on a rêvé.

On reverra tout ça plus tard, ou jamais. De nouvelles fêtes auront lieu un jour, avec de nouvelles actrices, de nouveaux acteurs. Pour l'instant, c'est la crise. Excellentes, les crises. Elles permettent d'apprécier les forces d'oubli, la vivacité de la mémoire, le grand futur du passé. J'ai confiance dans les prénoms suivants, tous décalés : Luz, dans *La Fête à Venise*, France, dans *Les Folies Françaises*, Dora et Clara, dans *Passion fixe*, Maud, dans *L'Étoile des amants*, Ludivine et Nelly, dans *Une vie divine*, Viva, dans *Les Voyageurs du Temps*, Minna, peut-être ma préférée, dans *Trésor d'Amour*, l'incroyable Lucie, dans *L'Éclaircie*. Je suis seul à les aimer ? Peut-être. Mais on a vu des tableaux s'affirmer avec le temps, on ne sait jamais.

Ce qui me paraît acquis, en revanche, c'est la précision de mon enquête. Femmes de tous les milieux, des plus populaires aux plus intellectuels ou « branchés », de tous les pays et de toutes les nationalités (Françaises, encore un effort !), plongées dans l'Histoire, la grande comme la petite, la violente comme la pacifique. La guerre des sexes est sans doute fatale et immémoriale, mais, que voulez-vous, il y a des pauses, des intervalles, des éclaircies. Mieux on fait la guerre, mieux on goûte la paix. La paix en pleine guerre, voilà le sujet.

Crise, mais surtout, sous des airs de libération, régression profonde. Jamais le 19e siècle n'a été à ce point ranimé. Madame Bovary est de retour, la plupart des romanciers sont sinistres, le désastre sexuel des classes moyennes est à l'ordre du jour, les meilleurs (Philip Roth, par exemple) ont baissé les bras ou se complaisent dans une impasse de désespoir. À les croire, c'est la fin du monde et de l'homme, l'apocalypse. La « littérature féminine » en rajoute dans la prison programmée. Vous nous énervez avec votre 18ᵉ siècle ! Il n'a jamais existé !

Et pourtant, moi aussi je suis peintre ! La peinture a disparu, mais je la reprends à travers les mots. Voyez toutes ces femmes dessinées en couleurs ! Ces Titien, ces Tiepolo, ces Watteau, ces Fragonard, ces Manet, ces Picasso ! Voyez l'intensité *poétique* de cette poissonnière ou de cette musicienne, de cette philosophe ou de cette pharmacienne, de cette gynécologue ou de cette tireuse d'élite, de cette boulangère de génie ou de cette cantatrice célèbre ! N'est-ce pas une *exposition* toute faite, à installer d'urgence à la Dogana de Venise, à la place des déchets de l'art contemporain ? Stupeur et succès garantis, je m'en charge.

Il n'en reste pas moins qu'un des personnages féminins les plus réussis de mes livres est, à mes yeux, celui de Reine dans *Le lys d'or*, mon roman le plus éreinté par la critique (malgré ses paysages enchanteurs). C'est le récit d'un échec, suivi d'une réussite ambiguë. Le narrateur est amoureux, elle se refuse, signe avec lui un contrat où il doit lui raconter sa vie, elle ne censurera rien, elle achète. Il s'ensuit une description minutieuse de la frigidité féminine chez cette jeune aristocrate inflexible. On est dans le contraire exact de *L'Amant de Lady Chatterley*, cette mièvrerie naturiste. La frigidité n'est pas une limite physique, mais une passion spirituelle d'orgueil, une sorte de sainteté à l'envers. Là encore, un modèle a joué son rôle, avec plusieurs raccords d'expériences diverses sur ce continent peu exploré. Voilà le « continent noir » en pleine lumière. Cette dimension négative aura été décrite au moins une fois, après quoi le navigateur a hâte de reprendre la mer.

Paradoxalement, cette frustration engendre, dans le roman, les meilleurs passages « chinois » de paysages. Vases communicants : privation d'un côté, prolifération de beauté de l'autre. C'est aussi une sorte de psychanalyse à l'envers, puisque le patient (si on peut dire) est payé pour écrire, ce qui, au lieu de l'inhiber, l'encourage. Cette prude est un comble de perversité. Cette petite catholique noble piétine ses origines. Elle est progressiste, ultradémocrate, elle n'aime que les poétesses russes, elle serait aujourd'hui, sinon communiste authentique, du moins adepte du dalaï-lama. Tout, plutôt que son château en Touraine, son milieu social, ses portraits de famille, la France et son passé englouti et, bien entendu, la sexualité, cette souillure.

C'est une vierge intrépide, cuirassée, sublime, une Jeanne d'Arc de l'intérieur corporel. Elle lutte à mort contre l'admirable perversion catholique qu'elle ressent en elle tout au fond, ce vice si mal utilisé par les imbéciles prêtres catholiques pédophiles. Elle proteste de toutes ses forces, elle est protestante, dans le sens de l'Histoire, en somme. Elle donne une leçon sévère à ce curieux professeur de chinois, beaucoup trop taoïste. Elle le récuse, comme une religieuse qui serait, aujourd'hui, au Tibet. Elle aime ses chevaux, pas les hommes. Elle pourrait être lesbienne sans rien ressentir. Mais *cet homme-là*, elle prend plaisir (drôle de plaisir) à le détester.

La haine est plus ancienne que l'amour, et la *hainamoration* est intéressante et mal étudiée. Il fallait qu'un explorateur se dévoue dans les glaces. Inutile de dire que l'accueil réservé à cette expédition hautement scientifique a été glacial. Je n'ai pas revu le modèle de Reine dans l'existence, mais je suis sûr de partager avec elle un vrai secret. J'ai beaucoup pensé à Laclos pendant cette liaison dangereuse, mais une liaison sans danger n'est pas vraie. À un moment, Valmont écrit à Merteuil : « Je ne sais pas pourquoi, il n'y a plus que les choses bizarres qui me plaisent. » Aller jusqu'au bout de la guerre des sexes *en s'amusant* est un art. *Le lys d'or* est le plus bizarre de mes romans, à cause de sa composition serrée et de son intrigue. C'est aussi un drôle de livre d'amour.

Sade, Laclos, Baudelaire, Balzac (*La Fille aux yeux d'or*), Stendhal, Proust, Bataille, Céline, voilà l'occasion de rappeler, une fois de plus, que, sans certains Français, on ne saurait pas grand-chose des forêts passionnelles. Proust, dans l'équation montée de la mémoire et des paysages, est incomparable. Plus il est jaloux d'Albertine, plus la nature lui parle. Le venin du soupçon est une drogue de parfums, de lumières, de sons. Bonjour tout de même, en passant, à Joyce et à Nabokov. Qu'un homme ait pu être Molly Bloom et Lolita est exceptionnel. Casanova a écrit en français, il a agi de même. Cette langue-là m'est tombée dessus, et c'est avec elle que je me déplace, de plus en plus seul, mais qui n'est pas seul dans son art ?

Je vois à l'instant, à la télévision, un vieil indigné humaniste en train de se faire remettre une écharpe blanche par le dalaï-lama, lequel clôture une manifestation sur le bonheur ayant attiré des foules. Le message de l'ancêtre est le suivant : il a atteint le bonheur, et il peut vérifier qu'il rayonne autour de lui. « Le bonheur est contagieux », dit-il, avec un grand sourire. Ce béat heureux se trompe. Le bonheur, s'il existe, est tellement rare qu'il est toujours jalousé à mort. Les innocents bouddhistes n'ont pas l'air de s'en rendre compte. Ne les réveillons pas.

Le bonheur, pour les peintres, a souvent été de trouver des collectionneurs avisés. Ils ne vendent rien, personne ne comprend leurs tableaux, et soudain surgissent des individus singuliers qui anticipent sur leur gloire future. Ils s'appellent Vollard, Ephrussi, Chtoukine, Kahnweiler, Rosenberg. D'où leur vient ce don, ce flair, cette *avance* ? On ne sait pas trop, mais il doit y avoir une forte jouissance à posséder ce que personne ne voit sur le moment et verra (peut-être) plus tard. Le marché n'aime pas ces amateurs fortunés, et les a remplacés, depuis longtemps, par des hommes d'affaires à tout faire. Ceux-là n'ont pas une ou deux passions fixes, mais des dizaines, au gré de la rotation spéculative de la laideur. L'art officiel a toujours été *pompier* et soucieux des ventes. En littérature, pareil. Le dernier best-seller américain, croûte épaisse, le prouve.

J'ai donc eu, dans ma vie, des *collectionneuses*. C'est le sujet du *Lys d'or*, c'est aussi celui de

*L'Éclaircie.* La collectionneuse ne confond pas le réel et le virtuel, le temps court et le temps long, un mari et un amant, un amant et un amour. Elle peut se tromper sur des maris, des amants, des amis, mais pas sur elle-même. Vollard *était* Cézanne, Ephrussi Manet, Kahnweiler Picasso. Ephrussi n'a pas eu son portrait, mais une botte d'asperges *plus une*. Les deux autres sont rentrés vivants dans la peinture de grand style, ce qui n'est pas rien.

Mes collectionneuses voulaient entrer dans des livres. Avec ou sans argent, c'est pareil, puisqu'ici tout ce qui compte vraiment est gratuit. Après tout, les modèles ont bien leurs idées sur leur vie posthume. Elles trouvent que leur corps vaut mieux que des robes, des bijoux, des fourrures, des photos, des films. C'est le contraire de l'impermanence bouddhiste. L'écrit, pour elles, garde sa fascination.

Elles peuvent d'ailleurs ignorer que vous êtes « écrivain », et n'en avoir rien à faire. Tout de même, elles sentent qu'elles n'ont presque jamais été observées et écoutées de cette façon. Vous les intéressez à elles-mêmes, mieux que les hommes, cela va de soi, mais mieux aussi que leurs meilleures amies ou copines. Vous êtes un vampire, tant mieux. Elles sont mariées et ont des enfants ? Et alors ? Elles ont des amants ? Et alors ? Vos atouts sont la gratuité, le détachement, l'ironie, l'athéisme sexuel radical. Comment, *vous n'y croyez pas* ? Allons, allons, une conversion est toujours possible.

Je parle ici de mes années avec « suffrage à vue » (merveilleuse expression de Casanova), qui ont duré au moins quarante ans (15 ans-55 ans). Le suffrage en question est souhaitable pour voyager et gagner du temps.

Désormais, sans aucune mélancolie, je me récite parfois ces vers de Rimbaud dans *Une saison en enfer* :

> « *Donc tu te dégages*
> *Des humains suffrages,*
> *Des communs élans !*
> *Tu voles selon...* »

Vivre encore, et encore, c'est apprendre à voler *selon*.

Eugenia s'appelle Concha dans *Une curieuse solitude*, et, très longtemps après, Maria dans *Studio*. Dominique, dans ce roman, devient Ingrid, et il y a beaucoup de Julia dans la Judith du *Secret*, mais aussi dans la Maud de *L'Étoile des amants*. Les personnages principaux ont donc des IRM, des Identités Rapprochées Multiples, comme les différents narrateurs. La vie romanesque les fait surgir ou res-surgir, selon les rencontres ou les précipités de mémoire.

Je ne m'attendais pas à l'apparition de Lucie dans *L'Éclaircie*, sous les traits de l'une de mes sœurs, Anne. Les mères, les filles, les tantes, les sœurs, les nièces ont chacune leurs couleurs : noir, blanc, rouge, bleu, vert, jaune, orange, grenat, violet, mauve. Les prénoms, comme les voyelles, sont des couleurs. J'ai déjà celui d'une femme d'un prochain roman, que je ne dirai pas avant de l'avoir fini, c'est magique.

L'amour libre est celui du « pouvoir aimant ». Une des clés de cette musique est la tendresse et son intimité. L'amitié amoureuse existe, elle est exceptionnelle, mais indestructible. Encore un don d'enfance, rare s'il y a eu un contact physique, encore plus rare si tout est resté en suspens. Le modèle en est Marion, dans *Studio*, une Anglaise qui travaillait dans les services secrets, comme Viva dans *Les Voyageurs du Temps*. Les femmes sont plus douées que les hommes pour le renseignement, la clandestinité, l'espionnage. Elles savent, de source sûre, que la vraie vie est cachée. Il vaut mieux les avoir pour amies dans cette dimension des choses.

Je conseille au débutant, avant d'atteindre une sérénité méritée, de commencer très tôt, et dans toutes les dimensions possibles. Il est déjà expérimenté sur son propre corps, l'autoérotisme n'a pas de secrets pour lui, il a beaucoup d'imagination, il la satisfait sans culpabilité notable. Il a 12 ou 13 ans, le « suffrage à vue », il vit dans un milieu privilégié, où les employées de maison, cuisinières et femmes de ménage, ont pour lui des attentions particulières. Il les observe, tourne autour, capte leur curiosité. Il a compris tout de suite que c'est à elles de faire des avances. Elles les font. Leur tempérament du Sud-Ouest s'y prête. Elles ont 30 ou 40 ans, ce sont des mères d'origine paysanne expertes, leurs caresses sont informées et précises, c'est le paradis sur terre.

Il y a Jacqueline, garçon réussi, avec qui je fais du vélo, Thérèse, aux seins magnifiques, Denise, au regard de feu, Louise, dans les garages, et enfin

85

Eugenia, pour les expériences plus sérieuses, fondées sur la « première fois » (pénétration, possession). C'est le début, à 15 ans, des « grandes histoires » en style amoureux. Ce débutant-là, déjà passionné de lecture et de poésie, deviendra sans doute « écrivain », puisqu'il se raconte ses sensations et ses gestes.

La précocité a ses avantages, mais aussi ses inconvénients. Le débutant essaie quelques filles bourgeoises de son âge, mais elles ne savent rien faire, sauf de la mauvaise littérature sentimentale sur fond de trucage social, mariage et enfants futurs. C'est consternant. Une fois installé à Paris, le débutant veut des contacts concrets, rapides, expéditifs. Il a quelques moyens financiers, il va donc, en dehors de toute morale, utiliser la prostitution. Il a ses plans, il marche sans arrêt dans la ville, il sait où trouver ce qu'il lui faut, du côté de la gare Saint-Lazare ou de Montparnasse. Il noue quelques habitudes joyeuses rue de Provence, jette un coup d'œil, l'après-midi, sur la terrasse de *La Lorraine*, où des femmes mûres (les meilleures) attendent le client. Voilà tout un monde disparu, furtif, au signal, celui des hôtels de passe, comme l'inoubliable maison de rendez-vous de la rue Sainte-Beuve, donnant sur le boulevard Raspail.

On peut s'étonner de ce genre de dérive systématique, mais le débutant, à Paris, ne connaît personne et n'a aucune envie de s'agréger à un milieu social, quel qu'il soit. En somme, il poursuit ses études. Les femmes mûres sont un peu étonnées de lever un garçon si jeune. Bien entendu, en souvenir d'Eugenia, il demande souvent deux femmes à la fois, c'est possible, action, souplesse, amusement, géométrie dans l'espace. Autres études : quelques stages dans des endroits « échangistes », histoire de noter la dissimulation intéressée des femmes et la bestialité répugnante des hommes. Les prostituées, au moins, ne font pas semblant de jouir, elles sont honnêtes et même scrupuleuses. Parfois, cependant…

Vite fait, bien fait, savoir immémorial et populaire, avec Paris comme capitale incontestable, du moins dans cette époque lointaine. À part *La Lorraine*, les meilleurs coups se trouvent en terrasse de *La Coupole* ou du *Dôme*. Les hôtels complices sont rue Chaplain, et, le soir, on peut encore traîner dans des bars comme *Le Parc aux cerfs* (pas possible ? mais si, mais si !), *Adrien* (piano), *Elle et Lui*. Dans ce dernier lieu, merveilleusement mal famé, on peut se laisser séduire par des travestis, tous plus féminins les uns que les autres. Voilà l'université du débutant, qui n'accorde aucune importance à sa présence fantomatique dans des amphithéâtres sinistres. Il a ses diplômes de bordel, c'est bien suffisant.

Il connaît quand même des échecs. Il a beau boire et reboire, consommer et reconsommer, il n'arrivera pas à convaincre cette sublime entraîneuse, qui partira à la fermeture, vers trois heures du matin, avec un autre client plus âgé. Il se retrouve ivre et furieux sur un banc, du côté du Luxembourg. Il fréquente d'ailleurs beaucoup les parcs, le bois de Boulogne (rien à faire, trop industriel), le parc Monceau (rien à faire non plus, femmes rangées et enfants), mais, que voulez-vous, il a besoin de verdure, d'arbres, de fleurs.

Je viens de dire « Paris, capitale de la luxure », mais là, je suis injuste avec Barcelone, qui aura été un vrai paradis. Picasso, très jeune, a obtenu là ses diplômes, comme Manet les a brillamment raflés, jadis, à Paris. La rue Saint-Denis, convulsive, appartient pour toujours à Georges Bataille (*Madame Edwarda*). Les relations de Giacometti avec les prostituées de Montparnasse ne sont plus un secret pour personne. Henry Miller, explorateur intrépide, a découvert, à Pigalle, l'antipode de l'Amérique. On me dit que l'Amérique latine (notamment Cuba, à La Havane) est pleine de femmes sensibles et faciles. Si je me réfère à mon expérience espagnole, je le crois volontiers.

De temps en temps, je dois vérifier les écrits de jeunes gens aux grandes ambitions. Je lis entre les lignes la nature de leurs expériences sexuelles, mais je tombe le plus souvent sur des visas douteux, voire des certificats de complaisance. Rien de probant, les jeunes filles en fleurs, à fanaison rapide, occupent le fond des tableaux. La psychologie revient comme chez elle, les actes sont conventionnels et sourds. Ils ne seront jamais de vieux robots primaires, genre DSK, et pas davantage des déprimés profonds, style Houellebecq. Ils manquent de corps, comme s'ils n'avaient jamais rencontré des corps.

J'ouvre Le Clézio, rien, Modiano, élégant brouillard, Quignard, mélancolie et traumatisme de la naissance. Chez ce dernier, une triste figure apparaît dans toutes les pages, celle de la raide Isabelle Huppert. Il s'est sûrement passé quelque chose de terrible dans ce pays, mais quoi ?

Vous posez cette question à une femme : « Supposons que vous changiez de sexe, vous aimeriez les hommes ou les femmes ? » Réponse immédiate la plus courante : « Les hommes. – Vous seriez alors homosexuel ? » Léger trouble. Je peux aussi ajouter : « Décidément, nous n'avons pas les mêmes goûts. »

Les lesbiennes, drôle d'histoire (rebonjour Baudelaire !). En principe, sauf dérapage, un homme n'entre pas dans ce château fort, et c'est normal, puisque, la plupart du temps, il s'agit d'amour courtois sur fond de tribadisme fiévreux. Je suis allé deux ou trois fois dans des endroits spécialisés (j'avais un passeport), et, comme de juste, je m'y suis beaucoup ennuyé (le débutant, ici, se souvient d'un bar d'autrefois particulièrement sinistre, *Le Monocle*). Ça ne m'a pas empêché d'avoir de fortes attirances de ce côté. Il y a, sur ce point, une photo célèbre et sublime de Cartier-Bresson, deux

femmes ensemble (au Mexique, je crois), enlace-
ment de toute beauté, pris, à la dérobée, à travers
une porte entrouverte, sans doute la plus belle
photo du monde. Eugenia était bisexuelle, et
c'était, pour moi, un de ses charmes les plus
puissants.

Les homosexuels, eux, m'ennuient vite (sauf
exception), les femmes jamais. Les homos ne
voient pas la moitié du ciel, drôle de vision cléri-
cale. Ils vieillissent tous, même les plus « virils »,
en fausses femmes, région prévue de l'enfer. Ils
manquent d'enfance, et restent, même les plus
obsédés sexuellement, très sentimentaux. Les
Mères, toutes-puissantes, surveillent dans l'ombre
ce continent du Spectacle. Sur ce miroitement
désertique, Genet a tout dit.

Je revois certaines prostituées dans le temps : ma
reconnaissance les accompagne, leur *humanité* me
touche. Expédier des corps, et, parfois s'attarder sur
l'un d'eux, fait partie de la science de la vie, donc de
la mort. On veut interdire la prostitution ? Si la vraie
raison est d'empêcher l'esclavage organisé et les
filières criminelles mafieuses, elle n'est pas discutable.
Mais quelque chose me dit qu'une source noire plus
profonde est à l'œuvre : on veut empêcher le débutant de faire ses études, d'apprendre le dessin, la couleur, la grammaire, la logique, et, tout simplement,

ne serait-ce que par contraste, la pureté, la raison, le goût.

Dernière étrangeté : les femmes qu'on n'a eues qu'en rêve. Je parle ici de vrais rêves nocturnes, avec grand élan, grand accord, grande satisfaction réciproque. Conclusion : ça aurait été moins bien dans la réalité, il fallait passer dans une autre géométrie, s'atteindre physiquement dans une quatrième dimension d'accueil. Je ne donne pas de noms, mais je pense surtout à l'une d'elles : on n'a jamais fait l'amour, et on l'a fait au moins dix fois en dormant, très loin l'un de l'autre. Si elle lit ce livre (peu probable), je suis sûr qu'elle se reconnaîtra.

J'aurais aimé connaître Suzanne Manet, Victorine Meurent, Berthe Morisot, Méry Laurent, et, à vrai dire, toutes les femmes des anciens peintres. J'imagine cette boulangère vénitienne posant pour Titien pour une Vénus ou une Assomption. Elle fluidifie son pinceau pendant des heures. Ensuite, j'interroge Victorine Meurent : « C'est bien vous, dans l'*Olympia* et *Le Déjeuner sur l'herbe* ? » Je l'entends me répondre : « Oh, vous savez, Manet avait une vision très spéciale des femmes. – Mais enfin, c'est bien vous ? – Si vous voulez, mais je ne vois pas ce que ça me rapporte, d'ailleurs je vous signale que moi-même je peins. » Même scène avec Berthe Morisot : « Ah non, écoutez, c'est trop douloureux. Mais que pensez-vous de mes toiles ? » Et

Suzanne : « Un mari exquis, n'insistez pas. » Et Méry Laurent ? « Un très grand ami, je n'en dirai pas plus. » Au fond : « Il n'est plus là, et nous sommes toujours présentes, nos corps s'alourdissent, alors que lui n'a pas eu le temps de vieillir, il a fixé notre beauté que nous ne voulons plus regarder. »

Même type de réponse avec les femmes de Picasso, en beaucoup plus agressif. Picasso ? Un monstre misogyne, entièrement tourné vers lui-même. Un sadique, un pervers, un mégalomane absolu. Un obsédé sexuel, comme le montrent ses derniers barbouillages. Dora Maar pleure toujours, se met à peindre et devient mystique, pendant que Françoise Gilot peint de grands draps rouges ésotériques. Quant à Marie-Thérèse Walter et Jacqueline Picasso, elles se suicident après la mort de leur amour persécuteur. Tristes tropiques.

Mes meilleurs souvenirs de femmes au cinéma ? Sans aucun doute la bondissante Debby Reynolds, dans *Chantons sous la pluie*, sans oublier Cyd Charisse et ses jambes (d'où le personnage de Cyd dans *Femmes*). Et puis toutes les actrices de Hitchcock, surtout Janet Leigh et Tippi Hedren, enveloppées, dessinées, magnétiques, toujours au bord de l'hallucination ou de la folie. Pas de Françaises, pour moi, dans le cinéma. Pas de femmes convaincantes chez Godard, trop protestant pour ce genre d'approche (il remplace l'élément féminin par la couleur). De toutes les apparitions corporelles, je retiens cette jeune paysanne grecque, dans *Méditerranée*, de Jean-Daniel Pollet. Elle boutonne lentement son tablier bleu, visage dans le miroir, fond de mer bleue. Regardez ses mains et ses doigts, c'est la perfection naturelle même.

J'ai voulu savoir pourquoi la meilleure incarnation de la marquise de Merteuil, au cinéma, n'était pas française mais américaine. Je suis donc allé voir Glenn Close à New York, pour lui dire mon admiration (sa bouche, lorsqu'elle prononce le mot *war*). À ce moment-là, elle jouait une pièce absurde au théâtre, mais, après le spectacle, on a longuement parlé des *Liaisons dangereuses*, dans sa loge, en buvant du champagne. Elle a disparu tard, dans la nuit, dans une grande limousine noire. Intelligence surprenante, beauté charmeuse et sauvage. Je ne sais plus dans quel film elle apparaît tout à coup dans un peignoir bleu. C'est de loin mon actrice préférée. En revanche, j'ose à peine dire, quitte à choquer l'armée américaine tout entière, que l'admirable et tragique Marilyn Monroe me laisse froid.

Les musiciennes ? Oh oui, des génies. Au clavier, Clara Haskil dans Mozart, Martha Argerich dans Bach (une de mes plus belles rencontres, un soir prolongé, à Bruxelles). Au violon, encore dans

Bach, Julia Fischer. Les voix pour moi bouleversantes ? Kathleen Ferrier, Elizabeth Schwarzkopf, Cecilia Bartoli. Mais j'ai aussi des souvenirs de gratitude pour Marilyn Horne, Ann Murray, Judith Nelson, Emma Kirkby.

Les voix désagréables sont légion (il suffit d'ouvrir la radio et la télévision), et j'avoue volontiers être un malade du bruit et de la voix humaine. Entre une très jolie femme à la mauvaise voix, et une femme sans beauté apparente à la voix mélodieuse, je choisis tout de suite la deuxième, fût-ce au téléphone. La voix dit toujours la vérité, même si elle ment, ce qui n'est pas grave. Deux voix magnifiques : Dominique, Julia. Le rire, la voix, ça ne trompe pas.

La discordance entre le corps et la voix est une information de première importance. Exemple : Simone de Beauvoir, beauté mais voix pincée insupportable. Autre exemple : Duras, et son élocution forcée, saccadée, symptôme d'une volonté d'emprise constante. Voilà des voix qui n'ont rien à cacher : tout est dehors, d'emblée, de façon militaire. Aucun humour, évidemment. Des voix de commandement.

L'érotisme, *bien entendu*, est fonction de la voix et du dire. Une femme qui peut changer de voix quand il faut, passer sans transition du « vous » au

« tu », de la conversation subtile à l'intonation franchement canaille, est au-dessus de l'éloge. C'est, par exemple, Sophie dans *Portrait du joueur*, un comble.

La voix basse, la voix haute, le murmure, le chuchotement, le soupir, le sourire, la moue, tout ce qui a trait aux lèvres, à la langue, tout ce qui *dialogue* en parlant, devient signe. Épargnez-moi toutes les bouches refaites de la publicité, charcuterie immangeable. Ne touchez pas à votre peau, laissez-la-moi. Parle, et tu es à moi. Ris, et tu es à moi plus encore. Si tu as ri, et as dit « oui », c'est un vrai *oui* du jour dans la nuit.

L'accord sur les mots grossiers ou doux exige beaucoup de délicatesse. Une fausse note, et tout déraille. Vous devez discerner ce qu'une femme veut entendre en secret et qu'elle ne pourrait pas supporter à l'état normal. Cela suppose qu'elle-même a su deviner ce qu'elle doit vous dire ou éviter de vous faire entendre. Le point de rencontre est musical, pour la pornographie comme pour la tendresse. L'une n'empêche pas l'autre (parfois à venir), les partenaires s'admirent, et sont en droit de le faire, sinon c'est en eux l'infection larvée du social. Ils ont leur langage singulier qu'ils sont seuls à comprendre. Public, il exploserait dans un ridicule insensé.

On agit d'abord, on parle ensuite. C'est ma formule de Lucie dans *L'Éclaircie,* en entrant dans le studio en fin d'après-midi : « Désennuyons-nous. » On ne parle pas de la même façon avant ou après l'acte, raison pour laquelle les actions en fin de soirée sont à éviter. On a trop bu, on a trop parlé, trop attendu, la fatigue est là, c'est plus au moins raté, comme le lendemain en témoigne. Je me revois dans une ville étrangère, longue soirée flirteuse, vin et whisky, rien au lit.

Les mots crus sont les meilleurs en français, les mots doux ou les diminutifs ont leur efficacité dans toutes les langues, les noms d'animaux notamment. Les statistiques, paraît-il, le prouvent : les femmes embrassent plus que les hommes. Les théologiens et les philosophes se sont trompés : les femmes ont une âme. Je revois la traductrice américaine de *Femmes,* la même que celle de Duras, me demander quelques explications de texte, et s'arrêter sur une expression sur laquelle elle venait buter : « Elle m'embrasse au souffle. » Comment lui expliquer ? Elle n'avait visiblement aucune idée d'une performance de ce genre, et il n'était pas question d'entraîner cette femme sérieuse et d'un certain âge dans une démonstration pratique. Quand une femme vous embrasse (ou s'embrasse à travers vous), vous savez exactement où vous êtes. Admis ou pas. Notre époque n'est pas favorable à l'âme, d'où l'apparition du répétitif et misérable « bisou ».

À l'instant, comme une morsure mortelle, j'entends intérieurement la voix de Dominique : « Au revoir, petit chéri ! » Je pense à sa beauté et à sa noblesse. Sa fin m'évoque celle de cette comtesse du 18e siècle, morte en 1736, qui a rédigé elle-même son épitaphe :

> « Ci-gît, dans une paix profonde,
> Cette dame de volupté,
> Qui, pour plus grande sûreté,
> Fit son paradis en ce monde. »

J'ai devant les yeux, dans mon jardin au bord de l'océan, un bougainvillier grenat, dont la couleur éclate entre deux grands acacias. Son nom évoque Louis-Antoine de Bougainville (1729-1811) et son célèbre *Voyage autour du monde*, effectué entre 1766 et 1769. L'édition originale de 1771 se présente ainsi :

Voyage
Autour du monde
Par la Frégate du Roi
*La Boudeuse*
Et
*La Flûte L'Étoile*
En 1766, 1767, 1768 et 1769
À Paris
Chez Saillant et Nyon, Libraire,
rue S. Jean-de-Beauvais
De l'imprimerie de Le Breton,
premier Imprimeur du Roi
M.DCC.LXXI.

Avec Approbation et Privilège du Roi.

Vous avez bien lu, le roi a voyagé autour du monde, il était sur le pont de *La Boudeuse,* de *La Flûte,* de *L'Étoile,* il a fini par découvrir, en 1768, une île de Mélanésie (dans l'archipel des Salomon) dont on peut se demander pourquoi elle s'appelle encore aujourd'hui *Bougainville.* Le roi a tout fait, tout connu sans quitter Versailles, subi les tempêtes et les accalmies, le désespoir et les féeries, écrit et imprimé ses aventures, avec sa propre approbation, comme son privilège le lui permet, en tant que roi.

Vous imaginez *La Boudeuse* au large de l'Australie ? Heureusement que *La Flûte* et *L'Étoile* étaient là, je les vois d'ici, dans le couchant, à l'ancre. En tout cas, ne me dites pas que ce bougainvillier n'est pas une plante de rêve, et qu'il y a une plus belle couleur que le *grenat* (un *velours grenat*). Il est vrai que je ne connais pas encore une Mélanésienne, je suis moins savant que le roi.

Y avait-il des bougainvilliers dans les jardins de Voltaire ? C'est probable. La ravissante Pompadour n'a pas pu les connaître, puisqu'elle est morte en 1764, à l'âge de 43 ans. Regardez son portrait somptueux par Maurice Quentin de La Tour, et vous comprendrez pourquoi la Française est tombée de haut. On ne l'imagine plus, sauf exception, dans un pastel bleu de ce temps bleu. Le temps bleu est celui de femmes étranges par leur liberté, Mme Du Deffand, par exemple, à qui Voltaire, le 22 juillet 1761 (deux ans après la parution de *Candide*), écrit ce qui suit :

« Quand je vous aurai bien répété que la vie est un enfant qu'il faut bercer jusqu'à ce qu'il s'endorme, j'aurai dit tout ce que je sais. »

Émilie Le Tonnelier de Breteuil, marquise du Châtelet, est morte, elle aussi, à l'âge de 43 ans, des suites d'une grossesse intempestive, « couverte » par Voltaire. Berçait-elle son philosophe comme un enfant dans son château de Cirey ? Son caractère ne l'indique guère et le prochain château de Voltaire s'appellera, avant Ferney, « Les Délices ». Émilie était jalouse, ne voulait pas que son amant aille voir Frédéric de Prusse, mais, sur ce chemin, nous trouvons Mme Bentinck, « grande amie », que Voltaire décrit ainsi : « Haute en couleur, fraîche, grasse, appétissante. » Elle a une « taille majestueuse », alors que sa nièce et maîtresse, Mme Denis, est « petite et grosse ». Charlotte-Sophie Bentinck ? La voici : « La spirituelle, l'éloquente, la sucrée, la romanesque, la bavarde comtesse. » Leur histoire mérite, de leur part, les mots « destinée », « roman ».

La voici aux « Délices », quand il est en train de composer *Candide*. Elle écrit, dans une lettre à un poète allemand qui a rencontré Voltaire six ans avant :

« M. de Voltaire est présentement la divinité que tout le monde adore. Je n'ai jamais vu une idolâtrie plus poussée que celle que tout le monde a pour lui. Aussi sait-il bien la mériter par ses façons. Il est charmant, doux, égal, gracieux, sociable, enfin, Monsieur, vous ne le reconnaîtriez assurément pas. D'abord il est coquet, bien poudré, tiré à quatre épingles. Il se faufile agréablement avec la compagnie, il se prête à tous, il daigne se communiquer à chacun ; il soupe, il joue, il se promène ; il vit comme les hommes, et parle comme personne n'a jamais parlé. Sa maison est montée comme celle d'un prince. Il fait une dépense enragée, et il est le seul de ce pays qui vive de cette opulence. »

La spirituelle Mme Bentinck est, pour Voltaire, « celle avec qui je voudrais passer ma vie ». Il réclame d'« avoir l'honneur de vivre avec elle ». Il a, pour elle, « un zèle, un respect, un attachement infinis ». Il faut dire qu'elle le soutient de mille façons dans son conflit avec Frédéric. Ils pensent tous les deux être guidés par une « étoile ». Elle refuse ses propositions de vie commune (pas question de s'enfermer à la campagne), mais Voltaire garde pour elle une grande tendresse. Elle lui écrit encore, de Hambourg, le 17 avril 1778. Là, Voltaire ne pourra pas lui répondre, puisqu'il est mort à Paris, le 30 mai.

Émilie du Châtelet, malgré ses connaissances scientifiques, s'est laissé tardivement faire un enfant par le poète Saint-Lambert. Voltaire est catastrophé, convoque le mari d'Émilie, lui fait endosser la paternité, arrange tout (car on ne se brouille pas « avec une amie de vingt ans »), et voit sa camarade de combat mourir sous ses yeux en couches. À défaut de Charlotte-Sophie, il s'arrangera donc avec sa nièce, à qui il écrit des lettres très crues en italien. Mais enfin, qui est Cunégonde, la Dulcinée de Candide ? La conclusion du roman est sévère : Cunégonde est devenue « laide, acariâtre et insupportable ». Sa rédemption, dans le jardin « qu'il faut cultiver », fait d'elle une « excellente pâtissière ». Morale à la Ubu : « Vous êtes bien laide, ce soir, madame Ubu. Est-ce parce que nous avons du monde ? »

J'ai eu de la chance : pas de ressentiment ou d'esprit de vengeance entre les femmes et moi. Des folles à distance, oui, mais pas de « laides et acariâtres » proches. Il faut dire que je suis un explorateur méconnu : je n'ai pas fait le tour du monde, mais j'ai identifié très tôt, afin de le neutraliser, un organe microscopique, très difficile à localiser, source de toutes les manifestations atrabilaires, situé chez les femmes de façon presque invisible, mais ayant un grand effet d'usure toxique dans la vie des hommes. J'ai nommé le cœur de la rancœur, la VVB, la Vésicule Vaginale Biliaire. Ma découverte va beaucoup plus loin que celle de l'hystérie, devenue globale et banale. Ce pas sur la lune, de façon très injuste, ne m'a pas encore valu le Nobel.

Le 13 septembre 1758, Mme Bentinck est donc chez Voltaire aux « Délices ». Elle reste jusqu'au 3 octobre, et on ne sait rien de leurs conversations, pendant ce moment capital où Voltaire achève *Candide*. Il lui écrit peu après son départ, en parlant des opérations militaires en cours :

« Il y aura encore bien des faubourgs brûlés, bien des femmes grosses écrasées, et des princesses évanouies, et des familles réduites à la mendicité, et des héros à cinq sous par jour massacrés, avant que les choses soient ce qu'elles doivent être. Le meilleur des mondes possibles de Leibniz est un petit enfer, et tout paraît assez *mal*, sur ce petit globe ou globule, dans lequel Pope trouve que tout est *bien*. J'ai mes raisons pour renoncer au système de l'optimisme, mais si vous êtes heureuse, je pardonnerai un peu au diable qui se mêle des affaires de ce monde. »

On sait, par une autre lettre, que le départ de Charlotte-Sophie lui a rendu les « yeux humides ». Voltaire sentimental dix minutes ? Mais oui. N'exagérons rien : le diable ne règne que sur un « globule ».

On n'est pas obligé de suivre Dante au paradis, conduit par la main céleste de Béatrice, morte à peine adolescente, ni de souscrire à la formule finale du *Faust* de Goethe : « L'éternel féminin nous attire vers le haut. » Il n'y a plus de ciel ni de « haut », le paradis est ici, ou pas. Le vieux Goethe, à plus de 80 ans, était très amoureux d'une fille de 19 ans, fâcheux retour d'âge, poésie idéalisante. On peut, en revanche, en s'appuyant sur un violent sentiment contraire aux trous noirs, garder le dernier vers sublime de *La Divine Comédie*, « L'amour qui meut le soleil et les autres étoiles », et aussi cet hommage à Éros du vieil auteur de *Faust* : « L'amour forme tout, protège tout. »

Le Diable a ses ressources : on l'a vu à l'œuvre, depuis des millénaires, dans l'exploitation des femmes, à travers le mariage subi, les sabbats nocturnes, la maladie romantique, la folie des hommes. Des religieuses au voile et à la burqua, du harcèlement au viol, en passant par l'idéalisation poétique ou mystique, on aura tout vu, et c'est peut-être loin d'être fini.

Et pourtant, c'est fini. J'ai toujours fait l'apologie du mariage, le mien en tout cas, pas celui des autres. Le mariage a explosé, les divorces ne se comptent plus, les familles recomposées rament, mais le voici de retour comme protection et revendication de stabilité. Les jeunes gens, paraît-il, y reviennent par conformisme, les homosexuels le réclament et l'obtiennent, avec la possibilité d'adoption d'enfants. Dans un contexte dévastateur, cette renormalisation est étrange. Du patriarcat traditionnel en ruine, on s'achemine peu à peu vers un matriarcat contrôlable. Le mariage classique opprimait les femmes, le nouveau, en Occident du moins, est appelé à cadrer les hommes. Ils seront fidèles, transparents, loyaux, monogames, participatifs, utiles. Les Droits de l'homme sont faits pour ça.

En tout cas, le mariage, pour moi, a été une décision antisociale défensive. On aime quelqu'un, la société s'y oppose, on affirme son choix. Question de temps dans le temps. Si le « mariage d'amour » existe, il est menacé (s'il s'agit vraiment d'amour). Il faut donc le protéger, avec ses composantes particulières : attrait immédiat, confiance, travail parallèle, chacun son lieu et son argent, son nom. C'est une force. Là où ça coince, c'est dans la demande de transparence. Rien n'est plus faux, sur ce point, que le contrat Sartre-Beauvoir : on se dit tout, on se raconte tout, on ne fait rien sans le regard et le jugement de l'autre. Erreur, et méconnaissance des corps. Les femmes en ont souffert pendant des siècles (couvent, amour courtois, bovarysation, adultère, remariages divers), et les hommes, pour la plupart, ont tout à y perdre : routine, censure, surveillance propriétaire, châtrage banal. Sans aller jusqu'à demander à une femme de s'exclamer, de façon héroïque, comme la femme de Morand : « Un homme qui ne trompe pas sa femme n'est pas un homme ! », on peut quand même écouter ce qui se dit là.

Ceci : pas de discussion possible, entre hommes et femmes, sur la « sexualité ». Opacité, réflexions générales, mais, surtout, silence. Arrangez-vous, la loi n'a rien à faire dans cette histoire. Vous avez le droit d'abriter votre singularité dans le mariage, pas celui d'introduire la police, sauf mauvais traitements, dans votre intimité. Le mariage, en général, a été, pour la grande majorité, un enfer. À un moment, on voulait, Julia et moi, écrire un livre à deux voix, avec, pour titre : *Le Mariage considéré comme un des Beaux-Arts,* mais pourquoi se donner en modèles ? Le titre, seul, était bon. Pour le reste, sauf dans la fiction, la discrétion s'impose.

Vous êtes un homme, soit, mais vous êtes aussi un enfant. Vous êtes marié, vous avez un fils, vous avez connu beaucoup d'aventures, mais vous n'aurez pleinement réussi votre parcours que si vous vous faites accepter comme un enfant, *l'enfant que vous n'avez jamais cessé d'être.* Soyez l'enfant de votre femme, et, surtout, faites-la rire. Elle est particulièrement jolie quand elle rit.

J'écoute les femmes avec curiosité, je vérifie mes données de base. Autant de femmes, autant de petits romans concentrés. Ça ne va pas fort avec les hommes, toujours les mêmes questions : où sont-ils, que font-ils, pourquoi se dérobent-ils ? Foule de textos, l'attente, toujours l'attente, l'angoisse et la déception de l'attente. On leur cède son corps, et puis, le lendemain, ils ont peur, ils s'enfuient, ne rappellent pas, craignant sans doute la demande d'enfant ou d'installation. Ils ne se rendent pas compte de la merveille qui leur est offerte. Si l'un d'eux accepte l'appropriation, il sera trompé. Normal : finalement, il est ennuyeux, on se demande si c'est un vrai homme.

Rien de plus pathétique qu'une femme qui s'accroche à un homme. Aucun obstacle ne peut la dissuader, c'est une dévote qu'aucun refus ne rebute. Lisez *Rendez-vous*, de Christine Angot, ou *Un homme dans la poche*, d'Aurélie Filippetti, deux très bons livres. Au moins, ces deux-là ont trouvé la force d'écrire, et c'est courageux. Ce sont des filles de pères ou de grands-pères spéciaux, et toute une histoire les rattrape dans leurs aventures : lutte des classes, conflits ethnique ou culturel, omniprésence d'un drame familial, conséquences de la déportation, mort de la mère. Elles vont en psychanalyse, et ça irait encore plus mal si elles ne le faisaient pas. Ces séances peuvent durer des années, des siècles. Leurs enfants les empêchent de s'effondrer, elles attendent de voir leurs petits-enfants, elles traversent comme elles peuvent les soucis sociaux, et, parfois, l'enfer politique.

Le cinéma, la mode, la publicité font leur travail. Une femme doit être une image, elle est d'abord photographiable et filmable, sinon elle n'existe pas. Non seulement elle est une image, mais elle doit se comporter sans cesse selon cette image : s'habiller, ne pas grossir, maigrir, sourire, soutenir les productions en cours. Pour les célibataires, il y a plein d'annonces, toutes plus attractives les unes que les autres, par exemple, cette pub télévisée « Attractive World, pour célibataires exigeants ». Si vous me plaisez, vous m'épousez. Une femme quelle qu'elle soit est un argument de vente. Dans la conversation, c'est pareil : faire sa propre publicité, dire du mal de tout le monde à tout le monde, en essayant de ne pas trop « se couper », et, surtout, rendre la concurrence impossible, « Une autre femme que moi ? Vous n'y pensez pas ! ».

Au cas où elles sont classées, et plus ou moins pénalisées, comme « femme de » (politiciens, intellectuels, artistes, sportifs), elles s'indignent et le font savoir. Quel rapport y a-t-il entre un compagnon ou un mari et leur propre identité professionnelle ? Aucun, c'est l'évidence. Leur protestation est mal comprise, parce qu'elles ne vont pas jusqu'à dire : « Si vous saviez comme je m'ennuie à la maison ! » C'est pourtant le cas, conflit automatique entre images. « On ne voit que toi. – Ah non, on ne parle que de toi ! » Les journées sont journalistiques, médiatiques, stratégiques. Les rumeurs, les réseaux, les tweets vous poursuivent

jusque dans votre salle de bains. Ça parle énormé-
ment, d'où, parfois, des bulles en surface. « Brasier
de complots », dit quelque part Saint-Simon, qui
serait très surpris (mais peut-être pas) que l'humanité en soit là.

Mon fils, David, a eu, lorsqu'il était enfant, deux
mots charmants à mon sujet. Comme je passe la
plupart de mon temps, seul, à écrire, il a dit un
jour : « Papa est comme Dieu, il existe, mais on ne
le voit pas. » Et, une autre fois, formule étonnante :
« Papa est un célibataire heureux. » Fameux compliment, et qui a fait rire sa mère.

À l'opposé du malheur féminin, programmé par des siècles d'obscurantisme, et grâce aux avancées de la science et de la technique, il existe de plus en plus de femmes autonomes et libres. Le spectacle, le plus souvent mécanique et navrant, de la société, ne les impressionne pas. Je les ai rencontrées, ces artistes de la vie, tous mes romans parlent d'elles. Elles sont reconnaissables au fait qu'elles ont dû surmonter des situations difficiles et des tonnes de préjugés. Elles connaissent le noir, elles aiment le bleu. Une sorte de gai savoir les accompagne. Je leur dois beaucoup.

Une artiste de la vie ne perd pas de temps, identifie au coup d'œil les contraintes qu'on veut lui faire endosser, gagne sa vie, n'a pas peur des compromis, sait que les meilleurs arrangements sont les plus commodes. Elle suit son cap « à la chinoise ». Elle est douée pour l'amour, mais aussi pour l'amitié. Même si elle est mariée, c'est une célibataire exigeante. Elle est drôle, sensible, discrète, elle sait voyager et juger. On se rencontre, on se reconnaît.

Toutes ces femmes auraient été brûlées au Moyen Âge comme des sorcières, elles n'ont pas le temps de se venger, n'appartiennent à aucun parti ni groupe de pression, font travailler leurs réseaux pour elles seules ou leurs complices, un jour absolument nouveau brille pour elles. Elles pourraient reprendre à leur compte la déclaration de la Juliette de Sade : « Le passé m'encourage, le présent m'électrise, je crains peu l'avenir. » Ce ne sont pas des « espèces » (comme dit Mme de Merteuil). Elles n'ont aucun penchant pour la cruauté, sauf pour se débarrasser des fâcheux, des fâcheuses. Ta liberté plus la mienne, ça fait une sacrée liberté.

Paris, si on sait s'en servir, est toujours une fête. Autant de villes civilisées dans une seule ville : un quartier, une vie, un autre quartier, une autre vie ; encore un autre quartier, et, de nouveau, une autre vie. Je me répète : mon héros de Paris s'appelle Manet. Regardez-le passer sur le boulevard des Italiens. Suivez-le dans son atelier, et admirez une fois de plus le *Bar aux Folies Bergère*.

J'ai été heureux dans le 17ᵉ arrondissement, le 9ᵉ, le 5ᵉ, le 6ᵉ, le 7ᵉ, le 14ᵉ, le 15ᵉ, parfois dans le

8ᵉ, rarement dans le 16ᵉ, assez souvent dans le 13ᵉ, jamais dans le 19ᵉ, une seule fois (mais mémorable) dans le 1ᵉʳ. Voici mes partenaires : elles travaillent tôt et beaucoup, conduisent vite et bien, leur ordinateur est savant, leur téléphone aussi. Les bars ou les restaurants simples et un peu cachés n'ont pas de secrets pour elles, et si j'en retrouve une à New York, Londres, Barcelone ou Rome, ses plans sont parfaits. Personne ne sait où me conduit ce taxi dans la nuit, personne n'a jamais su non plus ce que je faisais, *exactement*, à Venise. Une femme qui me permet d'écrire plus, et mieux, est un don du ciel. Il est impératif qu'elle aime la musique. Laquelle ? Le vrai flamenco, le jazz, et Bach, toujours Bach, encore Bach.

Des artistes de la vie, des femmes-miracles. On est ivres, on rit, on passe la nuit dehors, on s'embrasse, on se sépare, on se reverra bientôt. Tiens, qu'est-ce que je fais dans l'herbe de Hyde Park, entouré de canards et d'oies ? Je ne sais pas, il faut demander à Julia. Saveurs des petits matins à Paris, dans l'île de Ré, à Venise, déploiement silencieux des oiseaux. Une femme dort, on la laisse dormir, ou bien c'est elle qui vous réveille, thé pour elle, café pour moi. C'est le moment enfantin des joues, des yeux, des parfums. Il pleut, ou le ciel est rouge. La circulation commence, ou alors calme plat sur l'eau, pas un bruit.

Je ne sais plus quel Concile a défini l'âme comme étant la « forme du corps ». La formule est très juste. La forme du corps est à peine visible à l'œil nu, c'est une enveloppe, un halo, une aura, un nimbe. Il y a des corps sans âme (les mannequins, par exemple), et d'autres qu'on devine à travers la voix, les mains, la peau. Il y a aussi, hélas, des âmes sans corps, qu'on dirait promises à un malheur de mort. Séparer l'âme du corps, et le corps de l'âme, est une erreur grave et constante. En revanche, je n'ai jamais vu de preuve plus manifeste de leur unicité que les derniers jours de Dominique, beauté corporelle *formée* par son âme. Lumière sur lumière, grâce sur grâce, défi à la mort.

Rimbaud a compris ça, dans la dernière phrase, saisissante et soulignée, d'*Une saison en enfer* : « Et il me sera loisible de *posséder la vérité dans une âme et un corps.* » Et aussi : « Mon âme éternelle, / Observe ton vœu, / Malgré la nuit seule, / Et le jour en feu. »

On n'a jamais vu, je crois, avant Rimbaud, un homme tutoyer son âme comme une femme. Tout de même : « Mon enfant, ma sœur… »

Jusqu'où accepter les défauts de l'autre ? Disons 30 %. Au-delà de ce pourcentage, des questions se posent, et mieux vaut ne pas arriver à 40 %, car, à ce moment-là, même les meilleures qualités faiblissent. J'accepte, de mon côté, d'avoir 30 % de défauts, j'essaye de ne pas dépasser ce coefficient, sauf si j'ai décidé de me rendre insupportable. Plus de 30 % de défauts peut bondir assez vite jusqu'à 70 %, et, là, plus rien à faire, l'ennui s'installe. Toute rencontre devient toxique, une femme met son discours « en boucle », elle ne vous voit plus, ne vous entend plus, interrompt vos phrases, change de sujet en pleine conversation, semble avoir complètement oublié votre existence. C'est dit, c'est cuit. Les ruptures les plus rapides sont les meilleures. Les liaisons de longue durée, au contraire, sont stabilisées avec humour à 30 %. Après tout, 70 % de qualités, c'est énorme.

Je publie de temps en temps un roman que mes amis trouvent en général excellent, ce qui me console un moment des critiques négatives (« ce n'est pas un vrai roman », etc.). Le temps passe, et, par jeu, il m'arrive de demander à l'un ou à l'une s'il (ou elle) se rappelle du prénom du personnage féminin principal de tel ou tel livre. Ils (ou elles) ne s'en souviennent pas. Est-ce pour m'embêter, me ramener à leurs réalités difficiles ? Non, ils ou elles ont carrément *oublié* Maud, Viva ou Minna. Ils, ou elles, ont lu (ou du moins feuilleté) ces romans, dont les femmes, tout à coup, sont absentes.

Mes amis hétéros sont jaloux, mes amies femmes censurent les personnages de femmes, mes amis homos font comme si elles n'avaient jamais existé. Difficile d'imaginer un peintre dont les proches ne verraient pas les tableaux, ou un musicien entouré de gens sourds à toute musique. Après tout, bon, ils ne sont pas obligés de connaître la peinture ou la musique. Avec les livres, ça devrait aller mieux, puisqu'ils utilisent sans cesse des mots et des phrases. Eh non, c'est pire. Expliquez-moi.

J'insiste sur l'effacement des femmes dont j'ai, chaque fois, fait minutieusement le portrait. La conséquence de cette oblitération est que je me demande parfois si j'ai vraiment vécu ce que j'ai vécu. Mais oui, aucun doute, il s'agit bien de ce printemps-là, de cet été-là, de ce merveilleux automne. Jamais les Zattere, à Venise, n'ont été aussi lumineux et beaux, jamais ce bateau n'a mieux fendu l'eau, jamais cet appartement près de l'Hudson, à New York, n'a connu deux amants semblables. Il faut se faire une raison : mes amis, mes amies, ont tendance à me priver de ma vie. Au fond, c'est une famille imaginaire. Pour elles et eux, je suis un cousin gênant.

Le plus frappant, ici, est la perte de mémoire de certains modèles. Elles vivent avec intensité le moment où elles jouent, mais plus du tout dans ce qui en est décrit. Elles doivent avoir un autre récit des mêmes événements, mais comment le savoir sans détails concrets ? Peut-être, d'ailleurs, n'ont-elles aucun souvenir, ou alors très vague. « Un homme, disent les Chinois, ne laisse pas plus de traces dans une femme qu'un oiseau dans le ciel. » Il n'y a pas de mémoire de l'eau ni du ciel.

Disparition de la lecture et de la mémorisation qui devrait s'ensuivre. J'ai autrefois conseillé à une amie qui n'allait pas bien d'apprendre par cœur un poème, et de se le réciter de temps en temps, à voix haute, à elle-même. Baudelaire est un excellent antidépresseur, le mal social ne résiste pas à ses fleurs. Elle a commencé, ça lui a fait le plus grand bien, et puis elle a oublié de continuer, les poèmes sans voix s'évaporent.

Effacement ou falsification des femmes, c'est-à-dire, en fait, de la nature. Un monde contre nature s'édifie, imagé, bavard, insensible, bourré de produits de beauté, de soins médicaux, de gymnastique, de suppléments d'âme sans âme, de puritanisme et de spiritualisme à gogo. Les produits bio et la poudre de perlimpinpin prolifèrent. Si vous en doutez, regardez, après une solide publicité, les émissions religieuses du dimanche matin (surtout les bouddhistes, à mourir de rire).

Comme c'est curieux : une vraie femme apparaît, et le monde, soudain, devient vrai. C'est ce que raconte un ami de Manet, lequel, à la fin de sa vie, souffrait beaucoup de sa jambe gauche (il va être bientôt amputé) : « Manet souffrait constamment, mais il suffisait qu'une femme soit là, n'importe laquelle, et il allait mieux. » Ce « n'importe laquelle » m'enchante. Pourquoi Mozart fait-il chanter à Don Giovanni, avant qu'il disparaisse dans les flammes de la bien-pensance, « Vive les femmes, vive le bon vin, soutiens et gloire de l'humanité ! » ? *N'importe laquelle…*

Eh non, justement, pas n'importe laquelle. Celle-ci, celle-là, et sûrement pas la « jeune débutante » (appelons-la Cunégonde). La petite brune ronde remporte la partie au poker. Elle surgit, elle rit de façon déraisonnable, se met au clavier, et gagne. Je cherche une figure séduisante d'aujourd'hui dans l'audiovisuel français, je fais défiler les images, j'hésite, je ne vois personne, mais si, cette petite châtain mutine, genre noisette chaleureuse et impertinente, une Française comme on n'en fait plus, qui, un soir d'émission télé, sur Canal +, m'a laissé passer sur Stendhal. Comment s'appelle-t-elle déjà ? Elle a un prénom mythologique et un nom de mauvais musicien français du 19e siècle. Voilà : Ariane ! Ariane Massenet ! Ariane, vous n'en avez rien à faire, mais je vous aime.

Le cousin imaginaire gênant n'est pas communautaire. Il n'a même pas appartenu à la puissante secte de la « Communauté inavouable », fondée par un grand Inquisiteur du 20ᵉ siècle, connu pour avoir répandu la terreur chez les esprits forts. Il a écrit *L'Arrêt de mort*, ce qui veut tout dire. Que signifie « communauté inavouable » ? Quelque chose qu'on ne peut pas *avouer* ? Ce terme d'« aveu », outre sa connotation religieuse ou judiciaire, est problématique. S'agit-il d'un acte sexuel sadien particulièrement atroce ? D'un plaisir solitaire déclenché, à heure fixe, chez tous les participants de cette communauté communiste d'un nouveau genre ? Seul l'Inquisiteur a connu la vérité, mais il l'a emportée dans sa tombe.

Une des saintes locales de cette religion imprévue, toute dévouée à l'Inquisiteur, a obtenu un grand succès avec un roman, *L'Amant*. Mais elle a aussi écrit un livre, dont le titre, *La Maladie de la mort*, fait signe vers le rituel ultra-secret de la secte. Tous les membres, en tout cas, semblent avoir une grande vénération pour la Révolution française, et surtout pour la Terreur. Leur tableau préféré est, bien entendu, celui de David, *La Mort de Marat*. Des spécialistes discutent encore pour savoir si un jeune écrivain flamboyant, très ange blond des ténèbres, mort du sida, était, oui ou non, adepte de la confrérie, comme son livre *La Mort propagande* paraît l'indiquer. Parmi les précurseurs de cette vague noire, on peut citer l'auteur de *La Mort à Venise*, en 1912, film culte en 1971. Mais on n'en finirait pas, et l'Inquisiteur, là, tient la corde. Il s'intéressait d'ailleurs beaucoup à Dominique, après la mort de son deuxième mari. Elle a fui.

En 1986, Marguerite Duras fait cette déclaration fracassante :

« Ce n'est pas seulement sexuel l'homosexualité, c'est beaucoup plus vaste que ça. Beaucoup plus terrible. Infernal. Du point de vue de Dieu, on peut expliquer la finalité de presque tout. Sauf ici, ici, on ne peut pas l'expliquer, c'est exactement de la même façon que la mort. Dieu s'est réservé ces domaines-là. Dieu a décidé que l'inexpliqué de sa création, ce serait ces deux choses-là : la mort et l'homosexualité. Ça ne relève pas de la psychanalyse, ces histoires, mais de Dieu. »

On voit que Dieu, ici, reprend du service pour fragiliser la psychanalyse et entraîner les homosexuels dans une dimension métaphysique dont la plupart se passent très bien. Mais Duras est une visionnaire qui copie, de façon confuse, la description que Lautréamont fait de Dieu dans *Les Chants de Maldoror*. Là, pour la première fois, Dieu est montré comme homosexuel et criminel. Pas mort du tout, très actif au contraire, dans un bordel. L'Inquisiteur, bien informé, mais pas jusqu'au bout, a d'ailleurs écrit un livre important sur cette région infernale : *Lautréamont et Sade*. Mais ne troublons pas le 21e siècle : Dieu poursuit sa course de mort, les homosexuels se marient, les laboratoires s'occupent de la transmission de la vie mortelle.

Dans le livre *Les Parleuses,* où elle s'entretient avec Xavière Gauthier, Duras trouve que je suis le seul homme avec qui les femmes peuvent parler à l'époque. Pourquoi ? « Parce que Sollers est désespéré. » Quelle idée ! Je me souviens d'un dîner très lourd avec ces deux voyantes, lequel s'est terminé, de façon pas du tout désespérée, entre Xavière et moi. Elle m'a emmené chez elle, on n'a pas beaucoup parlé, mais le sous-entendu, bien sûr, était : « Duras, quelle raseuse. » Élégante Xavière, excellent souvenir.

La sorcière Duras a dû être avertie de cette trahison, puisqu'au moment de la parution de *Femmes,* elle m'a violemment attaqué dans la presse, allant jusqu'à comparer mon physique à celui d'un moine servant de publicité pour une marque de fromage. J'ai dû répondre qu'elle n'était elle-même qu'un vieux crapaud, ou quelque chose comme ça, ce qui ne l'a pas empêchée de m'embrasser fougueusement, un soir, dans la rue. Il est vrai qu'on prenait assez souvent des verres au *Pré aux clercs*, à côté de la rue Saint-Benoît, où officiait, parfois, l'Inquisiteur. Autre figure très présente dans le discours de Duras : François Mitterrand, dont elle n'arrêtait pas de faire l'éloge. L'Inquisiteur et elle avaient une fixation négative et haineuse : de Gaulle. Ce n'était pas mon avis.

Toute cette agitation a eu un quartier général légendaire, les Éditions de Minuit. Je n'aurai garde d'oublier une autre sorcière, célèbre pour ses séances de magie sexuelle, qu'elle a d'ailleurs racontées avec talent : Catherine Robbe-Grillet, spécialiste sympathique du grand minuit des organes. En ai-je assez dit sur la « communauté inavouable », qui me semble avoir disparu, comme le *Titanic*, dans les glaces ? Je suis sûr, en tout cas, que tous mes livres, après *Femmes*, ont beaucoup gêné ses activités.

Sans aller jusqu'à parler, comme le stupéfiant docteur Artaud, de la « maladresse sexuelle de Dieu », il suffit de rappeler les dates :

*Femmes*, 1983, commencement plus qu'abrupt : « Le monde appartient aux femmes, c'est-à-dire à la mort, là-dessus tout le monde ment. »

Déclaration de Duras sur Dieu, les homosexuels et la mort : 1986.

Pauvre Dieu, pauvres homosexuels ! Comme s'ils étaient dans le coup de ce qui se trafique vraiment, depuis des millénaires, à travers les femmes !

J'écris ces lignes en pleine crise économique, avec effondrement de l'euro et des banques, dans un *autre monde*, donc. Je sors dans mon jardin, il fait beau, je vois un gros pigeon, visiblement en rut, conscient de son importance, qui appelle sans arrêt à l'amour, à travers les arbres. Il ressemble comme deux gouttes d'eau à DSK. Je déchiffre son code, et c'est poignant, entêtant, tragique. J'entends nettement « Nafissa-tou-Diallo » – « Nafissa-tou-Diallo ». Le lendemain et le surlendemain, même topo. « Nafissa-tou ! » – « Nafissa-tou ! » Il n'a pas obtenu de réponse.

Je n'ai jamais porté plainte pour harcèlement, mais j'aurais pu, au moins huit ou dix fois. Sauf qu'un type qui porte plainte pour harcèlement féminin a l'air ridicule. Il est grotesque ou mythomane, pour qui se prend-il ? Ce genre de folie existe pourtant bel et bien : messages incessants, envois de Kleenex avec rouge à lèvres, filatures dans la rue, attentes dans les escaliers, lettres à l'employeur, etc. Harcèlement psychique qui finit presque par forcer l'admiration, malgré le dégoût. Une femme qui a choisi de vous *occuper* est d'une ténacité redoutable. Elle n'attend évidemment aucune réponse, mais le vide décuple son offensive absurde. Qu'est-ce qu'elle veut ? Rien, *vouloir*.

Elle perçoit sur vous, de loin, des effluves de femmes. Ça l'enflamme. Les plus déjantées vous prennent pour une poubelle et vous envoient, pêle-mêle, des flacons, des colifichets, des tickets de caisse, des débris de publicité : *elles vident leur sac.* Je passe sur les envois poétiques ou romanesques, les lettres interminables, les halètements télépho-niques, les photos tocardes, un vrai foutoir. Rien de « sexuel », bien entendu, pas la moindre inven-tion de ce genre. Du sentimental déchaîné et du mauvais goût à hurler. Tout est sexuel, parce que rien ne l'est.

Voilà, au contraire, une exception remarquable : le très beau livre de Catherine Millet, *La Vie sexuelle de Catherine M*. Une femme s'offre à tous les hommes, sans culpabilité, par désir et curiosité. L'auteur, une amie de longue date en toute amitié, a un sens visuel aigu, et restitue les scènes porno-graphiques avec une précision extrême. C'est un chef-d'œuvre de liberté, le seul dans son genre. Son succès a été très révélateur, d'autant plus profond et durable que le livre suivant portait sur la jalousie à l'égard de son partenaire fixe, s'il avait une liaison féminine. Être la seule femme pour tous les hommes, oui, mais pas d'autre femme dans mon lit. Démonstration impeccable.

L'époque étant à la régression brutale, on imagine mal un nouveau livre de cette ambition aujourd'hui. Catherine Millet est « critique d'art », elle sait regarder, et elle a écrit un livre lucide sur Salvador Dalí. Nul doute : les historiens de l'avenir se demanderont comment ce cas a été *possible*. Je ne pense pas qu'elle me démentira si je dis que *Femmes*, en son temps, a ouvert la voie.

Une amie intime me dit : « C'est curieux, on est passés par une longue passion physique torride, et maintenant *on rit*. » Preuve par le rire, la seule. Quelles que soient les épreuves tragiques qu'ils ont traversées, un homme et une femme se sont vraiment rencontrés s'ils rient.

Je colle un timbre français rouge sur une enveloppe, et je vois un profil de femme, latin-grec, entouré d'étoiles, avec un curieux bonnet de bain sur la tête, dont je sais qu'il faut l'appeler « phrygien », coiffure des affranchis dans la Rome antique, et symbole de la liberté pour la Révolution française. Je suis français, je suis tenu de respecter cette Marianne *affranchie*, même si j'ai l'impression que son buste omniprésent est là pour empêcher toute autre intrusion de femme. Le jour où la République française aura une femme comme présidente n'est pas encore en vue.

Une vieille loi monarchique, dite « salique », interdit aux femmes d'occuper la fonction royale. Des reines, donc, mais pas au sommet. Alors que les maîtresses de Louis XIV et Louis XV occupent les imaginations (Montespan, Maintenon, Pompadour, du Barry), la présence d'étrangères comme « premières dames » semble refoulée, voire maudite. Et pourtant, que de femmes étranges, dont on a envie de faire le portrait.

Marie de Médicis (femme de Henri IV, mère de Louis XIII), Catherine de Médicis (fabuleuse Régente criminelle), Anne d'Autriche (une *Espagnole*, mère de Louis XIV et de Philippe d'Orléans, et son amant, le cardinal Mazarin), Marie-Thérèse d'Autriche (femme de Louis XIV), Marie Leszczynska (plus jolie que prévu, polonaise, femme de Louis XV, *dix enfants* de lui), Marie-Antoinette (l'Autrichienne décapitée), Marie-Louise d'Autriche (l'impératrice de Napoléon), Eugénie de Montijo (l'Espagnole, impératrice de Napoléon III, qui a lancé la mode du Pays basque, d'où peut-être le choix du prénom de mon Eugenia).

Ça fait beaucoup d'Italie florentine, d'Autriche, d'Espagne. Il faut parfois que je souligne que mon pays, l'Aquitaine, a longtemps été une province anglaise à cause d'Aliénor et du Prince Noir (qu'on trouve au début des *Essais* de Montaigne). Les Médicis de Florence avaient au moins deux siècles de civilisation d'avance sur les Français, et on ne les voit pas devenir calvinistes, ce qui n'était pas une raison pour ensanglanter Paris avec le massacre de la Saint-Barthélemy. Mettez-vous, si vous le pouvez, à la place de Catherine de Médicis : ces protestants sont de dangereux iconoclastes, Coligny est d'une raideur à faire peur, ces gens sont des barbares, ils brûleraient Florence s'ils le pouvaient.

Toutes ces figures, donc, sont maudites, et Marie-Antoinette a payé pour elles toutes. N'empêche, je les entends bavarder en italien, en allemand, en espagnol, se moquer de l'arriération du goût des Français (qui a stupéfié Mozart), on ne voit pas trop, pour l'instant, ce qu'ils peuvent faire en peinture. Si je vais là, en vol plané, jusqu'aux épouses républicaines, j'ai l'impression d'étouffer chez des ménagères. Qui se souvient de Mme Thiers (le massacreur de la Commune), de Mme Loubet, de Mme Auriol, de Mme Coty ? Yvonne de Gaulle, c'est entendu, est une sainte. Petite détente chez madame Pompidou (mais non, elle n'est pas sexy). Rien sous Giscard, rien sous Mitterrand (à part l'épisode de sa fille cachée, avec son prénom de bibliothèque, Mazarine), encore une sainte chez Chirac, grabuge chez Sarkozy (malgré, retour du refoulé, une chanteuse italienne), dissolution de la fonction chez Hollande, avenir obscur. Restent la reine d'Angleterre, bientôt remplacée par un roi, et la chancelière Angela Merkel, qui dissuade tout fantasme érotique.

Une hypothèse n'est jamais évoquée : Anne d'Autriche a mis très longtemps à être enceinte de Louis XIV. Un membre viril s'est-il dévoué pour cette action de grâce, qui a poussé Louis XIII à vouer la France à la Vierge Marie (encore une étrangère) ? Ce n'est pas impossible, et expliquerait l'étonnant acharnement de Louis XIV à légitimer ses bâtards. Il se sentait, ou se savait, bâtard lui-même, comme Philippe d'Orléans (époux d'Henriette d'Angleterre puis de la Princesse Palatine), père d'un autre Philippe d'Orléans, le Régent, lequel, autre bâtard possible en tant que fils de bâtard, a cassé le testament de Louis XIV en faveur de ses bâtards. Comment expliquer, d'ailleurs, l'obsession et la rage de Saint-Simon sur ce point génétique crucial, lui dont la *légitimité* de fils unique est sacrée ?

On voit qu'on est désormais à des années-lumière de toutes ces histoires, de leur cocasserie tragique, mais aussi de leur extraordinaire grandeur, que n'a pas la biologie dans son règne.

Passons maintenant à ma reine préférée, à la reine des reines. Il faut aller la chercher très loin dans le temps et l'espace, à un moment de mutation décisive pour le monde entier, c'est-à-dire en Égypte, peu avant notre ère. J'ai nommé Cléopâtre. La voici.

Le *nez* de Cléopâtre a beaucoup fait rêver. Pascal pense que la face du monde aurait été changée s'il avait été plus court (autrement dit, ne pouvant pas séduire à ce point Antoine). Lautréamont le reprend ainsi :

« Si la morale de Cléopâtre eût été moins courte, la face du monde aurait changé. Son nez n'en serait pas devenu plus long. »

Cléopâtre ? Vous faites allusion au cinéma en Technicolor, à Elizabeth Taylor aux prises avec Richard Burton ? Au couple maudit d'Égypte ?

Non, non, Shakespeare, lui seul. Dès que j'ai lu, très jeune, *Antoine et Cléopâtre* (1606), j'ai cherché Cléopâtre partout. Elle passait dans les jardins de Bordeaux, je la suivais en Espagne et en Italie, je la poursuivais dans les rues de Paris, elle m'échappait toujours, comme l'Égypte elle-même. L'Égypte, ses mystères d'Isis... Ses pyramides, ses tombeaux, ses peintures magiques, ses chambres secrètes, ses ruses, ses philtres, ses drogues, son art sexuel immémorial, ses mariages royaux entre frères et sœurs, sa peau cuivrée, sa culture, ses caprices, son charme. Pas de doute, je suis Antoine, « infatigable luxurieux » à qui « aucune femme n'a jamais dit non ».

Toute femme est une Cléopâtre en puissance. Elle est endormie, il suffit de la réveiller. Regardez bien ce nez, et encore ce nez. La séduction absolue, c'est elle, beaucoup plus que Carmen, Phèdre ou la marquise de Merteuil. Elle vous veut, elle vous trouve, elle vous joue, elle vous retient, elle vous possède, elle vous trahit, elle vous aime, elle meurt si vous mourez, c'est parfait.

Pour sa rencontre avec Antoine, la voici sur le fleuve, dans une barque, assise sur un trône étincelant comme des flammes posées sur l'eau. La poupe du navire est de l'or battu, les voiles parfumées sont de couleur pourpre, les rames d'argent suivent le rythme des flûtes. Laissant voir ses formes, elle est mollement étendue sous un dais de drap d'or mêlé de soie. Jamais un coup de dais n'a été donné dans des circonstances aussi éternelles. Le hasard est aboli : il y a ici mieux que Vénus et mieux qu'Aphrodite. Deux Cupidons, tenant des éventails de toutes les couleurs, la rafraîchissent. Elle est entourée de ses dames de compagnie, des Néréides, des Sirènes, plus gracieuses les unes que les autres, avec des mains plus douces que des fleurs. D'ailleurs, une Sirène tient le gouvernail, pendant qu'un impalpable parfum embaume les rives.

Voici Cléopâtre, acte II, scène V, à la pêche de l'homme choisi :

> « Qu'on me donne mes lignes, allons au fleuve,
> Mes musiciens joueront à quelque distance, je
>      tromperai
> Ces poissons aux écailles sombres, mon hameçon
> Transpercera leurs mâchoires visqueuses,
> Et en les retirant de l'eau je rêverai
> Que chacun d'eux, c'est Antoine, et je m'écrierai :
> Ah ah, le voilà pris ! »

Voilà la bonne pêcheuse originelle. La suite est rapide :

> « Ah ce jour-là ! Beau jour parmi tant d'autres !
> J'avais tellement ri qu'il a perdu patience,
> Mais avec d'autres rires, la nuit venue,
> Je l'ai apaisé, et au matin,
> Avant neuf heures, au lit je l'ai mené ivre,
> Et je lui ai mis ma coiffure et je l'ai couvert de
>      ma robe,
> En ceignant, moi, son épée, celle de Philippes. »

Ce passage a encore sur moi un effet foudroyant. Il faut quand même que j'avertisse le lecteur ou la lectrice que Philippes (avec un *s*) est une ville de Macédoine aux confins de la Thrace. En

42 av. J.-C., Antoine et Octave y ont vaincu Brutus et Cassius (les assassins de César). Saint Paul y a séjourné en 50 de notre ère, drôle d'enchaînement. Enfin, mon prénom est là, en toutes lettres, *au pluriel*. Je participe à la scène, je suis Antoine féminisé, et Cléopâtre à l'épée.

Ils vont mourir l'un et l'autre après la défaite d'Actium (31 avant J.-C.). Elle a 39 ans, lui 53. Comme elle le trahit, il lui fait, avant de se repentir, des scènes furieuses :

« Vous étiez déjà à moitié flétrie, avant qu'on ne se connaisse… Vous avez toujours été inconstante et fausse… Je vous ai ramassée, comme un peu de viande froide, dans l'écuelle de César mort… À cause de votre luxure, vous pouvez bien rêver ce qu'est être chaste, jamais vous n'en saurez rien… »

Cet Antoine est idiot, il le sait, sa maîtresse est une « *great fairy* », une reine magicienne, une éblouissante sorcière, une enfant irrésistible. Un témoin l'a vue, très jeune, sauter à cloche-pied dans une rue, rester sans souffle, mais, haletante, parler avec grâce, « faisant alors de son insuffisance une perfection ». Elle ne manque jamais d'air, Cléopâtre, elle sait que la meilleure défense est l'attaque, il n'est pas question d'abandonner son Antoine, qu'elle pousse d'ailleurs à la mort pour mourir avec lui dans un suicide indépassable. Ce seront les petits serpents du Nil, cachés dans un panier de figues, dont la morsure mortelle, sans souffrance, a été expérimentée par elle sur des tas de victimes.

Elle est la seule femme au monde, elle défie l'Empire romain, elle lui prend le meilleur de ses généraux (Shakespeare lui-même). Octavie, la femme d'Antoine ? Une veuve, vieille déjà de 30 ans, une naine à la voix sourde et morne (il ne pourra pas l'aimer longtemps), une statue sans vie et sans musique, qui se traîne au lieu de marcher, une idiote au visage trop rond, au front bas couvert de cheveux trop lourds. Pas de voix, pas de musique, pas de mouvement, c'est l'Occidentale absurde, alors que Cléopâtre, elle, est à elle seule tout l'« Orient ». Antoine, en revenant sans cesse vers elle comme à la lumière, l'appelle « mon rossignol ». Que faire contre un rossignol ?

Elle aime son Antoine, et, mort, elle l'aime encore plus :

> « *Son visage était le ciel,*
> *Il y avait en lui un soleil, une lune,*
> *Ils suivaient leur cours,*
> *Ils éclairaient ce o minuscule, la terre.* »

La terre est un « globule », un zéro, un point négatif par rapport aux deux astres de la nuit et du jour. Cléopâtre, au moment de s'appliquer le petit serpent venimeux sur le sein, n'a plus rien d'humain comme Lady Macbeth, mais, à l'inverse de celle-ci, accomplit sa liberté dans une métamorphose :

> « *Ma décision est prise, et je n'ai plus rien*
> *De féminin en moi. De la tête aux pieds,*
> *Je suis de marbre, je suis immuable, je n'ai plus*
> *L'insaisissable lune pour planète.* »

Ça y est : Isis en personne vous parle. Elle va rejoindre son époux humain, trop humain :

> « *Je viens ! Je suis feu, je suis air,*
> *J'abandonne mes autres éléments*
> *À la simple existence mortelle…* »

On peut, dans ce genre de disparition, « se séparer doucement de la nature », ce qui prouve que « l'atteinte de la mort est un aimant qui agrippe et fait mal, mais qu'on désire ».

Elle est donc couchée et paisible. Une de ses suivantes parle :

> « *Si tu nous quittes ainsi, c'est dire au monde*
> *Qu'il ne vaut pas la peine d'un adieu !* »

Tout cela serait simple, s'il n'y avait pas, dans cette scène étourdissante (j'y suis ! j'y suis ! je sens tout ! je vois tout !), les deux suivantes de Cléopâtre, Iras et Charmian. Cléopâtre, avant de mourir, les embrasse, et leur donne « la dernière chaleur que dispensent ses lèvres ». Et, tout à coup, cette pensée jalouse (qui prouve qu'elle n'est pas de marbre) : supposons qu'Iras, qui vient de se suicider, rencontre dans l'au-delà « Antoine aux belles boucles ». Il la voudra, il la couvrira de baisers (comme dans la vie ?). Être trompée dans la mort ? Pas question. Ordre au serpent, donc :

> *« Viens donc, être de mort, d'un seul coup de ta*
> *dent aiguë,*
> *Tranche le nœud inextricable de la vie.*
> *Pauvre bête, tout en venin, mets-toi en colère,*
> *Dépêche-toi ! Oh, si tu pouvais parler, et que je*
> *puisse*
> *T'entendre traiter d'âne le grand César*
> *Qui n'aura rien prévu ! »*

Non, non, on ne veut pas que cela finisse. C'est la fin de l'après-midi à Alexandrie, il fait très chaud, comme il fait très chaud, à Venise, quand Othello étrangle Desdémone, et aussi à Londres dans l'encre noire de Shakespeare. Charmian (quel prénom !) vient de s'écrier, à propos de Cléopâtre :

> *« Étoile du ciel d'Orient ! »*

L'autre lui répond :

> *« Paix, paix !*
> *Ne vois-tu pas mon bébé à mon sein,*
> *Qui tète sa nourrice au point qu'il va l'endormir ? »*

Une nourrice de serpents, drôle de lait transformé en sang. Charmian n'en peut plus, elle crie :

145

*« Oh, brise-toi, brise-toi, mon cœur ! »*

Et l'autre :

*« Antoine, doux comme un baume,*
*Tendre comme les vents les plus légers ! »*

Allons, il y a un autre petit serpent mortel dissimulé dans les figues. Elle le met, non plus sur son sein, mais sur le bras :

*« Toi aussi, je te veux !*
*À quoi bon rester... »*

Charmian continue sa phrase :

*« Dans ce vil univers ? Soit, adieu !*
*Et enorgueillis-toi, ô mort, puisque tu tiens*
*Dans tes bras cette fille que rien n'égale,*
*Fenêtres voilées de soie, que je vous ferme !*
*Que des yeux si royaux ne te contemplent plus,*
*Phébus couronné d'or ! Votre couronne*
*Est de travers, je vais la redresser. Après,*
*Je pourrai m'amuser jusqu'à... »*

Charmian va s'amuser à mourir. César ne trouvera, comme traces de cette hécatombe (pas de sang, trois femmes endormies), que des traînées de *bave* des serpents dans les figues. Avant de mordre venimeusement des chairs délicieuses, les serpents ont *bavé*. Comme toujours, Shakespeare est cru et précis, comme aucun auteur avant lui. Quant à

« Phébus cuirassé d'or », le soleil, c'est évidemment Apollon dans sa royauté surplombante. Cette invocation a son intérêt : avec la mort de Cléopâtre, on arrive aux derniers moments de l'Égypte hellénistique. Les Romains sont là, ils ont déjà trafiqué les dieux grecs, changé et affadi les noms, remplacé Zeus par Jupiter (au secours !) et Athéna par Minerve (mon Dieu !). Seules Isis et Cléopâtre ont compris cette catastrophe. Antoine aussi, déserteur héroïque d'un monde qui aurait pu être tout autre, et qui, du moins, l'a été le temps de cette passion effrénée.

Cléopâtre, étoile d'Orient, étoile des amants, apparaît entre Iras et Charmian, la colère et le charme. Ne comptez pas sur le cinéma pour vous montrer Antoine avec ses trois femmes d'Orient, et ne comptez pas sur lui non plus pour vous donner la moindre idée de la conjonction improbable entre le soleil et la lune, Apollon et Isis. La censure veille partout, et les sorcières de Macbeth sont devenues les vraies prophétesses : désormais, le beau est laid, le laid est beau, le faux est vrai, le vrai est faux. Alors quoi ? Le Diable ?

Les Romains ont vaincu, ils vont bientôt s'effondrer à leur tour, de longs siècles nous séparent encore de la Renaissance, c'est-à-dire du retour des Grecs, c'est-à-dire de l'Italie. Encore quelques siècles, et je retrouve, en catimini, Cléopâtre à Venise. Elle s'est débrouillée, elle a un passeport secret et sûr. Elle trouve que je ressemble à Antoine, on fait vivre cette ville à deux, comme jamais.

Selon les renseignements de Shakespeare (la grande poésie est toujours très bien renseignée), la magicienne s'est aussi appelée Jessica, cette fille ravissante qui a trahi son père, le buté Shylock. Elle lui a volé ses bijoux pour rejoindre un patricien vénitien, qui aime, comme elle, la musique. Scandaleuse Jessica, dont on parle encore (pas assez). Elle aussi est passée dans ma vie, j'entends sa voix, je revois ses yeux verts, son cou, ses bras, son sourire.

Maintenant, c'est le soir, les quais sont de plus en plus lumineux et rouges. Aucun doute, les dieux sont là, les mâts des bateaux flambent. L'amour est présent, se cache, survit. Cléopâtre, désolée de m'abandonner, mais forcée de poursuivre son parcours céleste, me laisse, dans un souffle, son dernier message : « Au revoir, petit chéri ! »

L'anglais appartient à Shakespeare, comme le français à Saint-Simon, ce petit duc dont raffolaient Proust, Stendhal et Céline (« le français est langue royale, il n'y a que foutus baragouins tout autour »).

Proust a beaucoup *étudié* Saint-Simon, il a rêvé de lui ravir l'« esprit Mortemart » pour le transfuser dans celui, décadent, des Guermantes. Il a de grandes réussites, mais plutôt dans le genre populaire. Les joues d'Albertine :

« Blêmes, chaudes et rouges aux pommettes, avec quelque chose d'ardent et de fané comme en ont les filles des faubourgs. »

Et aussi :

« Ce petit bout de museau, ce signe où se résume la personnalité permanente d'une femme, cet extrait algébrique. »

Les sœurs Bloch :

« À la fois trop habillées et à demi nues, l'air languissant, hardi, fastueux et souillon. »

On sent la copie, voici l'original :

« Mme de Castries était un quart de femme, une espèce de biscuit manqué, extrêmement petite, mais bien prise, et aurait passé dans un médiocre anneau : ni derrière, ni gorge, ni menton ; fort laide, l'air toujours en peine et étonné ; avec cela une physionomie qui éclatait d'esprit et qui tenait encore plus parole. Elle savait tout : histoire, philosophie, mathématiques, langues savantes, et jamais il ne paraissait qu'elle sût mieux que parler français ; mais son parler avait une justesse, une énergie, une éloquence, une grâce jusque dans les choses les plus communes, avec ce tour unique qui n'est propre qu'aux Mortemart. Aimable, amusante, gaie, sérieuse, toute à tous, charmante quand elle voulait plaire, plaisante naturellement avec la dernière finesse, sans le vouloir être, et assenant aussi les ridicules à ne les jamais oublier ; glorieuse, choquée de mille choses avec un ton plaintif qui emportait la pièce, cruellement méchante quand il lui plaisait, et fort bonne amie, polie, gracieuse, obligeante en général, sans aucune galanterie, mais délicate sur l'esprit et amoureuse de l'esprit où elle le trouvait à son gré. Avec cela, un talent de raconter qui charmait, et, quand elle voulait faire un roman sur-le-champ, une source de production, de variété et d'agrément qui étonnait. Avec sa gloire, elle se croyait bien mariée, par l'amitié qu'elle eut pour son mari ; elle l'étendit sur tout ce qui lui appartenait, et elle était aussi glorieuse pour lui que pour elle. Elle en recevait le réciproque, et toutes sortes d'égards et de respects. »

Dommage que Mme de Castries n'ait pas été jolie, mais enfin, tout se paye, et je me tais ici de respect. J'aime l'expression « roman sur-le-champ ». C'est ce qu'il faudrait faire.

Saint-Simon dit aussi que Mme de Montespan parlait parfois « extrêmement français », ce qui veut dire avec autorité.

Le français est-il devenu une langue morte ? Tout le monde le prétend plus ou moins, ce qui peut signifier qu'il n'y aurait plus d'autre autorité que celle, muette, des marchés financiers. Mais non, je suis vivant, et tous ces portraits de femmes respirent.

Allez donc maintenant, très tôt le matin, place de la Concorde. Vous entendrez peut-être des cris d'une très jolie femme qu'on s'apprête à guillotiner. « Elle criait tellement, raconte le bourreau, qu'on l'entendait de l'autre côté de la Seine. » Elle ne veut pas mourir, elle se débat, on n'arrive pas à la « boucler », on ne va quand même pas y passer toute la journée. A-t-elle vraiment dit « Encore un moment, monsieur le bourreau » ? On n'en est pas sûr, mais c'est bien d'elle. Elle vient d'avoir 50 ans, elle est encore charmante, elle a été la maîtresse de Louis XV à l'âge de 26 ans, c'est la comtesse du Barry, que vous pouvez admirer, à 38 ans, dans un superbe portrait fait par son amie, Élisabeth Vigée-Lebrun.

Quelle beauté ! Quelle insolence ! Quelle allure ! Il est difficile d'imaginer que sa tête va bientôt tomber dans la sciure. Il le faut, pourtant. Elle s'appelle Jeanne, elle a du goût, elle protège les lettres et les arts, elle envoie, par la poste, deux

baisers à un homme qu'elle admire particulièrement, Voltaire. Celui-ci, vieux et malade, lui
répond par retour du courrier :

*« Quoi, deux baisers sur la fin de la vie !*
*Quel passeport vous daignez m'envoyer !*
*Deux, c'est trop d'un, adorable Égérie,*
*Je serai mort de plaisir au premier. »*

Vous verrez aussi, peut-être, passer Manon,
39 ans, l'amie des Girondins, oui, Manon Roland,
qu'adorait Stendhal. Elle ne bronche pas, elle
console, dans la charrette, un des condamnés qui
craque, elle ne veut pas qu'il la voie mourir, *elle lui
cède la place* (c'est probablement son amant), elle y
passera ensuite. Le bourreau n'est pas content, ça
dérange le protocole. Enfin, voyons, il ne peut
quand même pas résister, lui dit-elle, à « la dernière
volonté d'une femme ». Soit, on la raccourcira en
dernière position (ici, on a compris que les Girondins sont mes amis). Manon a-t-elle crié, avant de
monter au supplice : « Liberté, que de crimes on
commet en ton nom ! » ? C'est bien d'elle, et il
suffit, pour s'en convaincre, de lire les minutes de
son procès. Délicieuse Manon, vive, spirituelle,
cultivée, courageuse, tendre. Voilà, elle ne parle
plus, elle paye ses mauvaises fréquentations.

Jeanne, Manon, Charlotte : trois Grâces. Charlotte, maintenant, la divine meurtrière de Marat,
avec son couteau de cuisine, acheté le matin même,

qu'elle enfonce dans la poitrine de l'Ami du peuple, dans sa baignoire. Charlotte de Corday d'Armont a pris rendez-vous avec le dénonciateur public pour lui fournir une liste de conjurés girondins à faire exécuter d'urgence. Elle est là, au contraire, pour venger ses amis, et saigner l'amateur de sang, prophète de la Terreur. Elle a 25 ans, toute sa tête (pas pour longtemps), sa main ne tremble pas. L'autre est très flatté de recevoir dans son bain une jeune et belle aristocrate *dénonciatrice*, il va hurler quelques secondes, tandis qu'elle ne manifestera ni regret ni peur en montant à l'échafaud.

Le marquis de Sade, secrètement admiratif, prononcera contre elle un discours célèbre à la « Section des piques », en la qualifiant de « monstre sorti de l'enfer » (c'est un spécialiste qui parle). Sade, lui-même condamné à mort pour « girondinisme », sera sauvé, au dernier moment, par sa maîtresse d'alors, qu'il appelle « Sensible », beau surnom pour une femme de cœur.

Jeanne, Manon, Charlotte : je préfère oublier Marie-Antoinette, guillotinée au même endroit, puisqu'elle détestait la comtesse du Barry.

Pensez quand même un instant, en passant devant l'obélisque de Louxor, en érection place de la Concorde, ex-place Louis XV, à toutes ces femmes sacrifiées à l'Histoire. Et n'oubliez pas Cléopâtre, ni les serpents du Nil.

*(Suite de la page du même auteur)*

**Dans les collections « L'Art et l'Écrivain »,
« Livres d'art » et « Monographies »**

*Le Paradis de Cézanne*, 1995.
*Les Surprises de Fragonard*, 1987.
*Rodin. Dessins érotiques*, 1986.
*Les Passions de Francis Bacon*, 1996.

**Dans la collection « À voix haute » (CD Audio)**

*La Parole de Rimbaud*, 1999.

**Aux Éditions Grasset**

*Vision à New York*, entretiens avec David Hayman (Figures, 1981 ; Médiations / Denoël ; Folio n° 3133).

**Aux Éditions Plon**

*Carnet de nuit*, essai, 1989 (Folio n° 4462).
*Le Cavalier du Louvre : Vivant Denon, 1747-1825*, essai, 1995 (Folio n° 2938).
*Casanova l'admirable*, essai, 1998 (Folio n° 3318).
*Mystérieux Mozart*, essai, 2001 (Folio n° 3845).
*Dictionnaire amoureux de Venise*, 2004.
*Un vrai roman, Mémoires*, 2007 (Folio n° 4874).

**Aux Éditions Lattès**

*Venise éternelle*, 1993.

**Aux Éditions Desclée de Brouwer**

*La Divine Comédie*, entretiens avec Benoît Chantre, 2000 (Folio n° 3747).
*Vers le paradis : Dante au Collège des Bernardins*, essai, 2010.

**Aux Éditions Carnets Nord**

*Guerres secrètes*, 2007 (Folio n° 4994).

**Aux Éditions Robert Laffont**

*Illuminations*, essai, 2003 (Folio n° 4189).

**Aux Éditions Calmann-Lévy**

*Voir, Écrire*, entretiens avec Christian de Portzamparc, 2003 (Folio n° 4293).

**Aux Éditions Verdier**

*Le Saint-Âne*, essai, 2004.

**Aux Éditions Hermann**

*Fleurs, Le grand roman de l'érotisme floral*, 2006.

**Au Cherche Midi éditeur**

*L'Évangile de Nietzsche*, entretiens avec Vincent Roy, 2006 (Folio n° 4804).
*Grand beau temps*, 2008.

**Aux Éditions du Seuil**

Romans
*Une curieuse solitude*, 1958 (Points-romans n° 185).
*Le Parc*, 1961 (Points-romans n° 28).
*Drame*, 1965 (L'Imaginaire n° 227).
*Nombres*, 1968 (L'Imaginaire n° 425).
*Lois,* 1972 (L'Imaginaire n° 431).
*H*, 1973 (L'Imaginaire n° 441).
*Paradis*, 1981 (Points-romans n° 690).

Journal
*L'Année du tigre*, 1999 (Points n° 705).

Essais
*L'Intermédiaire*, 1963 (Points-essais n° 464).
*Logiques*, 1968.

*L'Écriture et l'expérience des limites*, 1968 (Points n° 24).
*Sur le matérialisme*, 1971.

**Aux Éditions de La Différence**

*De Kooning, vite*, essai, 1988.

**Aux Éditions Cercle d'Art**

*Picasso le héros*, essai, 1996.

**Aux Éditions Mille et Une Nuits**

*Un Amour américain*, nouvelle, 1999.

**Aux Éditions 1900**

*Photos licencieuses de la Belle Époque*, 1987.

**Aux Éditions Stock**

*L'œil de Proust. Les dessins de Marcel Proust*, 2000.

Préfaces
Paul Morand, *New York*, GF Flammarion.
Madame de Sévigné, *Lettres*, Éd. Scala.
*Femmes mythologies*, en collaboration avec Érich Lessing,
    Imprimerie nationale.
D.A.F de Sade, *Anne Prospère de Launay : L'Amour de Sade*,
    Gallimard.
Mirabeau, *Le Rideau levé ou l'éducation de Laure*, Jean-Claude
    Gawsewitch Éditeur.
Willy Ronis, *Nues*, Terre bleue.

Mise en page par Meta-systems
59100 Roubaix

CET OUVRAGE
A ÉTÉ ACHEVÉ D'IMPRIMER
SUR ROTO-PAGE
PAR L'IMPRIMERIE FLOCH
À MAYENNE EN NOVEMBRE 2012

N° d'édition : L.01ELJN000391.N001 – N° d'impression : 83522
Dépôt légal : janvier 2013
(Imprimé en France)

# ONNA Rising

## Rei Kimura

**Demarche Publishing LLC**
P.O. Box 824
Yorktown Heights NY 10598-9998
http://www.demarchepublishing.com

The author does not guarantee and assumes no responsibility on the accuracy of any websites, links or other contacts contained in this book.

# ONNA Rising

PRINTING HISTORY
Demarche Publishing/2013

ISBN: 978-0-9845497-2-6
Printed in the United States of America

# ONNA Rising

## Rei Kimura

# ONNA Rising

With money and freedom, a growing pool of young, well-educated and ambitious Japanese professional women are no longer submissive, demure extensions of their menfolk. They are ready to enjoy life, and with power and position four women (*onna*) have formed a strong supportive bond. Their friendship has withstood romantic conflicts, the fast-paced, glitzy life of Tokyo, trials of the workplace and the insulting 'aninoko' label given to one of the four. Now sordid secrets from the past have emboldened a blackmailer, threatening the very foundation of the friends' bond.

## Praise for ONNA Rising

From cover to cover this gripping book gives readers a very honest look at life in modern Japan through its four main female characters. Whether you laugh or cry at the satire and bitter sweet humor of this book, it will make you feel and go on reading....

–Hanna Laura Noack, German writer.

# ONNA Rising

## Contents

# CHAPTER 1

"The night is still young—stay on for a bit more, Emi," the long-haired, vodka-swirling young woman with a body to diet and die for said, trying to make herself heard above the current Michael Jackson "This Is It" song craze in Tokyo.

Then as her friend mouthed the words,"What did you just say?" for the third time, Sachi Ishikawa slid off her seat and grabbed Emi's arm, mouthing back "Look, let's go outside for a while. I've just realized that I can't compete with Michael Jackson in here! Really, this guy is still hogging the music charts and almost every bar in Tokyo, as popular and controversial in death as in life. I wish we could be more like him!"

"You don't really want that, do you?" Emi screamed above the blaring music. "Do you know what his life was like?"

"Why not?" Sachi screamed back. "At least his life and all its messiness was challenging and impacted a lot of people all over the world—for better or for worse!"

Outside, the brisk early autumn air raised goosebumps on their bare arms and shoulders, but it felt refreshing after the smoke and heat of hundreds of gyrating bodies inside one of Shibuya's many hip disco bars.

"Oh, the fresh air feels so good," Sachi said, breathing deeply. She immediately contradicted herself by taking out her favorite LV cigarette case and lighting up. Her hands shook with the nervous energy of a young and restless woman, let loose in Tokyo with the money and freedom enjoyed by a growing pool of young, well-educated and ambitious Japanese professional women.

"Look at you," Emi laughed. "I thought you just said the fresh air is so good and here you are, lighting up at the drop of a coin! You really shouldn't smoke so much, Sachi."

"Says who? This is Tokyo and I work as hard as I play. I can do anything I want as long as I don't break the law!" Sachi retorted good naturedly, knowing that Emi was still so ingenuous that there wasn't a mean bone in that flat- chested, small-waisted little girl body of hers. Emi didn't smoke, drank very moderately, didn't do the boyfriend-hopping thing the rest did and held a sane, down-to-earth job at a blue-blooded bank in Tokyo. Frankly, sometimes Sachi wondered what the hell she was doing hanging out with them.

*****

The truth was that the fresh-faced Emi reminded Sachi uncomfortably of her conservative roots back in Matsumoto, where her mother still bowed the correct number of times and the correct number of angles, according to the rank and closeness of her visitor. Sachi's father, Michio Ishikawa, lived his life very correctly as required by the city office bureaucracy he had been working for almost his entire adult life; he was truly a firm believer in Japan's employment for life rhetoric. Sometimes Sachi pitied her father, who had to submit himself daily at the city office to the demanding taxpayers who paid his salary — then when he returned home, he had to hand himself over to his quietly domineering wife.

In fact, Sachi wanted to laugh whenever she read books or documentaries by Western writers and "experts" on Japanese society portraying Japanese women as submissive, demure extensions of their men folk walking at least three shuffling steps behind. But then, who could blame them? Look at her mother, for instance; who would imagine that behind that soft, demure face and sweet, gentle nature lurked a woman, hard as nails and twice as astute, who controlled the family's purse strings with ironclad fists and could quell her supposedly superior husband with just one silent, reproachful look?

And then there was the money issue. How many Western writers lamenting Japanese women's second-class status really knew about "salary men," like her father, who dutifully handed over his whole pay packet every month to her mother and waited for her to dole out his "lunch and pocket money?"

Sachi would never forget the day she saw her father stuff a wad of 10,000 yen notes behind a picture and warn her not to tell her mother about it. Even at 12 years old, she could already empathize with him for having to hide any additional money he made just to have some economic independence from his wife! Of course, Michio lied about his annual bonuses and held back a little of his hard-earned money for himself. Sachi remembered the fun she'd had being a willing accomplice to these "scams."

Her mother ruled the family with a silken glove. She seldom raised her voice but, somehow, it was still understood that her word was law in the house. On weekends, Matsumoto would join the league of housewives who needed to de-stress from a week of hard homemaking and throw the children at their overworked, exhausted husbands. These fathers entertained the kids with compulsory trips to the zoo, baseball and soccer games, fishing spots or Disneyland and amusement parks—if there were any— just to keep them away from their stressed-out mothers.

Sachi started off by pitying her father and his weekend duties because her mother had her weekends but her exhausted, overworked father couldn't even sleep in on a Sunday and never seemed to have any time off for himself! But as she grew older, Sachi realized the wisdom of such weekend interactions with her father because it was the only time they actually saw each other.

Michio, like most of the "salary men fathers" all over the country, left home no later than 7 a.m. each morning before their children were up and often came home late at night, especially on closing of accounts seasons, long after they had gone to bed. Sometimes Sachi could go for weeks without seeing Michio on working days and if not for those enforced weekend-bonding sessions, Sachi was sure she would never even have known her own father.

The weekend trips started as soon as she was old enough to ride the toy horses in the park and carry plastic pails and spades to dig for imaginary crabs and shells in between the doddering sand castles she built at the nearby beach. All of this happened under the bored supervision of her chain-smoking, newspaper-wielding father. Michio had strict instructions never to smoke in front of his daughter because the smoke was hazardous to a child of her age, but who was to know or tell on him? So Michio whiled away the time answering Sachi's endless questions absent mindedly while he lit up. But when Sachi grew old enough to tell on him, the smoking abruptly stopped, then was replaced by something infinitely more rewarding and powerful.

By the time she was 8 years old, Sachi had become a friend, companion and useful ally for Michio against her mother; she was no longer just a weekend duty her father had to endure to escape the cold and reproachful silence of his wife. They began to actually have fun pitching with the other father and child teams at a nearby field reserved for predominantly weekend amateur baseball in a nation obsessed with the game. Some weekends, Sachi and her father trudged down to the mammoth Arakawa river to spend hours hunched over their fishing rods and discuss anything from his work and clients to her studies at school. Sometimes, they'd have at least one good therapeutic session to bitch about the person they called the Minister of Finance and Home Affairs, the woman of the house, Michiko Ishikawa.

One day, their conversation took on a more serious tone as Sachi asked her father a question that had been bothering her: What was she going to do with her life? She was just 12 years old and already being pushed unceremoniously into punishing after-school, tuition classes to prepare for the harsh entrance exams into the best jyuku or cram schools in the area. The Ishikawas did not have a son and Michiko was determined that her only child would get into the best local cram school so she could hold her head up high among the neighbors who either had sons to carry on the family name or had children already proudly ensconced in the best schools and jyukus. So Sachi was pushed even harder than many of her peers and she resented losing her precious weekend outings with her father to more tuition classes, which wore her out even before the weekend was over.

One day she heard her parents fighting over her punishing weekend study schedule, and it was the first time she had ever seen Michio so angry.

"Everyday after school, Sachi is already balancing piano lessons with more tuition in math and science; now even weekends, you are insisting she goes to cram schools to prepare her for THE cram school you want her to enter!" Michio shouted. "Really, Michiko, do you know how many children in Japan are committing suicide because they just cannot cope with their parents' demands on them? Do you want to push our only child to that?"

"I don't know why you are so angry and shouting at me like that, Michio! All I've ever done is for the good of this family!"

"Yes, and it's good for Sachi to be pushed beyond her endurance just so that you can tell the neighbors that your daughter got into the best jyuku in this area? I won't accept every weekend in cram school, Michiko!"

When Sachi's mother saw that her husband had dug his heels in for once and would not budge, she reluctantly agreed to a compromise and Sachi's outings with her father were thankfully restored, at least every other weekend.

The young Sachi could not understand her mother and as she grew older, the complexities of Michiko's mind became even more perplexing.

"Why is it, father, that Mother fights so hard for me to go to the best cram schools, the best high schools and now is fighting for me to get into the best universities and then she tells me it's all right to get a good job after graduation for the main purpose of finding a good husband? And after that, I can quit my job and spend the rest of my life caring for my husband and children!" she confided in her father on one of their fishing trips. "She never asks me if that is what I want! It's almost as if all that hard work and money spent on my education is just to be in the right place at the right time to find a good husband and nothing more! Can you see any sense in that?"

"I guess to your mother, there is nothing wrong with this mindset because she too walked the same route as her mother before her. Do you know, she was a Waseda University graduate and was working in a bank when she met me? When we got married, it just seemed so natural for her to resign from her job and stay at home without a thought about whether she was wasting a perfectly good education in finance. If she had wanted to continue working

I would never have stopped her, but I couldn't insist otherwise her family would have thought that I was reluctant to fulfill my duty to provide for my wife and that I wanted her to bring home a pay packet as well!"

"Oh my God, did Mother really graduate from Waseda University? Do you know how many students—myself included—want to get in there? Looking at her now, no one would believe she once graced the blue-blooded halls of Waseda University!"

Sachi shuddered as she thought of the prospect of becoming like her mother and continued. "No father, I would much rather be a career woman and I mean a *career* woman and not an office tea-and-coffee lady many female university graduates seem satisfied to be. And if I scare off the men with what Mother calls my 'unfeminine ambitions,' so be it!"

"You can be anything you want Sachi chan, provided you work for it. I am not the kind of father to clip your wings. But you will have to fight a system that does not place women in a very high priority for long-term careers, a system you can't really blame because women like your mother have encouraged it as their desired role in society."

Sachi looked at her father and her eyes shone with love for him. Unlike other fathers who would have gladly relinquished their roles of weekend child-minders, Michio had actually fought to maintain the status quo of their weekend bonding. He really cared about her and was no absentee father, like so many of her friends' fathers were. Sachi decided that this alone would make her different, for good or for bad.

*****

"Penny for your thoughts," Emi's voice cut into Sachi's nostalgic memories of her childhood and growing-up years in Matsumoto. "You have been standing there with that scowl on your face for a long time. I've been to the ladies' room and back and you're still here with that scowl! What on earth are you thinking of?"

"Just thinking of my father and how much I miss him and those innocent childhood days when he was the center of my life!" Sachi replied. Then she let out a scream as the cigarette she had been holding burned to the quick and scorched her fingers.

## Onna Rising

The moment was broken. Someone opened the door of the bar and a blast of music drenched them like a sudden rain shower and Sachi shouted above the din, "Come on let's get back in there!"

# CHAPTER 2

It was 6 a.m. and a few streaks of dawn light had just started to brighten the sky over Tokyo. In a small but cozy apartment in upmarket Shibuya, a kinky pink alarm clock (which had been set for that unearthly hour, as always, on weekdays) released its loud, relentless squawking that was fit to wake the dead. There was a shuffle and a golden brown mop of curly hair on the pillow a few feet away from the clock moved and groaned.

A hand reached out and flung the offending object across the room, but the alarm clock had become immune to such daily assault and continued to ring indignantly, undeterred and louder than ever, as if to protest its abuse.

After a while, Suzue Tanaka, the owner of the golden brown mop of curly hair, gave up and padded across the room to retrieve what she called her "daily morning bully." God, how she hated having to get up each morning almost at the crack of dawn! Some days she even wondered why she didn't give up the struggle and just get married and be a home-maker—that way her life would not be controlled by pink alarm clocks and "must have, can't lose" clients who set tight deadlines to punish and terrorize their agencies.

Suzue had studied communications and upon graduation joined a major advertising agency in Tokyo, exchanging her comfortable home in the spacious Kyushu countryside for a small 1DK apartment in order to take the job. Her family and friends waited for her to find a husband from the pool of energetic, attractive young men she worked with and announce her resignation, but

# Onna Rising

Suzue had disappointed them because nine years into her job she was still there, steadily climbing from a junior accounts executive to her current position of senior accounts director. Recently, her massive contributions to the company and large pool of clients had even gained her a place in the boardroom among the poker face "corporate suits" who obviously didn't like a skirt in their midst.

One enviable corporate position and impressive remuneration package later (not to mention the acquisition of a beautiful apartment in trendy Shibuya), Suzue's mother was won over. However, her grandmother was still not convinced that this was how a Japanese woman should live her life—single and in the fast lane.

"Today will be an adrenalin-charged day," Suzue declared grimly to the face she hated most, the naked one that stared back at her from the large, uncompromising bathroom mirror each morning, pale but glistening with the shine of overnight moisturizers.

God, Suzue shuddered, how could her latest ex- boyfriend ever think that her plain, unmade up "morning face" was her best? "Men can be so dumb and self-absorbed," she mused. "If Taki had been less of both, we might still be having fun together!"

Then her mind switched to the high-value pitch her team was making that day for a mega pharmaceutical client; they'd be fighting tooth and nail with their arch enemy, a competing agency. Suzue shuddered again at the thought. Had she make the right decision? The room would be full of traditional male suits and she could imagine the look on their faces when they realized that the woman at the head of the long shining conference table was not the agency's "tea" lady but a top-notch director who would be spearheading the pitch for the day.

Some of her other clients had good naturedly dismissed the agency's habit of having a woman spearhead its major accounts as one of the idiosyncrasies of advertising agencies; after all, gays and women in suits went so well together! It was annoying but Suzue had learned the hard way as a junior accounts executive that what mattered most was not morals, justice or even ethics—it was about who could ruthlessly elbow anything and anyone out of the way to get a coveted account.

Still, should she have caved in to her coordinator's insistence that for this pitch, at least, they send in the male directors?

Conservative Japanese pharmaceutical men in blacksuits did not take women seriously, and the account was too huge to risk losing just because of gender issues. "After all, winning the account is all that matters, right?" Takuya, the other senior account director, argued. Suzue seethed at the open condescension in his voice and dug her heels in even more. All of the hard work had been done by her and Fumiko, her assistant; chain smoking, caffeine-ridden days and nights of merciless research, strategic planning and stroking the balls of petulant and demanding lower-level executives of the client company who wanted to feel important. No way in hell was she going to hand over all this hard work to a couple of male directors and watch them get all the glory and credit if the pitch was successful!

"Why? Just because people in Japan still think women should only be serving tea and bowing at the right angles in the work place?" she had fumed to Emi, a banker, and the newest member of what Suzue called "the four pillars." They were friends, representing the new generation of Japanese professional women. The other three pillars were herself, Sachi, a fashion designer and owner of her own fashion house and Tomoko, a financial advisor and hard-talking lawyer. The pillars met at least once a week, drawn together by a common goal to work hard and play hard. They had broken away from the chains of tradition to compete alongside their more privileged male counterparts in hard corporate careers, refusing to budge even if they had to work at least two or three times harder than the men, just to prove themselves.

Poor Emi—she was the most feminine, soft spoken and nurturing of the four of them, and she always had to listen to all their garbage. Whenever a relationship went wrong, it was on Emi's decidedly calm shoulders that they cried on. But it was Suzue herself who provided the launching pad when some real character assassination and aggression was needed. Sometimes Suzue felt that she was so cynical and hard because of all that angry energy the girls loaded on her. But she knew that was not really true. She had been resentful and rebellious for as long as she could remember, ever since she became old enough to realize that her family was different and she was a kind of pariah in the tight and judgmental small town Japanese society she grew up in.

*****

16

# Onna Rising

One day when she was six years old and they had all just sat down to dinner, Suzue popped the tiresome question of why, unlike the other children in her yochien (kindergarten), she did not have a father. Instinctively, Suzue knew that she had asked a taboo question because of the sudden silence and shadow that fell over a dinner table which had been bustling with small talk between her mother and grandmother and the cheerful clatter of chopsticks and simulated lacquer miso shiru soup bowls.

A dark, angry shadow raced across her grandmother's face and her mother, Rumiko, muttered an excuse and ran out of the room. The sudden tension frightened the child and she shivered. Baba, as Suzue called her grandmother, cleared her throat after a while and said reproachfully, "Never bring up that subject in front of your mother again, Suzue chan. It's something very painful we don't talk about in this house."

"But why?" Suzue whispered. She was terrified at the unhappiness she had caused and yet she couldn't stop herself from persisting til she got her answer. "Everyone has a father so why can't we talk about mine? Is he dead?"

"Someday when you're older and can understand things better, we'll tell you about your father but for now, please stop asking about him! Can't you see, child, how much you're hurting your mother? You want her to be happy, don't you?"

Suzue nodded and stopped asking about her father but the mystery about him was always there, gnawing at her inside. It was about that time that she really looked at herself and realized with a shock that something else differentiated her from the other children, apart from her lack of a father. Her skin was a dusky color, at least a couple of shades darker than the normal Japanese skin tone, and in a nation where the women, in particular, were obsessed with fair skin, she stood out quite a bit.

Suzue remembered how her mother and grandmother would make sure that she did not swim under the hot summer sun and get her skin even darker. They were obsessed with her skin color and regularly subjected her to all kinds of herbal creams and whitening soaps. Finally they gave up and accepted that Suzue's skin tone was genetic and there to stay.

Eventually, when it became increasingly difficult to hold on

**17**

to a good job and make ends meet in a small community where Rumiko was not well received, the whole family moved to Chiba prefecture nearer to Tokyo to start a new life, returning to their beloved Kyushu only years later when Suzue had practically left home for her studies in Tokyo.

But the controversy over her "unique" looks continued and one day she overheard her mother saying, "Thank goodness—apart from her skin which can actually pass her off as a Japanese from the south or Okinawa—Suzue chan can quite easily blend in." There were a million questions she wanted to ask such as why she had to be "passed off" as a Japanese from the south—wasn't she a true Japanese? And then her so-called best friend at school, a girl called Mariko, told her one day, "My mother said you are different from us and that you are not a pure Japanese. She called you an Ainoko."

When Suzue asked her mother that night what ainoko was, Rumiko's eyes filled with tears and she cried out, "Who dared to call you an ainoko? That's a lie, you are just as Japanese as anyone else, do you hear that?"

Alarmed at the emotions she had unleashed in her mother, Suzue lied. "No one called me an ainoko, mother, it was just something I heard at school, that's all." She tried to find the meaning of ainoko, but no dictionary had such a word . It was only days later that she found out from a visiting teenage cousin that it meant an illegitimate love child or a half-baked, mixed-blood child. The insinuation made her blood curdle and ignited the flame of anger and defiance that would grow and unwittingly shape her life in later years.

The very next day, Suzue confronted her friend and demanded to know why she had been called an ainoko but Mariko had no answer beyond a muttered, "My mother says you have a darkish skin and your face is different from us so you're not one of us."

"Well, I don't care much what your mother thinks but you're my best friend, so tell me, do you believe that?"

There was a long silence and Suzue held her breath. They were only eight-year-old primary school children but how Mariko answered would determine whether she would still have a best friend for life.

"I don't know…it's ok with me, I guess, but still…mother says I should mix around more…," Mariko replied, furiously nibbling at her finger nails, an instinctive habit whenever she was nervous or distressed.

Suzue had heard all she wanted to hear and although her heart felt like it had been ripped apart, she replied with the brittle, devil-may-care defiant front she would adopt from then on: "It's fine, perhaps your mother is right and you should go find some other friends. I'll be all right."

She turned on her heels and started to run, slowing only when she had rounded a corner and gone out of sight of Mariko, who still stood rooted to the same spot, confused and bewildered. The little girl's face crumbled because she knew she had hurt her best friend irreparably. But when you are only eight years old, it is difficult to disobey the orders of a domineering mother.

Suzue didn't exactly know where she was going until she ended up in a little craftwork woodshed at one extreme end of the school grounds. She had lost her best friend and, at just eight years old, felt as if her world had been cut up into pieces, some of which didn't fit any more. Suzue had never been much of a crier, perhaps because despite the absence of a father, there had never been any reason to cry in her relatively peaceful and contented household. But now the tears flowed. However, when she dried her eyes after this, it would be a long time before she cried, if ever, again.

That night Suzue took a good look at herself in the mirror and she had to admit that Mariko was right. She was different. Apart from her permanently sun-tanned skin, her hair was not straight like most Japanese girls but floated around her face in tight crinkly curls. As she grew up, the difference would become more pronounced in the full chest she tried so hard to flatten, til she realized that it was an asset rather than a curse, as were the double eyelids coveted by other girls who paid a ton of money to have their eyes "done" by plastic surgeons.

A few days later, a conversation Suzue overheard between her mother and her Uncle Masao, who had come to visit them from Hokkaido, both frightened and made her angry.

"What are you going to do with Suzue chan's future?"

Uncle Masao asked when they thought Suzue was out in the tiny patch of grass they called a garden playing with the new model car he had brought her.

"That worries me sometimes and then I just push it aside and don't think of the future," his sister replied. "But you're right, marriage into a good family will not be easy—and what kind of job can she hope to get? Look at all the mixed children in Japan; it's not easy for them to find acceptance and fully integrate. Those who succeed in life are mostly in the entertainment industry. It's so cruel, this polite and subtle discrimination against those not of pure Japanese blood, right here in their own country. All right, I made a big mistake once in my life when I was very young and idealistic but society doesn't have to punish an innocent child for it!"

"I don't know what to say, onesan," Uncle Masao said. "And you know the kind of work you do doesn't help improve Suzue's social acceptance. Haven't you thought about giving it up for something more, shall we say, respectable?"

"Don't say that, Masao!" Rumiko cried. "I cannot give it up because what other job will bring in as much money to support us in this way? Can you not remember that I am the sole bread winner of this family? I know you've tried to help but you have a large family to support and a wife who is not exactly fond of me!"

A shiver ran down Suzue's spine because her Uncle Masao had done it at last: addressed the perplexing question of what exactly her mother did for a living. As soon as she was old enough to notice things around her, Suzue would watch as her mother dressed up in gorgeous kimonos almost every evening and a black sedan whisked her off to work. She was always asleep by the time her mother got back so she never quite knew what time Rumiko returned home each night.

But she loved to watch the daily ritual of her mother slipping into her kimono for the night and the tying of the breathtakingly ornate obi, meticulously, layer by layer. On good days, Rumiko could get her obi right in a matter of thirty minutes but on bad days, she had to tie, untie, and re- tie for at least a frustrating hour or so. It was a fascinating ritual that intrigued Suzue.

Most of all, Suzue was amazed at the transformation of her mother as soon as she slipped into a kimono, tabi socks and zoshi slippers. In western clothes, usually a one piece dress or a simple skirt and blouse, Rumiko was just like any other busy and harassed Japanese mother and home-maker. But the minute she stepped into a kimono, she metamorphosed into a beautiful woman, long neck exposed by the elegant sweep of her hair into a chignon. Every pore and imperfection on her face was eliminated by a mask of white powder, and even the way she walked changed to the small shuffling steps of the traditional geishas Suzue often watched on television.

"Oh Mother," she breathed. "You look beautiful, like a swan!"

"Oh, go along with you, Suzue chan," her mother laughed tousling her hair in a rare burst of humor, although Suzue could see she was happy with the compliment. But on a more serious note, Rumiko added "Do you know, it's said that in a kimono, even an ugly woman can look beautiful and elegant? And there is something so pure and noble in the elegant beauty of the kimono, don't you think?"

These words would be responsible for Suzue's penchant for elaborate kimonos in later years, a partiality that made her the brunt of good natured jokes about why a high-flying corporate woman would shed her corporate suit and easy western clothes to be imprisoned in the tight restraining confines of a kimono with its cumbersome obi and the neccessity of having to shuffle around with demure steps.

"There is no escaping history and environment in the shaping of a person's life, character and aspirations," Suzue always told her earnest, fresh-faced account executive trainees who arrived straight from Tokyo's finest universities rearing to learn and climb in Japan's competitive advertising world. "But you can change the constraints of your past and fight your way to achieving what you want and you will get there — no matter how brutal it gets."

*****

Suzue was thinking of this now as she went through *her* daily ritual of applying heavy make up to create the face she wanted to show to the world at work. She did that every morning because a naked face made her feel vulnerable and exposed.

She would never forget the day when she was twelve years

old and she discovered quite by chance that her mother was a club hostess at an exclusive members' club in Ginza and it was her job to entertain rich and powerful businessmen each night, pouring drinks for them, pampering and soothing them by listening to their problems and feeding their egos with every compliment a well-trained courtesan should have in her bag of tricks.

That day, her grandmother had suddenly decided that the two of them deserved an outing to Tokyo. The trip started in the tranquil Meiji Jingu gardens, progressed to the trendy streets of Harajuku and ended finally at the upmarket glitzy Ginza, the retail paradise of the rich and famous and home to some of Tokyo's most exclusive men's clubs and escort services. It was the first time Suzue had ever been to Ginza and her eyes shone at the luxurious designer goods displayed in the ritzy window fronts of the many lofty boutiques lining the broad boulevards. The smell of money and prestige was powerful and Suzue, standing at the windows looking in, wondered what it would be like to afford such goods with the staggering price tags of a whole month's salary or even two!

It was already late and Baba hurried her along the famous Ginza crossing or yon chome to the station and it was as they were walking past a low building with a classy impressive frontage and soft lights that a side door opened to the tinkling sound of laughter and girlish chatter. As soon as a distinguished looking man and a slender woman in a kimono emerged, a sleek black limousine drew up from nowhere like a ghost and Suzue remembered thinking what an important man he must be.

Although her grandmother tried to hurry her along, Suzue lagged behind to watch, fascinated, as the man proceeded to plant a kiss on the woman's cheek and ducked to avoid her playful swipe before slipping a fistful of notes down the front of her kimono and entering the purring limousine. The woman stood bowing til the limousine had pulled away and then she turned to re-enter what was clearly one of Ginza's famous hostess clubs where rich men came to flirt and unwind.

The lamplight lit up the woman's face and Suzue gasped, almost suffocating. Was she hallucinating or was it her own mother she was staring at? Suzue started shivering when she realized that

Rumiko, her mother, was the slender coquettish woman who had just flirted with the distinguished looking man and graciously accepted a fistful of money from him! Quickly, she was gone.

"Baba," she whispered. "I saw mother with a man just now. Is this where she works?"

"Hush, child," her grandmother replied sharply. "You never saw anything! Come along now. We have to hurry if we want to catch the next express train back home."

But Suzue stood her ground and refused to move and right in the middle of Ginza, with its well-heeled crowds swirling around them, she cried out, "No, Baba, don't treat me like a baby and keep everything I ought to know away from me! I'm already twelve years old and if there is anything about my family that I'm being teased about at school, it's only fair that I should know enough to defend myself!"

Suzue's voice had risen in her agitation and a few people turned round to look at them. Embarrassed by the attention they were attracting, her grandmother took her by the arm and whispered, "Keep your voice down, Suzue, people are looking at us! All right, let's go to that coffee shop over there and I'll tell you about your roots."

They walked in silence to the fancy little coffee shop her grandmother had pointed out and even in her distressed state, Suzue was anxious about the price they would have to pay for drinks at this notoriously expensive keisaten. But she didn't say anything; after all, her mother just had a thick wad of notes pushed down her kimono front, so what were a couple of overpriced drinks anyway?

They ordered green tea which came with a pair of sweet bean paste rice cakes served on a beautiful real lacquer plate. Suzue also had a soft drink, and it was only after they had finished their rice cakes that her grandmother began to speak.

"I guess we can't hide this from you forever but promise me one thing, Suzue chan. Promise me that after you've heard what I have to say, your feelings for your mother will not change."

Suzue nodded, not trusting herself to speak because her heart was thudding unsteadily and there was a very big lump in her throat.

As if from a long distance, she heard her grandmother's voice drone on. "Your father was a half black American armed forces officer who had come to our prefecture with a team to help with some engineering construction work. Your father's unit set up a small temporary base near the school where your mother taught classical dancing. I was the last one to know it, but they started a secret relationship. All those trips your mother told me she had to make with her students for performances were lies to spend time with your father. I only discovered this when your mother could no longer hide it from me because she had become pregnant with you.

"I was devastated. My only daughter not only pregnant out of wedlock – but with the baby of a gaijin of a different skin color. How would such a child be accepted in Japan, obsessed as the country is with homogeneity? How would we be viewed by the neighbors who were already whispering about the lack of a man in our household?

"I guess your father panicked or just didn't want the responsibility of a child but in any case, he packed his bags and disappeared back to America and was never heard from again. Your mother made some attempts to trace him but gave up in the end. I was angry for a long time because my daughter's life had been destroyed by an untimely pregnancy out of wedlock with a man of non-Japanese origins and although she tried to hide it, I knew how much she had loved your father and had been shattered by his ultimate rejection and betrayal. Because it was such a sad and painful subject, we mutually decided never to speak of him again.

"It's the story of a naïve woman's life, you may say, but when it happens to your own daughter, it's very different and heart-breaking. We were left raising a child of mixed origin in a conservative society that tolerated but didn't accept a mixed-blood Japanese. Even the neighbors whispered about us, and to avoid being judged and stigmatized in our close-knit community, we moved to a much bigger town in the prefecture where we would be less conspicuous and hopefully melt into the larger population.

"It was a difficult decision moving from the inaka we always loved and your mother had to leave her job at the school. The official explanation for the absence of a husband in our new home was that your father had died in a car crash. Before we left Kyushu, it was a very difficult time, trying to hide your mother's pregnancy from the curious stares of the neighbors and making ends meet on our savings.

"I was afraid I was going to dislike you because, after all, you were the cause of all our problems and practically ruined your mother's life in Japan. But do you know, Suzue chan, the day you were born, everything changed. The minute I set eyes on my little granddaughter, I was lost. A strange kind of energy flowed between us and we would be bonded for life. True, you would never have the skin color of a Japanese girl and there would be stares and even snide comments, but that never affected my love for you."

Even after her grandmother had finished her story, Suzue remained silent for a long time. The old lady peered at her granddaughter's face anxiously, and continued speaking.

"You're angry with your mother, aren't you, for bringing you into the world in such circumstances? It wasn't entirely her fault, you know. She was a victim of love and whatever mistakes she made, she has paid her dues. Please don't judge her harshly, child."

Suzue shook her head. She couldn't seem to find her voice because the lump in her throat had grown bigger but somehow the silence between them had no tension, only a kind of poignant sadness.

"Thank you for telling me everything, Baba," she whispered at last. "I know that I asked to find out, but it's too much to swallow in one day so please pardon me, Grandma, if I take a little time to think about what you just said. But one thing is for sure—my feelings for Mother have not changed. In fact, I admire her even more for being strong enough to accept all the stigma she faced to have me. Now I understand that it was all because she loved me."

It was her grandmother's turn to nod and almost in silence the old lady and her granddaughter travelled back to their home in Matsudo, a riot of emotions going through their minds and hearts. When they reached the house, Suzue went straight to her room and stayed there til the next day. She needed time alone and her grandmother understood that and didn't try to intrude.

Suzue was surprised at how calm she felt, even slightly

detached. There wasn't even any anger or reproach at her mother's transgression. In fact, knowing about that part of her mother's life brought Suzue closer to her; it was almost a relief to know that her family was different from other Japanese families because it justified her own feelings as she became older. She knew the teachers in her school tolerated her because they pitied her for being a child of mixed parentage, sure to be left out of mainstream Japanese society. So Suzue grew into a rebel who could not conform.

As for her mother's work life, Suzue was relieved to know at last how her mother earned the money to comfortably support them. To be honest, she did not find working as a club hostess anything to be ashamed of. Far from it, she found her mother's opportunities to hob nob with fabulously rich and successful men fortuitous, and it was one of those rich patrons who placed Suzue in a major advertising agency after she graduated from a top notch university in Tokyo. It was a position she could not have even gone near, despite her sterling university degree, if not for her mother's patron.

She had been so good at her job that within two years she was promoted to Senior Accounts Manager and Suzue learned that in life what mattered was power and position. Once she had made it, Suzue was suddenly the most sought after executive in the advertising industry, even in Japan, and no one cared what color her skin was!

\*\*\*\*\*

Suzue was thinking of this as she put the finishing touches to her impeccably made-up face and stood up determinedly. She was thinking too much these days, and that wasn't good for her own peace of mind and the calculated shrewdness she needed, to be good at her job. The phone rang and Suzue was glad for the interruption that put an end to her morning soul searching.

It was Tomoko, one of the four pillars, wanting to find out when they could do dinner and Suzue smiled as she took the call, in control of herself and put together once again.

# CHAPTER 3

Tomoko Akita shoved the sheaf of papers she had been studying for the past hour into her briefcase. She leaned back to rest a little as the JR bullet train, Nozomi, hurtled into the dusk on its journey back to Tokyo. Each second took her further and further away from her family home in the beautiful and peaceful Nigiita mountains.

As always, Tomoko left her aged parents behind with a lingering feeling of guilt. Long after the train pulled away, she could still see her father's wistful face and her mother's teary eyes because their only child was leaving them and they would be alone again till her next much-awaited visit. God, it must be awful to grow so old with nothing to look forward to but the occasional visits of your children when they can spare the time to travel from the city!

Darn it, why did they always make her feel so bad to leave them behind? Tomoko got rid of these feelings of guilt by unloading them all angrily on Emi when Emi met her at the Tokyo station.

"It's not my fault they have to live alone, is it?" Tomoko fumed. "How many times have I asked them to come live with me in Tokyo? But no, they want to stay on in Niigata because their friends are there. When I asked them how many of their friends are left, they said only one couple — and the husband is dying of cancer!

"But then again, I guess they could never be happy living in a big, busy city like Tokyo closed up in an apartment the whole day," Tomoko continued. "My father needs his little plot of land to grow vegetables that are cheaper in the markets than the fertilizer and seedlings he spends on this hobby and my mother needs her little senbei and ramen shops. But how can I stay on in Niigata?

What kind of work could a corporate female lawyer — and I stress, female lawyer — get there?"

Emi muttered something soothing to calm down the frazzled Tomoko. They had been friends long enough to know that sometimes Tomoko asked questions which were better left unanswered, and this was one of those times. The long weekend had rested her body and cleared her mind of what her father called the "urban dust" of Tokyo and all her favorite childhood home-cooked meals — with their attendant memories — had been food for the soul. But now that Tomoko was back in Tokyo, she realized how much she would miss this vibrant heartbeat of Japan if she were to stay away for any extended period of time.

It was well after 10:30 p.m. but the mammoth Tokyo station was still teeming with throngs of commuters and long distance travelers amassed on its criss-crossing maze of platforms, alleys, lobbies, shopping lanes and wicket gates. The station's sheer size and efficiency had amazed Tomoko when she first came to Tokyo and it still did after so many years in the city. For a moment she felt disorientated after experiencing just a few days of her inaka's tiny single-track railway stations, micro wooden station buildings and the slow local pre-war trains which totally reflected the pace of life there.

But within minutes of getting out of the Yamanote subway line at Shibuya where her apartment was, Tomoko came alive again, every nerve responding to the bright neon lights of the advertisements on all the major buildings in the Shibuya Station vicinity. Those lights competed with the flashes of brilliant colors from the giant TV screens mounted on at least three or four buildings across from the station.

Emi got off of the train in the exclusive neighborhood of Mejiro, where she lived with her well-heeled parents in a huge bungalow house with a real garden filled with sculptured shrubs and elegant matsu trees. It was ironic that Emi, the only one among them to be born and bred in Tokyo, was also the least materialistic and streetwise of the four of them. Her friends attributed that to her pampered and sheltered life, including an education in blue-blooded schools like the Sacred Heart School and the Gakushin University. Sometimes they wondered what Emi was doing hanging out with three women who had gone through rough and tumble lives and clawed their way to professional recognition with a hardness that was uncompromising and brutal—character traits that Emi certainly was not used to, especially in women.

The cool early autumn night air hit Tomoko's face as soon as she emerged from the protective confines of the station to stand for a moment at her favorite spot, next to the stone sculptures of Taro, the famous Japanese Shiba dog. Legend had it that Taro waited patiently at the station every night for his late master's return from work till his own death, his dream of reuniting with his master in life, unfulfilled.

To be honest, although she would rather die than admit it, Tomoko had fled back to Niigata to escape the unpleasantness of an acrimonious split from her boyfriend of four years, an up-and-coming public prosecutor she had met while working on one of her well-publicized money- laundering cases.

The first year of their relationship had been heady and exciting and Tomoko had even neglected her girlfriends and cut back on her punishing work schedule to spend more time with Masao. She flinched now when she remembered the many times she stood up her three other pillars just to wait for Masao. God, she had been a total ass and was lucky that Sachi had soothed the ruffled feathers of the others with her persuasive "have a heart" logic.

"The woman's in love—or thinks she's in love—so leave her be! You know how fuzzy even the most level-headed woman can get when Cupid's arrow strikes! All these bubbles will burst and she will be herself again; we just need to wait for that event!"

Sachi was right of course. In the beginning it had been wonderful, meeting up after work and wining and dining at the trendy bars in Roppongi where they both worked. The sex had been awesome too, wild, uninhibited and if the neighbors heard their unrestrained cries of passion through the thin walls of even the most concrete "mansion" in Tokyo, they couldn't care less.

Masao was never a gentle lover and Tomoko could not remember many tender moments they shared together but she was quite the sex animal herself so they were a perfect match. True, his sexual fantasies could be kinky but Tomoko, herself an unconventional lover, could live with that.

Things started to frazzle when she made the decision to move in with him to save time shuttling between their two apartments in Shibuya and Roppongi. Life settled into a routine of getting up at the fifth ring of their alarm clock and bickering over godforsaken chores like who should do the laundry, the cooking and cleaning of the apartment. Suddenly they didn't feel sexy or wild about each other anymore.

Masao started taking her for granted and things about Tomoko which had been angelic to him before suddenly irritated and inflamed him. The last straw came six months after they started living together when Masao shouted during an argument, "You know what's wrong with you, Tomoko? You behave like a man; there's no feminine softness about you! God knows, I need someone who is a real woman!"

Those words really hurt and irreparably affected Tomoko's feelings for Masao. Exhausted from hours of bickering and sad at how her partner of four years had changed, Tomoko picked up her keys and left the house.

It was a Friday night and the streets of Roppongi were filled with afterwork young revelers, in groups or in couples. They thronged the broad pavements in laughing anticipation of the night of drinking, eating and dancing ahead, just as she and Masao had done.

Her cell phone rang at least five separate times before stopping and she could picture Masao shouting, "Fine, if that's the way you want it — go ahead and sulk!"

God, the man could be so childish and insensitive!

*That's the trouble with Masao and me, we never have tender moments; it's either wild, sometimes kinky sex or talking about work.* Tomoko mused as she observed others on the street. *We're never like that couple over there and there and there, all cuddly and star struck! I guess that's what he meant by saying I feel like a man to him, there's no softness in our quirky relationship at all!* Tomoko sighed. *Maybe that's all we are, sex partners, a good formula for occasionally hooking up in hormone-infused environments but not for moving in and trying to share all the other infinitely less sexy aspects of our lives!*

"That's it! That's what's wrong with Masao and me — we

don't share anything except sex!" Tomoko burst out as she settled that night on the extra futon in Sachi's comfortable 2LDK apartment in the upmarket Meguro area.

"Funny, isn't it that when a woman is in a relationship or in love or whatever, she has eyes only for her man but when things go wrong it's always to her girlfriends that she runs to for a shoulder to cry on," Tomoko continued. "Thanks for having me for the night, Sachi, my long-suffering friend! What would a woman do without girlfriends?"

"You know, Tomo," Sachi sighed, "I think we should be like Suzue. She uses men like disposables and she has an expiration date for them—two years maximum—because in her opinion, the first two years of any relationship are the best. Past the expiration date, like food, everything goes stale and it's time to throw them out!"

"I thought Masao would be different, being western educated and all that, but he's just the same," Tomoko said. "I can see him becoming my father in as little as ten years' time!"

That night Tomoko surprised herself by sleeping well and fretting less about her imminent split from Masao than she had expected. Her cell phone rang just a couple more times and then stopped.

The next day, Tomoko went to work dressed in one of Sachi's "power suits" and she could feel Masao's panic as her cell phone rang more insistently now and at shorter intervals. Tomoko felt an odd satisfaction because she knew how focused and disciplined Masao was at work and how he seldom made any personal calls, yet here he was, flooding her mobile phone with missed calls. He had to be pretty desperate and she couldn't care less.

During a short break between clients, Tomoko decided to take his call—and if she had begun to doubt her decision to split from Masao, the first words out of his mouth convinced her she had been right.

"Where have you been after just taking off last night like that?"

Tomoko sighed. As usual, there were no tender or soft words. In fact, Masao sounded peeved and even accusatory—as if everything was her fault. It was really hopeless!

"So what time are you coming back today?" Masao asked when she did not reply.

"I'm not coming back, Masao," Tomoko said at last. "Things are just not working out between us and I've decided to end it."

There was heavy breathing on the other end of the phone and she could just imagine Masao's face criss-crossing with disbelief and then indignation. She could almost hear the thoughts going through his mind: He was young, tall, incredibly handsome, well-educated and extremely successful in a highly respected career. What woman could say no to him? Yet here was Tomoko Akita calmly giving him the brush off in a cold, faceless, cell phone conversation!

Masao's stomach knotted up in anger and he retorted, "Fine, if that's what you want, but you'll regret it! I'll send your stuff over by takyubin tomorrow and please don't call me anymore."

It was Tomoko's turn to be angry. The cheek of that guy — telling her not to call him. What a jerk!

"I promise I won't be calling you anymore and thanks for sending my stuff over. Goodbye, Masao, and have a good life!"

Coincidentally, her work that afternoon involved the splitting up of enormous assets in a high-profile divorce case and Tomoko was a bitch, cutting through the negotiation process with a razor sharp knife. By the end of the afternoon she had secured an impressive amount of assets for the wife whom she represented. She had also earned herself a fat fee for her efforts.

That night Tomoko moved back to her own apartment in Shibuya. For just a moment it felt a little bit strange to have her own space back, to eat whatever she wanted when she felt like it, to do things only for herself and not have a partner's feelings, moods and needs with which to contend. Tomoko was sure that there would again be times when she'd miss the company of a man, but for now she was just happy to have her life back.

She threw open the windows to let the cool autumn air clear away the mustiness of her closed-up apartment and just then her cell phone rang. It was Suzue, the pillar they all went to if they needed a cynical and streetwise hand to keep overflowing emotions in check.

"I heard," Suzue said simply. That was one of the nicest

things about Suzue—the fact that when things went wrong, she never judged or asked painful and uncomfortable questions. "Let's pub crawl tomorrow—just the girls. It's Saturday so we can drink ourselves silly. And by the way, that was very convenient of you to split up on a Friday!"

They were both still laughing when Tomoko put the phone down and ran the bath for a good soak in the near scalding water of a typical Japanese ofuro.

# CHAPTER 4

In a studio in Akasaka, Emi folded up her work for the day and prepared to leave. She was glad to be going out with the girls that night; God, it had been a trying day!

Work aside, her mother had gone on a rampage again after returning from the wedding of an old classmate's daughter. Held at the upscale Four Seasons Hotel, it had all the splendor of a picture perfect match, at least on the surface, between two blue-blooded industrialist families. Emi had attended a few such weddings with her parents over the last couple of years; long, painfully-formal affairs which seemed to go on forever. The tension and pressure to have everything perfect was great for illustrious unions where the public face and pride of two powerful families were at stake, and Emi found it a real chore to attend such weddings.

Like most girls from Japan's elite families, Emi had attended the prestigious Sacred Heart School with the bride, Hiroko, daughter of the founder of one of Japan's giant car makers. Emi remembered Hiroko as a fun-loving mischievous girl with a wild nonconformist streak. Naturally, that streak was frowned upon and discouraged by the custodians of the school, entrusted as they were with the responsibilities of turning their charges into elegant ladies to be launched into high society for brilliant matrimonial matches.

Emi and Hiroko had gone on to different universities but their paths crossed enough for Emi to know of Hiroko's penchant for long-haired boys from rock bands and her occasional desire to cross-dress. Emi could have also sworn that Hiroko had dabbled in a lesbian relationship and smoked pot in her university years but Hiroko was exceptionally intelligent and the predominantly male professors in the engineering faculty grudgingly awarded her the highest scores for her finals, far surpassing those of the male students. Emi had always been in awe of Hiroko, who dared to go places and do things Emi herself was too timid to venture into.

Hiroko's parents were proud of her amazing academic scores, but they weren't impressed enough to encourage her to utilize that talent, preferring to stick to the centuries-old tradition that the daughters of blue-blooded families should not have to seriously work for a living. They were totally in the dark about the pot-smoking, cross-dressing, wild-child side of their daughter; they were aware only of the Hiroko who could easily assume the mantel of a demure debutante moving among Japan's higher echelons of society and who attended charity balls and auctions in elegant designer dresses or gorgeous kimonos with almost indecent price tags.

After their university years, the next time Emi saw Hiroko was at the wedding. Brokered and arranged through an omiai, Hiroko married the son of another blue-blooded family. This was a union of two fabulously rich families and emotions like love were not in the equation.

At the wedding, Emi eyed her former classmate with amazement. Only a few months ago, Hiroko was a scruffy girl riding on the back of a boyfriend's motorbike, clad in tight faded jeans and a leather jacket, with at least four earrings dangling from her much pierced ears. How on earth did Hiroko's family make her turn around to conform so fast and so thoroughly?

"Oh my God," Emi punched out a text message to Sachi. "I am at the wedding of the daughter of one of my dad's business acquaintances. I used to know the bride in school and she was really hot! I always thought she would end up with some gaijin or someone from the entertainment industry but look at her — marrying the heir of the Nakhoda family, yes THE Nakhoda family and looking like a maikosan! Hiroko? Pinch me, someone!

"I simply can't believe it! She's buried her real character in layers of makeup and a wedding kimono that, I swear, is sewn with real gold threads! You know what — she is actually shuffling behind her new husband, head averted and eyes downcast — and there's no trace at all of the modern 21st century woman who used to ride on the back of a motorbike in a leather jacket! I will never cease to wonder at the Japanese woman's supreme ability to crossover from modern to traditional and back again at the drop of a coin!"

But even as Emi gaped at Hiroko's "crossing over", she knew that she herself was a more likely candidate to end up the same way than any of her other friends simply because of her family background and the fact that her mother was trying so fiercely to steer her in that direction. She had no doubt at all that soon, an omiai would be knocking on her door!

Emi had to admit that her mother could be very focused and determined if she wanted to achieve a particular objective and it had been a hard and unpleasant battle when after her graduation Emi accepted an offer to work for a bank without consulting her family.

Her father had been less hard but there had been hell to pay with her mother who tried everything from psychological blackmail, tears and finally threats to tell the bank's president, a business associate of the family, not to employ her. It was one of the few times Emi dug her heels in and refused to budge, and it was only when she packed her clothes to leave the family home that her mother grudgingly caved in and agreed to let Emi "try out" the bank job for a while. She fully expected her daughter to give up working after a couple of months and return to the privileged life of belonging to one of Japan's richest families, hefty punitive taxes permitting.

But Emi had proved her family wrong, and three years on, to her mother's despair and her father's whimsical tolerance, she was still working at the bank and enjoying every minute of it. It was at a major agency pitch for the advertising package of her bank that Emi met Suzue, and her calm, non-eventful life, outside of her mother's manipulations, took a dramatic turn.

They worked together for a few months, first on the pitch and then the advertising package, and it opened Emi's eyes to a world where dynamic, well-educated Japanese women had broken away from the stereotypical roles of corporate "tea ladies" to become powerful "skirts in the boardroom."

**36**

## Onna Rising

At first, Emi was both intimidated by the forceful presence of Suzue and dazzled by her extraordinary energy and talent—to which her dusky olive skin added a mystery that made people notice her. If she were homosexually or even bisexually inclined, Emi swore she could quite easily have been attracted to Suzue, not so much because of her unique looks, but because of the energy for life she exuded.

Suzue, on her part, had to admit that when she asked Emi out for a drink that first time, she was only thinking of using her as a business contact to strengthen her pitch with the bank. It was only later that she discovered that they connected so well that when Sachi had a birthday bash, she brought Emi along as a new friend, not a potential client.

The party had been a no-holds bash at a little bar tucked away in one of the smaller sidestreets of Shibuya. A well-hidden, back-alley-like street that should have been quiet. But when they arrived, disco music was already spilling out of the red splash of paint of no particular shape that represented the quaint entrance to the bar. The pavement outside was awash with pub goers, groups of young people standing around, smoking or sipping alcohol.

"My goodness," Emi yelled above the roar of music rising and falling to the opening and closing of the door as patrons went in and out of the bar. "This bar is ...for want of a better word, special!" she finished lamely as a couple emerged and kissed their way down to the pavement where they proceeded to make out in full view of everyone.

Emi belonged to the set that attended concerts, operas and musicals, and this rowdy, raunchy bar was a new experience for her—but God, she was already loving it! What a sense of freedom! She could stop pretending and talk as loudly as she wanted, sit with her legs wide open if she wanted instead of having them delicately crossed and laugh right from the depths of her stomach instead of the gentle giggles her mother had taught her to affect since she was a little girl. Who needed polite superficial conversation and concerts that put her to sleep when she could have real life with real people?

"Thanks for bringing me here, Suzue san!" Emi yelled above a metallic number that a bar reveler was belting out.

**37**

"It's not too loud for you?" Suzue yelled back.

"No, I love it because I don't have to be Emi Yokota here. In fact, I can be anyone I want and this anonymity is empowering!" Emi shouted and they burst out laughing at their shouting match of a conversation. They were having fun doing the two things not encouraged in Japan's orderly society: shouting and talking loudly in public places. Suzue was beginning to like Emi Yokota, the prim and proper banker who turned out to be more spirited and fun-loving than expected. Thank God she had taken the risk to invite Emi to the party. She'd found a new friend, not just a potential client, in the process.

"Come, let me take you into the private room we have booked and meet the others," Suzue mouthed as she ushered Emi through a door at the back of the bar to an area that overflowed with guests of the birthday girl.

Emi felt new energy flowing into her body that replaced the memory of a whole month's worth of sculptured weddings. She soaked herself into this totally different scene which was worlds apart from her family's world of snobbish "old money," sinfully expensive kimonos, tea ceremonies and ikebana lessons, and the tranquil gardens of her home in Meijiro that came complete with a koi fish pond and sculptured azalea shrubs and matsu trees.

But hip bars like these represented the heartbeat of the young and energized professionals of Japan who were not afraid to play as hard as they worked. Two young and vivacious women disengaged themselves from a group smoking in a corner and bounded over to them.

"Meet Tomoko, the lawyer of our group and Sachi, the high fashion entrepreneur for two years running — and, may I say, the best girlfriends ever!" Suzue declared, proud as any mother introducing her talented kids.

That night, downing a daring mix of beer, whiskey, cocktails and wine, a firm friendship was forged. Although her mother would have disdained these women as "common," to Emi, they represented emancipation from her snobbish family and their pre-war samurai mentality.

At midnight, Suzue stood up and declared, "I have a surprise for the birthday girl!" She signaled to someone at the door of the private room and shouted, "Bring in the surprise!"

There was a scurry and a young man bounded in. Emi's mouth fell open. He was the most gorgeous man she had ever seen, a million miles removed from the stuffy bankers and pompous industrialists that she was used to. From the tip of his luscious gelled hair to his beautifully sculptured hips and legs, this Adonis was irresistible and sexy.

Across the room, she could see Sachi frantically mouthing the words, "No, you didn't, Suzue! A male stripper?" But, acknowledging that since it was her birthday and she wasn't getting any younger, Sachi decided to go with the flow and enjoy her present.

The male guests put a few tables together to form a make shift stage and grumbled good naturedly that it was unfair they didn't get to have any ladies strip for them, but, ok, it was the birthday girl's night.

Although initially shy about such an explicit form of live entertainment, Emi eventually enjoyed watching the gorgeous Adonis on the stage as he peeled off his clothes piece by piece until nothing but a G-string brief covered his chiseled body. She understood how Suzue and the rest of the women gyrating to the music and dance moves of the stripper felt empowered to have a male stripper pleasure them in the same way that men had, for centuries, been entitled to seek and pay for the pleasure of women who did the same for them. It felt good to have a man dance and strip for their pleasure instead of being the ones on parade; it was a petty, frivolous victory but it made a statement, at least to the hitherto shy and diffident Emi.

What she didn't know at that point was that a male stripper hired privately to perform was really nothing to gawk about because — as incongruous as it seemed in a country where women were expected to take a back seat to men in most areas, including pleasuring themselves — Tokyo was full of stripper clubs where women paid to watch a line-up of gorgeous men strip and perform for them. There were also many male escort clubs scattered over the Roppongi, Shibuya and Shinjuku areas where successful women paid to be pampered, spoiled and "loved" by any handsome young man of their choice.

Emi smiled as she remembered how she finally discovered herself, right there in a room with flashing disco lights and gyrating bodies hovering around a near-naked man who egged on perfectly intelligent women to stuff 1,000 yen notes into his grinding briefs.

As Emi found herself responding very pleasurably to the sexual vibes their male stripper was dispensing, she decided that being a banker and having to keep a straight face and a straight back to bow at all the right angles was not what she wanted. Hell, she had a degree in journalism and *that* was what she had always wanted to do — report news or be in television! She had gone into banking because it was the only safe, sedate and ladylike job that her parents could be persuaded to approve of without too much of a fuss. But that night, Emi decided that she was through with always doing things that were expected of her.

Why was it that men in Japan, like her brother, never had to suppress their ambitions and could be anything they wanted to be? Women had to fight and struggle to be what they wanted; they had to cut through layers of prejudice not only from society but even from families like hers who wanted to push them back to traditional roles instead of encouraging them to surge forward. Whatever a man did, a woman had to work twice as hard to make a point or to prove herself.

"God," she thought. "No wonder, Sachi, Tomoko and Suzue are so full of angst — they've had to fight hard just to get their skirts into the boardroom!"

Emi became their fourth pillar and Suzue decided that they would "keep" her, even if the pitch failed and her agency did not get the account of Emi's bank.

Within days of making the decision to leave the bank, Emi sounded out a university mate who anchored a program at a major Tokyo TV station, and as luck would have it, there was an opening in the financial news section. Emi, an experienced banker, fit the profile of what they were looking for. In Japan, getting a good job was still all about being recommended in by someone prominent and Emi got the job after just one interview.

She fully expected to lock horns with her family, especially her mother, over her impulsive decision to quit the bank but Emi was pleasantly surprised when they seemed almost excited that she was going to be in television, declaring that at least it was a more glamorous job than hiding in a bank.

"We must make you look nice so that people will notice you," Emi's mother declared. "I can just imagine you appearing in your designer clothes; the young men from all the good families will be impressed and it will be easier to make a good match for you!"

Emi shook her head in exasperation. Didn't her mother ever envisage any future for her beyond auctioning her off to the highest bidder in the marriage market? But, although frustrated, Emi had long accepted that her mother belonged to the old school of thought, mired in traditions, class consciousness, old money and clinging on to the name of her noble samurai lineage. It was too late now to change her mindset.

"It's not all about glamour, Mother. It's also about going out there for grueling field work, doing interviews sometimes with people who don't really want to talk, being thick-skinned and going all out to gather news—there's certainly no designer clothes for that kind of work!"

That had been three years ago, a time when Emi started blossoming from a reserved, self-effacing conformist into a vocal, assertive journalist. She developed an amazing nose for scoops and financial scandals simply because of her special ability for making people open up to her. Her excellent journalistic skills eventually earned her the grudging respect of the media networks in Japan and pushed her channel to promote her to senior positions with greater autonomy to avoid losing her to rival channels.

But the early days had been tough—not so much because of the grueling 14 hours or more she often put in, but because of the way people didn't take her seriously because of her privileged background and her gender. Even now, despite her success, the character assassination continued.

"Can you believe it?" she fumed to Tomoko, whom she had met for a coffee. "The nerve of some of the men at the station! I swear they are badly henpecked at home so they need to take it out on their female colleagues—making snide remarks that I probably got my promotion because I slept with my department chief!"

"Oh you'll get used to it!" Tomoko replied airily. "In the

early days, I used to be affected by all the office gender politicking, just like you, but now I just shrug it off and tell my critics, 'Lucky me for having that option to sleep with the powers that be—so bite me!'"

"Come to think of it, my department chief is quite drop-dead gorgeous and I just wouldn't mind taking a nap or two with him—promotions aside!" Emi replied, as the two friends laughed heartily, drawing glances from the table next to them. A moment or two later, Emi dropped a bombshell.

"By the way, " she announced quietly, "I've volunteered to go with a crew to Africa to do a documentary on the plight of women in poverty stricken communities."

The open-minded and largely shock-proof Tomoko gasped. Emi— *"In Africa, doing a heart-wrenching documentary under such grim circumstances?"* Even now, clad in faded jeans and a nondescript T-shirt with her hair tied back in a pony tail and without a stitch of makeup on, Emi looked poised and elegant!

"What's wrong with that?" Emi demanded, peeved. "You think I can't do it? It's this rich kid stigma again, isn't it, even from you! Look, in case you've forgotten, the head of the UN human rights commission is a Japanese woman!"

"No, no, it's not that," Tomoko lied. "It's just that this is very sudden and I was taken by surprise. Do the others know yet?"

"No, I only made this decision yesterday and I haven't seen any of them yet but I'll break the news when we have our drinks session tomorrow night. My family will have my head for this, that's for sure!"

Tomoko reached over and took Emi's hand, realizing for the first time how firm and determined her grip was under its deceptively soft, white and extremely smooth exterior.

"Go and do what you want to do, Emi chan, and be all you can be," she said. "It's what we are fighting to achieve; to break away from society's role for us as women in Japan, the custodians of the nation's reproductive and babysitting services. We are the modern emancipated voices of Japan's professional women and we don't let anything or anyone affect our professional decisions. Good grief, don't they know how many brains and human resources they are wasting by pushing us to the backyard of this country's workforce? And then they scream that there is labor shortage in Japan?"

Tomoko had been so engrossed she didn't realize she had raised her voice till the woman at the next table clapped her hands ever so lightly in approval and was joined by her teenage daughter while the man of the family continued eating in glum silence.

Tomoko suppressed the desire to giggle out of a sense of social decorum but she whispered to Emi, "See? The men can feel the women becoming more assertive outside the home — and I don't think they like it one little bit!"

# CHAPTER 5

Sachi lifted the phone off the hook and went back to her makeup. She made a mental note to install caller ID on her landline as soon as possible so that she could screen the calls that came in. Kenji had been calling every hour almost on the dot—so much for his petulant declaration that she would regret breaking off with him and that there were many pebbles on the beach anyway!

God, he was pathetic! After having literally kicked her off his back, he wanted her back desperately—now that he realized she didn't want him anymore. That really hurt his male ego. In fact, Sachi was quite sure it was more his ego that was bothering him than actually losing her.

"What's it about men that they just can't bear to be dumped?" she asked her awakening face in the mirror. "It has happened to women since time immemorial and they're expected to take it. Well, not any more, Kenji san and your kind!"

Her cell phone rang; it was Kenji again. This time Sachi didn't avoid the call, but picked it up and said firmly, "Please stop calling! When you had me, you took me for granted and treated me with a carelessness and disrespect that I took for a while. Stupid me! Now you want me back—well, too bad and too sad! Is it because you miss the convenience of being able to have sex for free anytime you want?" Kenji tried to speak, but Sachi wouldn't let him.

"No, stop, " she continued. "Don't say you love me because for some men, love is a convenient excuse for sex on a regular basis. You know what? Stop calling me. Go find another woman to have sex with or pay someone more feminine for it! Remember how you threw it into my face that I'm not good enough for you? By the way—just so that you will remember this the next time—women don't forget that kind of cruel remark easily!" Sachi hung up the phone without even bothering to hear what her ex-boyfriend had to say.

"God, that felt good," she thought. "Two years past Suzue's expiration date and it's finally over. No more having my day determined by what kind of mood His Majesty was in, eating the kind of food he wanted, watching movies he liked and pretending to enjoy having boring, selfish sex with him. It's over."

She calmly returned to her makeup, watching her face transform from a sweet, fresh-faced, young Japanese woman to a sultry, head-turning beauty oozing with self-confidence. She never tired of watching this magical transformation that just a few pots of eye and lip makeup could do to a woman and it pleased her that tonight she looked icy, unapproachable and impeccably beautiful. Sachi's other three pillars called this her "fire and ice" look, which could drive a man crazy simply because she appeared to be so unattainable.

Maybe she was a little under the weather or maybe that scatterbrained receptionist had passed her cold on to her, but Sachi suddenly felt a little down and alone. She had to admit to her sophisticated face in the mirror that deep down, she still believed that men and women belonged together and should compliment each other and even try to grow old together. It was just so hard to find the right fit.

Sachi sighed and turned away from the mirror, a young woman with a healthy sexual appetite who sometimes got lonely for the touch and feel of a man. But she did not want the kind of man that Kenji had been.

*****

"Where have all the good, really nice men gone?" Emi echoed her thoughts later as they looked through the menu of the new Spanish tapas restaurant in a quiet part of Shinjuku. Tomoko had heard about the restaurant from a client; it was one of many western restaurants that had recently sprung up all over Tokyo's more affluent clusters to whet the appetite of the young, single and restless with purchasing power and no other mouths to feed.

"Perhaps there are none," Suzue replied, blowing rings of cigarette smoke and watching them swirl off to contribute to the smoky environment in the restaurant. She immediately got defensive. "I know, I know, I shouldn't be smoking so much, but Tokyo is one of the few advanced cities of the world where smoking is still allowed in restaurants," Suzue added hurriedly. "They're going to ban that soon for sure, so let me enjoy it while it lasts!"

"Getting back to the subject of men—perhaps we should be like you, Suzue. I know we make fun of it sometimes but your expiration date concept is actually becoming more appealing!" Tomoko laughed.

"Hurts less that way, believe me!" Suzue said. "Last month a guy from my creative department started sending out 'I am attracted to you vibes' and I looked him over. Nice firm body, excellent white teeth, the kind I like—so why not? He was wild in bed, but for some reason I got bored after two weeks and decided to end this dalliance. One minute we were touchy-feely lovers and the next we reverted back to slap-on-the-back friends and workmates. It was that simple. No fuss and no mess, and I'm still his boss!

"In fact, dinner is on me tonight, ladies, because I've just been promoted! My friends and pillars of strength, you are looking at the new Global Brand Director—with a foot in the boardroom at last!"

Suzue laughed as she tried good naturedly to fend off the flurry of arms as her three friends descended on her with congratulatory hugs and an excited chorus of "Omedeto, congratulations!" "Hey ladies, just buying a dinner doesn't deserve such an excessive show of affection and gratitude!"

"Another promotion—I don't know how you do it, Suzue!" Tomoko said. "I know you're very good at what you do and you work your heart out but I swear there's something else you have that is edging you into the boardroom!"

"Maybe it's because my skin is a couple of shades darker so I have the 'gaijin tsuyoi,' that strength and articulateness of a foreigner, Suzue laughed. "They leave me alone to create whatever I want without clipping my wings and I come up with these bizarre ideas and concepts that the clients seem to love because they're daring and different. And then my company realizes they need me and if I march up to them and demand a promotion, they give it to me even though I am a woman because they are so afraid to lose me to a competitor. You know how we Japanese – and I say "we" because I am a Japanese through and through no matter how many shades darker my skin is – are afraid of scenes and 'gaijin tsuyoi.'"

Suzue grew thoughtful. "You know, growing up, I used to hate my dark skin. I actually tried to scrub it off with whitening soaps and creams, but now I love it because my "difference" gives me the license to be as daring in my creations as I want and people just leave me alone. I see some of my colleagues trying to do more revolutionary creations and they are shot down and end up conforming. I know that some people routinely whisper that I sleep with my boss to be on the fast track, but I don't even care about that.

"Anyway, you should have seen the look on that sour-faced old woman from traffic when she saw my promotion letter. You know, the one who hates me and calls me the "ugly foreigner?" If looks could kill, I would probably be dead and cremated by now!"

Suzue smiled. "But enough of me; let's hear from the rest of you. Any good news, bad news, new relationships to share or split ups to grouse about?"

Emi took a big gulp of sangria and said, "I don't know if Tomoko has told you both, but I've volunteered to go with a team to Africa to do a documentary about abused and socially underprivileged women there."

At that moment, in one of the restaurant's whole-hearted attempts to be more Spanish than Spain, a couple dressed in flamenco dance costumes glided over to serenade their table with a rendition of 'Spanish Eyes' and the shocked silence following Emi's announcement was thankfully broken.

"Did I just hear you say that you're going to Africa?" Sachi shouted above the blare of the accordion playing to the clicking of the colorful dancers' wooden hand cymbals.

"Yes, you did, and don't you dare repeat what I already have had an earful of – that you can't imagine me being in Africa with my designer dresses," Emi shouted back, just as the flamenco dancers moved away from their table, taking their music with them and leaving Emi's last sentence ringing out loud and clear in the restaurant.

In the past, a reserved Emi would have been mortified with embarrassment as heads turned to identify the author of that bizarre statement, but a year into the media industry, Emi simply shrugged and continued as if people shouted out these statements in a restaurant every day.

"For the next two months, no designer clothes—only faded T shirts and jeans with my camera and netbook as my constant companions," Emi went on. "And I couldn't be more excited at that prospect! I've had too many comfortable urban assignments to let this one slip through my fingers! It's a chance I've been waiting for since I joined my network—so be happy for me.

"Now I have just one more hurdle to cross, and that will be even greater than the project itself : Convincing my mum to let me go without a big fuss and drama, because I will go in the end anyway—even if she objects. But it would be more pleasant to go with her blessing than with her tears and threats," Emi sighed.

" You know, you should really try to live on your own," Tomoko said. "Thirty years old and still living at home with your parents! How do you invite your friends home and if you find a guy that you like, how do you invite him over to spend the night? I think we've outgrown sneaking around love hotels with water beds and red, heart-shaped pillows!"

"I'm not suggesting that you disregard your parents' feelings, but at this age, Emi, you should be able to be your own person," Sachi agreed. "My parents are very important to me but I don't let them run my life. I pretty much decide on something and then inform them about it rather than ask for their approval before making any decision."

"Whoa! Whoa!" Emi held up her hand. "One thing at a time! Africa *and* moving out together? I don't think my mum would be able to take that double blow!"

"Ok, ladies—leave Emi alone. We're all products of our environment and one of us is no better or stronger than the other," Suzue interjected. "And anyway, what's wrong with love hotels? To be honest, I rather like the red, heart-pillows and kinky, mirrored ceilings so that we can see what we are doing and get even more turned on. How delectably erotic and sexually open; at least there's no need to pretend because we all know what we go to a love hotel for! I know I have a perfectly good apartment to bring guys home to, but sometimes I make them check into a love hotel just for the fun of it!"

"I don't know how the conversation got sidetracked from Emi's upcoming African trip to love hotels but, for sure, no one can say that the conversation at our table is ever boring!" Sachi laughed. She wasn't a very stronger drinker and the wine was getting to her.

They toasted Emi's exciting new project that night with round after round of sangria and hard liquor, and just managed to stagger back to Sachi's apartment—stone drunk but happy.

# CHAPTER 6

Suzue watched the plane becoming smaller until it disappeared into the thick clouds which had opened up eagerly, as if they couldn't wait to swallow that little metallic object. She shivered as she thought about how delicate life really was; all it took was for that flimsy tin box carrying her mother and grandmother back to their inaka to keel over and lose control and the two people she loved most in the world would be gone.

Despite all the business trips she had made criss-crossing Asia and the United States as a regional brand manager and then as her company's new global brand director, Suzue still hated flying because, for those few hours airborne, she could not control her own life and had to leave it in the hands of others.

Ever since that night in Ginza when she discovered what her mother did to keep them safe, warm and comfortable, Suzue decided she had to be tough and strong. Nothing and no one was going to make even the tiniest hairpin crack in the protective armor she would build around herself and her family. Her mother would not be able to do that kind of job forever. Someday she, Suzue, would have to be the breadwinner and take care of her family so she had to be strong, no matter what.

*"Stop being morbid and melodramatic; what's wrong with you?"* Suzue chided herself. But if the truth be known, the sight of that plane disappearing made her feel suddenly alone and vulnerable — emotions she hadn't allowed into her busy, self-sufficient life for a long time.

A few weeks ago, when her mother and grandmother had

announced excitedly that they were coming to Tokyo to visit her, Suzue had initially been flustered. She thought of the frenetic lifestyle she would have to put on hold while they were around and how she'd have to flurry to hide all the 'incriminating' evidence of that lifestyle. But when she saw them walking out of Arrivals at the airport, her heart just exploded with love.

Her mother was still a beautiful woman, but after she left her job at the Ginza club, Rumiko had gratefully forsaken her trademark thick and flawless make up for a simple, more natural dash of powder and lipstick. Looking at her, Suzue could hardly believe that she had once been a much sought after and immensely popular hostess of an exclusive men's club in Ginza.

Rumiko looked tranquil and totally at peace now, as if she had just stepped out of the glossy brochures filled with de-stressed women surrounded by nature, soaking in one of Japan's famous onsen or hot spring resorts. Yet, once, Rumiko must have been madly in love with Suzue's father; crazed enough to throw all caution of an unwise liaison with a 'gaijin' to the wind and bear him an 'ainoko,' or love child. Just for that one moment in her life, Rumiko Tanaka had accepted the challenge of following her heart and ignoring her head... and Suzue was the lifelong result of that 'challenge.'

Kyushu was hardly a three-hour shinkansen—or bullet train—ride away, but Suzue's grandmother had wanted to fly for the sheer experience of it, and despite the inconvenience of meeting them at the airport instead of the train station, Suzue was rewarded by the grin on the old lady's face. She had obviously enjoyed the plane ride tremendously and Suzue found her grandmother's shining eyes infinitely endearing because it took so little to make her happy.

Suzue sighed; when was the last time her own eyes had shone like that? These days, even diamonds didn't glitter for her anymore, and there were times when she wondered what would happen when she had achieved everything and there was nothing left to go out there to get.

Suzue's mother and grandmother stayed for almost a week and it gave her a warm feeling to return home to an apartment that was filled with laughter and chatter. The tiny kitchen of her bachelor pad seemed to spring to life, awash with the aroma of her favorite food and her grandmother's signature dishes. Suzue lapped up all the fuss and attention shamelessly. It felt nice to be taken care of for a change instead of always having to be strong and perfect. With her mother and grandmother, she could be herself, imperfect, dented, sloppy and vulnerable. Suzue knew she was going to miss all that 'homeliness' as she turned away from the deck and caught the train back to her dark, empty apartment.

Suzue was used to being alone. She usually didn't mind the solitude when she was not with her three other pillars or with a guy she felt attracted to sufficiently to spend a night with or even several nights and, a couple of times, even several weeks with. In fact, Suzue couldn't take too much 'togetherness' and needed her own space and time alone. But, somehow, today she did not feel like returning to her apartment so she made the impulsive decision to take the Tozai subway to Toyocho, a nice residential town on the outskirts of Tokyo to visit one of the few childhood friends she had stayed in close touch with after they went their separate ways.

Akiko Kobayashi had been Suzue's best friend from middle school right through high school. They had drifted apart when Akiko chose to study home science at a women's college instead of entering the university, but the ties that bind never really snapped and they stayed in constant contact even after Suzue's attempts to 'educate' Akiko on her right to build a career and be financially independent failed miserably.

"Don't take a back seat and stay in the background just because we are women and expected to do so," Suzue said. But her pleas fell on deaf ears. Her friend's response was that some women had to stay home to have children and mind them. Japan's aging population and declining workforce needed to be replenished, and these women were actually doing the noblest job of all. After all, without a constant supply of children, where would the future professionals, work force and entrepreneurs of Japan come from?

Akiko was born to be a wife and mother and like many women in Japan, all she wanted out of life was to find a good husband with a stable income, have two obligatory children, preferably a boy and a girl and ease comfortably into the life of a Japanese "okusan" or homemaker.

# Onna Rising

When Suzue realized that this was what made Akiko happy, she accepted her friend's decision. Six years later, Akiko got what she dreamt about: A comfortable 3LDK modern 'mansion' or apartment in the middle class Toyocho neighborhood, a salary man husband whom she waved off to work every morning at 7 a.m., and two beautiful children, exactly two years apart, a boy and a girl, of course, for whom she would eventually join the other homemakers to queue and fight for places in the best yochien or kindergarten—followed by primary, junior and high schools. And on top of this, the eventual fierce fight to enter the highly sought 'jyukus,' or cram schools, which would hopefully prepare them for the stringent entrance exams to the likes of Tokyo, Keio or Waseda University.

This would be Akiko's life; and in between she would fit in hurried shopping trips to the malls, tea sessions with her other friends to compare notes mostly about their kids' education, and the occasional all-ladies' trips to the onsens or hot springs to "de-stress." Not all the okusans were happy; in fact, most were in boring marriages and it was not unthinkable to pack condoms in their husbands' travel bags when they went on business trips.

"Far better to be safe than sorry," was their practical, matter-of-fact rationale. "After all, who knows what kind of "entertainment" the men may get when they are abroad."

When Suzue got out of Toyocho station it was already 4 p.m., the time when Japanese housewives did their marketing in the streets and supermarkets that formed the epicenter of every satellite town or urban pocket. Suzue felt the warm rays of the late afternoon sunshine on her face as she watched the trail of women with their shopping carts stop occasionally to exchange a few words with a friend or neighbor. They were like bees swarming towards a pot of honey and offered a warm, bustling scene, without the subterfuge and knife-edge tension of Suzue's working life inside and outside the boardroom.

It reminded her of those beautiful and simple childhood days when she would rush back from school each afternoon just to make this trip to the "machi" or shopping streets with her grandmother. For someone who would in later life dislike shopping for groceries and any form of domestic chore, Suzue had enjoyed those trips to the machi immensely. By the time they got there, the little side streets would be filled with shoppers crowding around stalls displaying colorful 'yamas' or mounds of fruits and vegetables and the voices of the stall holders shouting out their products, some cracking jokes and trying to outshout others.

It was incredible and yet touching that despite the great technological and economic advances Japan had achieved through the decades since she was a child, nothing had changed in this aspect of Japanese society and daily life.

Suzue had come to Toyocho on an impulse without even calling Akiko, and chances were that she might not even be at home and they would end up not meeting. For what it was worth, Suzue quickened her steps on the familiar paved road with its cheerful clover patterns, to Akiko's "mansion," which faced a canal flanked by beautiful weeping willows and sakura trees that blossomed into breathtaking pink wonders during the cherry blossom season in the first week of April.

Every year without fail, Suzue would visit Akiko to watch the cherry blossoms outside her apartment in full bloom and so they could have dinner together. This year, she was a lot earlier; by seven months, to be exact. Suzue chuckled as she thought how shocked the methodical and routine-abiding Akiko would be at this unscheduled visit.

Akiko's mansion was easy to spot as it was painted a kind of liver red with rows of neat cream colored doors. Suzue took the stairs to 02-02 and rang the doorbell, not expecting anyone to open it. To her surprise there was a shuffle of slippered feet and the door opened to a slightly -flustered Akiko wearing the trademark apron of Japanese housewives.

"Suzue, is that really you?" she screamed, clapping one hand instinctively to her mouth. "What are you doing here? Has something happened? Why didn't you call? I could have gone out and then we would have missed each other."

"I know, I know but it was just an impulse after I sent my mother and grandmother off at the airport. I suddenly missed my roots and the innocent and simple joys of my childhood. You are the only person in Tokyo from my past and I had this sudden desire to see you, so I just hopped onto the Tozai line without even thinking and here I am! I hope it's not an inconvenient time?"

"No, of course not; we have been friends since we were

twelve years old and that gives us certain rights and obligations towards each other!" Akiko replied earnestly. She never said anything she didn't mean, not even as a teen. "I was just taken aback when I opened the door and saw you standing there. You know me — always have to plan everything way ahead and jigsaw puzzles must fit perfectly!"

"Yes, I remember, especially about the jigsaw puzzles always having to fit!" Suzue laughed. "Your mum would groan every time you received a jigsaw puzzle as a present because you would not rest till you had every piece in place! Remember your 13th birthday when one of your uncles showed up with a 1,000 pieces jigsaw puzzle thinking that it would keep you occupied and out of your mum's way?"

"Yes, my mum nearly fainted and finally she negotiated a good price to buy it over from me!"

It was only when they stopped laughing that Suzue noticed that the comfortable 3LDK apartment was quiet and orderly without Akiko's two children chattering and running up a storm.

"The children have gone to Hokkaido to spend a week with Shintaro's parents — that's why I'm so free this week," Akiko said, busying herself by pouring piping hot barley tea and slicing up a cake she had just baked. She looked and sounded the same, and it was incredible how many years and lifestyles had passed between them. But, for better or for worse, it was Suzue who had changed.

"Look at you," Akiko said. "A global brand director, no less! I really admire you, Suzue, because you did it! I could never be the person you are. I haven't got the fight, the guts or what it takes to reach the top. I always knew that I couldn't do it, no matter how hard you tried to push me to travel alongside you!"

"I know, " Suzue said. "I was so horrendous that you were terrified each time you saw me! But as long as you're happy and this is the life you want, that's all that matters. You *are* happy, aren't you, Akiko?"

"Yes," Akiko replied simply. "I am. Although being a homemaker does have its downside, I am pretty contented, taking care of Shintaro and the children, and watching them grow each day. You could say this home is my boardroom and I am managing director of it!"

"You know, coming here and talking to you makes me realize that your life decision was right and in many ways, the role you play is much more important than high flying career women like me. Creative directors, lawyers, doctors — all these roles can be fulfilled by men but having children and bringing them up with a mother's love and care, no man can undertake that role! After all, no matter how advanced science becomes, no man can bear a child!"

"You are so right and I must remind Shintaro more often of that!" Akiko laughed. Then she sobered up and continued. "I have a confession to make, Suzue. When I said I was contented, I really meant it — but you know the jigsaw puzzle thing with me? There's one piece left to be fitted in to complete the whole puzzle of my life."

"Really? Tell me, please tell me. Your life always seems so organized that I can't imagine what piece could still be displaced!"

"Ok, here goes! Do you remember how good I was at creating costume jewelry?" Akiko asked a bit self consciously. "Well, I am hoping in a few years' time, when the kids grow up and don't need me so much anymore, to start a small business in fine costume jewelry and accessories. There, I've said it! That's the last piece I need to fit into the jigsaw puzzle of my life!"

"Oh my God, Akiko, that's a brilliant idea!" Suzue breathed. "Of course I remember your costume jewelry. I still have the pieces you made for me and I call them my good luck charms. Every time I wear them for any meeting I always come out of it the winner! I can see it: Akiko Kobayashi, entrepreneur and founder of Akiko's Creations!"

"Whoa, whoa! I was just thinking of a small business to start!" Akiko laughed. "I've started making a few pieces here and there, and to be honest, this idea was inspired by you, Suzue. Seeing your success has made me realize that I can do it too, and I will not rest till this last piece is successfully fitted into my puzzle!"

Suzue was smiling when she turned to wave at Akiko before hurrying down to the platform to catch her train back to Shibuya. *"My intrepid and shy friend, Akiko, has realized her potential and wants to start her own business — and she said she was inspired by me!"* was all she could think of as she shoved her way into the rush hour commuter crowd.

Suzue's cell phone beeped. It was Fumiko, her PA, reminding her she had a mega pitch the following day for a major airline account. Her heart soared. Suzue's adrenalin surged as she mentally returned to her familiar world of wheeling and dealing and all the bitching and scheming that went with it. The visit to Akiko had been refreshing, but this was her real world and she couldn't wait to get started on the pitch — the more challenging and punishing, the better!

# CHAPTER 7

Suzue noticed the new digital director who arrived from their London office as soon as he walked by her office. He was tall, even for a Caucasian, towering over everyone and just making it through the doors of Japan's notoriously low ceilings, even in a glass and metal modern building like theirs. He was not particularly drop-dead gorgeous like some of her dates had been but he had an interesting face. His snub-nosed ruggedness was arresting and his clipped British accent (with a strong hint of a Hugh Grant lisp) made her heart race.

Suzue had to admit that she was attracted to Robert Darcey and the feeling seemed to be mutual. He openly admired Suzue and his daily innovative excuses to drop by her office were both flattering and hard to resist.

"Just go have a fling with him," Tomoko suggested. "After all, it's been quite a while since your last boyfriend — the longest interval ever, as far as I can remember. You've become lazy, Suzue!"

"To be honest, something's stopping me from dallying with this one," Suzue replied. "It's not the language or culture divide thing because you know I've spent many years working and interacting with foreign clients and co-workers and once I even spent a summer interning in a media agency in Los Angeles. So I'm totally comfortable interacting with a gaijin and anyway, remember I am even considered one myself!

"It's Robert Darcey's intensity and seriousness about people and any potential relationship that makes me hesitate to take him on," Suzue continued. "This guy can get serious and bothersome and it might be difficult to shake him off and I really don't need a clinging-ivy complication in my life!"

"It might not be so bad, Suzue, being in a committed relationship for a change," Tomoko said popping a piece of forbidden fried chicken into her mouth. Tonight she was insanely happy because she had won a landmark case which would earn her a big bonus and probably the senior partnership she had been promised. In fact, Tomoko was so intoxicated by the power of her success and the large amount of champagne they had all drunk to celebrate this event that she was even prepared to not only break her strict diet code and eat fried food, but also tolerate the concept of committed relationships.

"Hey, this is Suzue you're talking to. Remember, I don't do committed relationships! Besides, he's a gaijin and although I can work very well with them, I'm not sure I really want to sleep with one on account of my no-show father being a gaijin and all! You must be drunk, Tomoko, but what the hell. We're all drunk so we can say whatever we want and take responsibility for it tomorrow!"

"Yes, that's the nicest thing about being drunk — you can let your hair just hang loose and when questioned the next day, put the blame on that one too many drink you had!" Sachi agreed.

"Legal observation: If you think about what you can do because you are drunk, you're really not drunk at all!" Tomoko declared.

"Hey, don't be a spoilsport," Sachi gave her a playful shove and the laughter that followed was as light and frothy as the bubbles in their champagne.

This was the first time Sachi, Tomoko and Suzue were meeting since waving Emi off to Africa at the airport three weeks earlier. Although they missed Emi's calm unruffled presence tremendously, they had every reason to be happy. Each was at the top of her respective career and had shaken off an uncaring and boring boyfriend or lover. They were footloose and fancy-free.

*"Well, almost footloose and fancy-free,"* Suzue mused to herself wryly, because for the past few days, she had definitely wasted more thoughts on Robert Darcey than she had on any other man even at the peak of a fling. It made her uncomfortable to know that her heart could still be jolted by a man and she had even started

flirting with Tomi from the buying department just to get Robert out of her hair. It hadn't worked very well because here she was, right in the middle of clubbing with the girls, and she was still thinking of Robert! Fools—that was what women were—fools because no matter how many times they were hurt, they still insisted on delivering their hearts to be slashed again!

When the suave young man from the next table who had been trying to make eye contact with her the whole night came over to ask her for a dance, Suzue readily accepted and threw Robert Darcey out of her thoughts.

After all, it was Friday night, a time for after office-hour reveling right into the early hours of the morning. The discos, karaoke lounges and bars of Shibuya, Shinjuku and Roppongi, their regular haunts, were spilling over with merry makers and pub crawlers—mostly single salary men and women and university students—who stayed till 5 a.m. when train service resumed to take them home.

After dancing to a few songs, a glistening Suzue returned to the table. "It's nice, isn't it, just us girls together like this without any boyfriends hanging around," Sachi said. "I know I disappeared on you ladies when I was with Kenji but he just took up so much of me that I didn't have the energy for anyone else. Oh my god, he wanted us to do everything together, even shopping for my ladies' stuff! Everywhere I turned, there was Kenji! I meant no disrespect to the old lady, bless her soul, but when his grandmother passed away in Hokkaido and he had to spend a week there, I was over the moon because for a whole week I had my own space. It felt as if I had my life back again! It was then I realized that Kenji was wrong for me. The fact that I didn't miss him at all, but instead wished he would stay on in Hokkaido permanently, made me take the plunge to break off with him. The next boyfriend I have has to be less needy, must value his own space as fiercely as I do mine and will preferably be there only when I need him!"

"Well, I can do much better than that. O.K., maybe not better, but infinitely more bizarre by normal standards!" Suzue said. "I would prefer my partner to stay in a separate room and have his own separate bathroom if we have to share a house. But if we can afford it, it's even better if we stay in separate houses—that way his face won't be the first I see when I wake up in the morning and the last one when I go to sleep at night! Think of what that can do for a relationship—not being there all the time to get on each other's nerves and see the worst realities of your partner!" Suzue smiled. "It keeps the freshness and goodness sealed in and the expiration date could be extended a bit more!"

Just then, Suzue's dance partner from the next table came over and started to get fresh, encouraged by Suzue's daring dance moves earlier. When she had had enough of his bold, open advances, Suzue leaned close to him and whispered something in his ear. The music was too loud for the others to hear what she said but whatever it was, she managed to shake him off and he beat a hasty retreat from their table.

"What on earth did you say to the poor man to make him scoot off like that? He didn't stay beyond the courtesy three minutes!" Sachi asked, laughing.

"Nothing sinister. I merely told him I am having a very heavy flow of menstruation tonight and I don't do sex during menstruation!"

"Suzue! You didn't say that to a total stranger!" Sachi and Tomoko laughed so much that they nearly swept their drinks off the small table crowded with beer mugs, whisky glasses and snack bowls.

"Sure I did!" Suzue retorted. "Proves one thing: All he was interested in was getting laid for the night! Talk about wining and dining a woman into the bed—guys don't even seem to think that is necessary anymore!"

"Well, to be fair, you did lead him on earlier on the dance floor," Tomoko pointed out. "I was watching you. He's just the average guy with hormones raging, but for you it was calculated. Somehow I got the idea that for you it was all about shaking off something or someone!"

"Yeah, you're right," Suzue admitted, after only the slightest hesitation. That was what the other pillars liked about their "main pillar" —her very unJapanese way of being direct and passionate about things that mattered to her. At work, she preferred to engage her subordinates and be upfront with them instead of ruling with the steely hand of hierarchy in Japan's corporate "Me Tarzan, You Jane" kind of way. It endeared her to her subordinates and softened somewhat the preconceived employee mindset of the lady boss from hell.

Suzue knew she was the envy of her male executive management colleagues and most definitely the unkind butt of their bawdy ribbing during toilet breaks. She was unfazed and if anything, it amused her to think of a row of black suited corporate men standing in a row with their pants unzipped, bitching about her.

But she also knew that centuries of corporate culture in Japan could not be shaken by one, two or even an army of women or men, for that matter. She only got away with her unconventional ways of handling her team because she was "different" — a 'gaijin' — and they preferred to leave her alone.

"Penny for your thoughts," Sachi's voice cut through Suzue's wandering mind and brought her back to the present. "You were saying we were right and then you just disappeared into your own world!"

"Sorry," Suzue laughed lightly. "I do that sometimes as you well know. Now, where was I? Oh, you were insisting I have some issues and I was agreeing with you. It's that wretched man, Darcey. I can't seem to get him out of my mind and it's driving me nuts! And the way he's walking by my desk once too often and placing little gifts when he thinks I'm not looking doesn't help! That man is either a shameless hustler or a sweet guileless schoolboy from our middle school days — take your pick!"

"Why don't you choose the sweet schoolboy from our middle school days, Suzue?" Tomoko suggested, a wicked gleam in her eyes. "Will be easier to handle him and do the karate chop, Suzue style, when the time comes!"

"That exactly is the trouble, ladies," Suzue sighed. "I don't think the classic karate chop will be easy here and a lot of blood will be shed — and you know I like my karate chops clean, with minimal bleeding!"

"All this talk of karate chops and bloodletting is giving me the creeps!" Sachi shuddered. "Maybe you are dramatizing the whole thing, Suzue. It's a case of wanting the fruit you can't or dare not eat! If you fancy this Darcey guy, why don't you just take him like the others. Then you'll find out that he's just the same, and you'll get bored and restless and do what you always do—walk away and never cast him a second thought again!"

"Yes, I agree with Sachi," Tomoko said. "You know what they call those Japanese girls who go for any Western man in pants? Yellow cabs! Well, let Mr. Darcey into your cab and after a few rides you might just throw him out. Or, on the contrary, after a few rides you may decide Mr. Darcey is the only passenger you want in your cab! Either way, it's a challenge and I've never known you to pass up any challenge! That's why you are such a loud and formidable voice at board meetings! I've heard stories about your boardroom antics from our mutual clients and colleagues that would make you blush!"

Suzue smiled. "All right, never let it be said that Suzue passed up a challenge—be it in the bedroom or the boardroom! So let's drink to Mr. Robert Darcey!"

The three women raised their whiskey glasses and shouted over the drone of disco music, "To Suzue and the poor unsuspecting Mr. Darcey!"

# CHAPTER 8

The week hadn't started well at all. On Monday, the busiest day of any executive's workweek, Tomoko took a tumble as she climbed a ladder in her stilettos to reach the top of the book shelves which lined her office, and broke a leg.

"Oh no," Suzue groaned when she got Tomoko's SOS text message on her cell phone while in the middle of a video conference. "How many times have I told that girl not to climb even a step ladder on stilettos?"

"Is everything ok?" Robert Darcey, who was seated next to her asked, placing his hand instinctively over hers.

Suzue moved her hand away, suddenly irritated with him. O.K., they had gone out a number of times and had started making out but that didn't give him the right to display proprietary control of her hand in full view of all the supercilious male corporate godforsaken suits! Didn't he know by now that this was still Japan and it was hard enough for her to get out of the societal mindset that a woman's place was to belong to a man and not in a boardroom? Didn't he know that she didn't have many friends in the corporate world and lots of criticism to deal with?

Still, Suzue shouldn't have rebuffed Robert in public and make him lose face in the Japanese sense. To her surprise, Robert wasn't fazed at all by her rebuff but merely gave her a Hugh Grant woebegone look that said "Oops, I put my foot in my mouth again!" Immediately, Suzue softened. It was impossible to be angry with Robert for long or at all! The corners of her mouth lifted imperceptibly and next to her, Robert relaxed as the late afternoon brainstorming session of creator directors began to wind down.

But their exchange had not been lost on Noburo Yamada, the junior director two notches below Suzue and her envious arch enemy in the envy department, due to her promotion above him. A diehard male chauvinist, Yamada made no secret of his resentment of Suzue and his desire to have her head on the chopping board as soon as possible. In fact, it had become a standing joke in the company that if Suzue's ideas were pitched to the directors and those who objected were asked to indicate by a showing of hands, Noburo's hand would be the first and often the only hand to be raised! It didn't matter that Suzue had brilliant and fresh ideas, was a daring strategic planner and had the amazing ability to win over clients to clinch for the company many enviable accounts; to Noburo she was still a woman, lest everyone else forgot that. Suzue was sure he was the most vocal of the male toilet-break complainants of women 'trespassers' in the boardroom.

One day, after a particularly trying run in with Noburo whose "uprising" had to be quelled using the emergency weapons she hated to deploy (hierarchal arm twisting and putting him down in public) Suzue met Tomoko at a nearby coffee shop to grouse.

"Just think of it, Suzue, maybe he will get so carried away by his insane jealousy of you that when he is at his toilet break bitching, he will imagine he is squeezing your neck when his hands are on his penis and he will squeeze so hard that he will crack his little man up!" Tomoko suggested wickedly.

"Yes, I like that idea…that would definitely make my day!" Suzue laughed so hard she almost fell off her chair. "Well, I'll certainly know what's up when I hear a commotion coming from the gents' room!"

Then she remembered: Tomoko! Oh God, how could she have forgotten, even for one second, about her friend's urgent SOS? Although Suzue's thoughts had drifted to her power struggle angst with Noburo, her pillars were far more important than all the Noburo Yamadas of the world. Even before the directors had filed out of the conference room, Suzue was on her cell phone to Tomoko, while she signaled for Robert to wait.

No answer; Tomoko must have left for the hospital to have her broken leg attended to. A call to her law firm ascertained that

Tomoko had indeed been taken to a nearby international hospital. Pushing Robert into a corner, Suzue gave him a tight hug, reached up to kiss him and whispered, "My friend, Tomoko is in the hospital and I have to go to her. Can you please cover for me for a few hours? I have two presentations with foreign brands to be conducted in English and here are my presentation notes; I'm only asking you because I trust that you'll be able to convince our clients. They love the 'gaijin tsuyoi' and heck, Robert, you are much more gaijin than me!"

"Just go, Suzue. I'll wrap up this for you," Robert replied, and Suzue kissed him again.

"Thanks, Robert, you're a gem," she said. Then, to lighten her anxiety over Tomoko's injury, she laughed and quipped, "Just look at us, my kohibito, two self respecting directors kissing behind a potted plant in this crème de la crème agency! Yamada san would love to catch us in this compromising position and add more spice to his toilet- break assassination of my character!"

Her laughter was still lingering in the little alcove as Suzue dashed off in her lavender silk dress, mean-looking, matching stilettos and her trademark bouncy "gaijin" curls, for the moment tinted a warm dark auburn. That was the way Suzue dressed, hip and unconventional, and unless there was an important client meeting, she would not be caught dead in those dark corporate suits that the company dress code had tried to impose on her till the powers that be just gave up. Suzue knew that if she wasn't so good at her work and with her clients, she would have gotten the axe long ago for flaunting so many company rules and refusing to conform.

Robert Darcey watched as Suzue exited through the swing glass door and stood there for a long time, his hands stuck deep in his pockets and a tiny line creasing the space between his eyebrows as it always did when he was in deep thought. What was it about this abrasive woman with the mindset and ambitions of a man — who liked to dress in flowy dresses and killer shoes — that just drove him mad for her? He was insane because Suzue Tanaka was what his mother back home in Northampton, England would call "trouble."

\*\*\*\*\*

## Onna Rising

When he first arrived in Tokyo, Robert did what most single, foreign men did: He went through the time honored "initiation" rounds of cruising the bars and raunchy discos of Roppongi, and it was only his traditional British upbringing that prevented him from accepting the open invitations of many young nubile and absolutely attractive Japanese girls. They were the "yellow cabs" with their trademark dyed blonde hair, tanned skin and doll-like false eyelashes who cruised the bars of Roppongi for the novelty and adventure of making out with foreign men, preferably Caucasian. Some of his friends weren't quite so circumspect and had absolutely wild nights of bedding a string of "yellow cabs" till they finally got tired of the Roppongi circuit and settled down to more stable lives in Tokyo.

Still, even without Roppongi, Robert knew that he could have any number of incredibly beautiful Japanese girl with the softest, most flawless skin he had ever seen on any woman on the planet, and he was just about to succumb to the shy but obvious "invitation to date" of a gorgeous Japanese girl from the accounts department when Suzue crossed his path and all hell literally broke loose in his life.

It hadn't been easy getting Suzue to notice him and even when she did, there were lines that he could not cross— the most important being getting her to recognize him as more than a casual office fling that just went on a little longer because he gave her such a good time in bed. Suzue herself was a fantastic lover; just as she was a perfectionist in her work, she threw herself into sex with uninhibited abandon and made love with such raw passion, completely open and unashamed of her need to pleasure and be pleasured that even now, standing in a room cold with glass and shining chrome, Robert could still feel the heat of their previous night's intense love making staining his cheeks and erotic zones. Suzue kept him on his toes and never gave him many moments of peace, and he loved every minute spent with her, which she loftily declared could not be too often—and certainly not on a daily and nightly—basis lest—they became "plodding along" lovers.

*****

"Darcey san, Mr. Darcey!" the frantic voice of Suzue's assistant, Fumiko, jolted Robert out of his thoughts. "Do you know

**67**

where Tanaka san is? She is due for a presentation in conference room 2 in 15 minutes and I've looked everywhere for her!" The poor girl was close to tears because she adored Suzue and couldn't bear to have her boss commit the virtually unpardonable crime of not showing up at an important presentation. Robert hastened to reassure her.

"It's all right, Tanaka san had to rush off on an emergency and she left me with her notes to do her presentations today, so I'll be taking this one," he said.

Fumiko looked at him dubiously as if she wasn't sure if he, or anyone else for that matter, would do as good a job as her boss and she blurted out, "But..but..Tanaka san didn't say anything about that.."

"Look, she had to rush off. She was worried stiff about her friend who is in hospital, so it probably slipped her mind," Robert explained patiently. "Don't worry. I'll charm and dazzle the clients so much I might even take them away from your Ms. Tanaka!" He was just trying to lighten the moment with a joke, but too late Robert realized that Japanese co-workers—especially devoted P.A.'s —had a very different sense of humor and could take his words very seriously.

"Oh, Darcey san!" Fumiko literally squeaked, her cheeks puffed up with indignance and bristling at the very thought of anyone touching her Tanaka san's clients.

"Wait a minute, don't take my words so seriously. I'm kidding, of course! Come on, you're stuck with me for today whether you like it or not so let's get going and go through these notes before the clients arrive. Remember, we've only 10 minutes!"

Without giving her any more opportunities to protest, he ushered the still indignant Fumiko into conference room No. 2 for a pre-presentation briefing.

*"God,"* he thought. *"The woman is like a nursing baby who only wants its mother and no one else!"* The thought of Suzue mothering and nursing a baby made Robert chuckle and he was still smiling as the suspicious Fumiko started reluctantly to go through the presentation notes with him in a monotonous voice.

On the other side of Tokyo, Suzue was running the 300 meters or so from the subway station to the hospital as best as she could on her stilettos, completely unaware of the waves she was making in Robert Darcey's life. The only thought she had of him right now was to wonder how he was handling her presentations and her suspicious assistant, Fumiko.

Poor Robert! In her anxiety over Tomoko, she had forgotten to text Fumiko about him taking over her presentation and no doubt, she was not giving him an easy time! But he was a big boy and he would know what to do. With that thought, Suzue promptly forgot about Robert Darcey and tiptoed down the long, linoleum-covered hospital corridor to Tomoko's four-bed room. She hated hospitals because they reminded her of the weaknesses and mortality of human life and one thing Suzue couldn't stand was to be weak, helpless and dependent on others.

Tomoko's face lit up when Suzue tiptoed to her side of the room, which was already filling up with flowers and fruit baskets from her many appreciative clients and co-workers. She had insisted on a four-bed room because, for all the "tough cookie" vibes she gave to people, Tomoko was also afraid of things she couldn't control, like death and ghosts and spirits. She was sure the bed she was lying on had seen a good turnover of dead bodies, perhaps even the pillow her head was resting on had hosted at least a few corpses, and it was always better in such circumstances to have at least three other fellow patients for comfort and company even though they were all too sick to exchange more than two words with each other.

"Oh my God, just look at you! How did you get yourself into this mess?" Suzue whispered. There was something about hospitals that made even the irreverent Suzue feel she had to whisper and walk on tiptoes, lest her stilettos beat a sacrilegious din fit to stop all the pacemakers in the hospital and wake up the dead in the basement mortuary.

"I know, I know — no stilettos on a ladder, not even a three step one!" Tomoko said, doing a near perfect rendition of Suzue's "I told you so" voice and they both burst out laughing. "Oh it's so good to see a friendly face! But you shouldn't have rushed over like this — what about your appointments and meetings? I messaged you just to let you know what happened, not to make you drop everything and come over like this!" Just then, her cell phone beeped, and Tomoko's face lit up a second time. "It's Sachi," she announced. "Oh my God, she's here too! I feel like a celebrity for the day!"

Tomoko's eyes misted over as Sachi entered the room. "When I was brought in here, all I could think of wasn't the excruciating pain I was in, but of being helpless and away from work for a few days, and this in the middle of a big public policy case," she said. "But now look at both of you — dashing down here to give me support in the middle of a Black Monday! What would a girl do without her best pals?"

Sachi and Suzue spent the whole afternoon with Tomoko and even ate dinner in the hospital cafeteria. They chatted with her, trying to make her forget the broken leg that was going to make her miss work for four days and then have to hobble around the office on crutches for at least another week.

Suzue's cell phone beeped at least three or four times during the visit with Robert updating her more than necessary about how the presentations were going under the watchful but slowly relenting eyes of Fumiko. She smiled because both of them knew Robert was finding any excuse to beep her and somehow, the thought of that made Suzue happy and a little guilty that she hadn't thought about him at all. God, what a bitch she was, not caring for Robert beyond fleeting thoughts! Well, she was certainly proving Sachi, the most romantic of them all, wrong in her dire warning that "Every bitch has its day and will eventually face her Waterloo!"

Suzue made a mental note to have a serious talk with Robert about how she was incapable of loving any man. What they had was purely physical gratification and perhaps he should move on to find love with someone else, if that was what he was looking for. She had tried to do that twice before, but he made her feel so damn good that she decided she didn't want to push him off yet. That had been six months ago and instead of getting bored with the same lover, Suzue actually found their physical intimacy getting better and more exciting!

"Goodness, it's not supposed to be that way! Am I starting to feel something for Robert? Is he becoming comfortable, like the old pair of shoes you keep looking for?" she asked Sachi as they sat in the dull grey hospital cafeteria over an equally unimaginative dinner of rubbery spaghetti with a sprinkling of lukewarm bolognese sauce. She wrinkled her nose both at the unappetizing hospital food and the idea of becoming emotional about someone who had started as being a mere "sex buddy."

Suzue's "sex buddies" concept chilled even the blood of diehard cynics like Sachi and Tomoko, who had objected to the use of those words as crude and demeaning. After some good-natured bickering over that, Suzue had agreed to call them her "playmates" instead, not that, in her view, it was any better!

"An old pair of shoes? Is that how you feel about Robert Darcey?" Sachi laughed and then continued in a more serious voice, "You know, Suzue, no one will think any less of you if you develop feelings for a man. With us, you don't have to be tough and hard all the time. Remember, we are the best friends you will ever have and we know everything about each other, so be upfront and don't be so Japanese!"

Suzue became very still. Sachi's innocent words "we know everything about each other" had struck a bitter chord in her heart and the familiar cold hand of panic began to stroke her back with a kind of smoldering power. No, Sachi was wrong, they didn't know everything about her. There was a dark secret in her life that she had never told any of the pillars and they must never find out.

In the beginning, as she started steadily to climb up the corporate ladder with dizzying speed, creating envy and hostility in the co-workers who were pushed back down a rung or two to make way for her to reach the top, Suzue lived in fear that someone would dig deep into her life and uncover this ugly secret which would spell her downfall. After all, in Japan, even powerful political figures had fallen from grace for lesser scandals than hers would be if it were ever uncovered.

The cafeteria door swung open and a whiff of breeze raised the hairs on her neck. Suzue shivered as she was reminded of that dark secret she longed to unburden onto someone to ease the heaviness of keeping it all inside her. How would people feel about her if they found out? Fumiko, Robert, her three pillars—would they still respect her if they knew? Yes, that dark secret was another reason why Suzue used men for her pleasure but would never give her heart to any one of them.

"Are you all right, Suzue?" Sachi's anxious voice cut through her thoughts. "You look sort of green and pukey!"

She peered up at her friend's white, mask-like face with concern. God, Suzue looked as if she had been possessed by one of the many spirits that must have escaped from the hospital mortuary downstairs!

It was on the tip of Suzue's tongue to blurt out the truth to Sachi so that she could feel the relief of sharing her burden with someone at last, but the moment passed and she replied lightly, "Oh, I'm fine. A little out of sorts perhaps, because hospitals just don't agree with me, but everyone has to be afraid of something. And now you know that I, Suzue, nasty bitch to my enemies at work, am spooked by hospitals!" she laughed, a loud brittle laugh which, even to her own ears, sounded false and hollow.

Sachi didn't look convinced but she could sense Suzue's reluctance to talk about whatever was bothering her so she replied quietly, "Something is bothering you, Suzue. I worry because you know how intense you get about things that bug you. Just don't let whatever it is bother you too much, OK? Promise and then I'll leave you alone."

"If I don't promise — then what?" Suzue laughed, the old wicked gleam back in her eyes. "You're going to do what my primary school class bully used to threaten? 'Go to the bathroom with me or I'll wait for you after school and there will be no escape.' Oh, those innocent days of childhood when we didn't even think to question *why* class bullies would be afraid to go to the bathroom alone! Think of what we could do today if we discovered such weaknesses in our rival co- workers!

"Yeah, when we were born we were really nice, innocent and trusting and look at us now — shamelessly corrupted by power, ambition, agendas and desires, not all of which are work-related, mind you!

"Sometimes, when I have time to reflect, I just look at myself. God, I've just been promoted and have gotten my foot in the boardroom and I'm already eyeing the next level, assistant CEO, perhaps. No wonder everyone in an usurpable position, if there's such a word, is suspicious of me — and I'm definitely not very well-liked. Sometimes, I stop and think that maybe I ought to be a bit nicer and be contented with what I've achieved thus far and stop edging everyone out of the way with my much feared stilettos, but then I get into the boardroom with its miles of shining, polished oak wood table and I see myself sitting at the head and all power hell breaks loose and I am very much in the race again!

"And it feels so good to have people saying 'Suzue is a woman but she is still a power to be reckoned with' instead of 'Suzue Tanaka? She is just a woman and there is only so much harm she can do to us!' I had the men who said those very words looking at me with real loathing and disbelief when I sailed past them up the corporate ladder!

"And when I got my first advertising award and clinched account after account with a few really coveted clients, they had to accept that this skirt in the boardroom had come to stay. You should see the way even Noburo san has to grit his teeth and congratulate me at award ceremonies because everyone is watching! I could even hear the sound of his teeth grinding and gnashing at the last one! And all of them think the same thing—she must be sleeping with the right people!"

Both of them were still laughing as they returned to Tomoko's room where a little commotion seemed to be in progress next to her bed. The center of dispute was a white tray with a single bowl of what looked like watery rice porridge. Two young bewildered nurses were hovering around Tomoko as she implored, "Please tell them, Suzue, that I have a distinctive aversion to porridge and there is no way in hell I'm going to eat that anemic paste!"

Then she turned to the nurses who still hovered anxiously and demanded, "Do you like snakes and lizards? Would you eat them if someone says you must?" The normally even tempered Tomoko was on a rampage, spitting out her frustration at being immobilized and 'out from work' and scaring the poor young nurses out of their wits.

Suzue hurried up to the sparring Tomoko and apologized to the nurses, adding that she would handle the matter and get their difficult patient to eat the porridge which did actually look nasty and totally unappetizing. She ignored Tomoko's silent 'if looks could kill' expression till the nurses had disappeared. Then she reached into her bag and produced two cartons of the Japanese bachelor girl's must-have emergency comfort food: Cup noodles!

"These never fail to work with us single girls," Sachi said as she saw the smile spreading across Tomoko's face.

"It's amazing, Suzue, how you think of everything, even cup noodles! What else do you have in that bag of yours?" Suzue smiled as Tomoko tore into her dinner. Moments later, the bed-ridden pillar spoke.

"Thanks, I really needed that! A good feast of comfort food with absolutely no nutritional value other than carbohydrates and a lethal mixture of sodium and MSG! My God, cup noodles have never tasted so good!" Tomoko declared. "Sorry about my childish display of tantrums earlier—I don't know why I snapped like that. I guess the porridge was just an excuse to spit out all my frustration. Can you believe it—a little while ago I couldn't even get up to go to the toilet and had to relieve myself in a bedpan! That's absolutely the pits! "

But despite her promise to be a better patient, by the time Tomoko was ready to hobble out of the hospital to return home, even the most patient trainee nurses bade her a very relieved farewell!

# CHAPTER 9

Suzue was walking on air. For the first time since Tomoko's accident she felt the familiar adrenalin surge of having snared a new major account, one she had not even made her best pitch for, at that, and was prepared to lose. On top of that, it was Robert's birthday and he had passed up a big birthday bash at one of Roppongi's more up market pubs for a quiet dinner with her. For some reason, Suzue was pleased that he wanted to spend his birthday with her alone. There was an intimacy about that that she found strangely erotic and she was sure they would make love afterwards with wild and unrestrained abandon.

*Sex is like power – wild, driven, addictive, irresistible and all consuming,* she thought as she dressed for her dinner with Robert. It was liberating to be able to express herself sexually, to take what pleasure she needed or wanted without having to suppress her desires behind a false veil of decency, modesty and whatever else a 'good' Japanese girl was supposed to do.

Suzue chuckled to herself as she remembered how shocked her grandmother had been one day when she declared, at barely six years old, that she was going to be bad because 'it was more fun to be bad.' She had later heard her grandmother complaining to her mother about "the bad genes of the foreign blood in that girl" and wondered whether they were talking about her because at that time she was too young to know she was considered 'foreign.'

Another time, when she was just starting to climb the second rung of what she called 'her corporate agenda ladder,' Michio, a former lover on the fast track of the diplomatic route at the

Foreign Ministry, had told her, tongue in cheek after a particularly memorable night in her apartment, "You're sensational in bed. It's a pity you're not the kind of girl I could bring back home to introduce to my family or take to Foreign Ministry functions."

What typical male chauvinistic garbage it was for him to presume that she would want to have any permanent relationship with him, much less be on the verge of begging him for marriage! Did he think she would give up a challenging and satisfying career for a life hanging onto his arm as a diplomat's wife? Did he really, really not see that she would rather be the diplomat herself than be a diplomat's wife?

Suzue knew she ought to do the 'right' thing—which was to be angry and deeply hurt by these insulting words and perhaps fly into a rage and throw him out—but she felt none of those things, just a vague decision that it was time to end this dalliance. True, the sex was fantastic, but it was just sex—easily replaceable and nothing to fret about.

In fact, eventually, it was the current favorite of the Foreign Ministry who looked worried and uncertain, even a little peeved, when Suzue said nothing. Instead, she just calmly walked into the bathroom to put on her makeup.

"My goodness, Suzue," he said. "Aren't you supposed to feel *something*?"

"No, should I?" Suzue replied, calmly applying foundation, her face expressionless.

"Yes, a normal woman should," Michio persisted. "My God, you're really cold!"

"Well, maybe I'm not a normal woman then," Suzue said and turning to look at him at last, she added. "It's over, Michio. I would appreciate it if you could leave my apartment now and don't contact me except, perhaps, as a friend or acquaintance. And oh, just leave the keys on the console table on your way out.."

"You cannot be serious! So it's over, just like that?"

Suzue almost laughed out loud at the look of disbelief on Michio's face. What was it with men, especially in Japan and with a man as successful and 'marriageable' as Michio, that they refused to believe a woman could dump them and walk away from the lure of all that brilliant career prospects and guaranteed financial stability.

# Onna Rising

Suzue could see and feel Michio bristling with indignance; her reaction was what he had definitely not expected at all. It was not that she wanted to lash out at him for giving her such a low priority in his life but Suzue simply couldn't be bothered to waste time on what she considered trivialities.

But with Robert it was different. He didn't put pressure on her by talking about the future, and they were kindred, sexually-compatible spirits—addicted to power and living for the present . They were together and yet apart, enjoying each other to the fullest and yet sacrificing nothing of their independent lives and careers. With Robert, Suzue could ask for time out which could last anything from three days to a month, no problem. And although she hated to admit it, they were perfect for each other.

Suzue also liked it that Robert Darcey respected her work. He believed in her and encouraged her to be all she could and even when she stole an award from him or was awarded better accounts, he was happy for her. She had more enemies in the company than friends, people waiting for her to make mistakes and mess up. It had been lonely in the boardroom among all the suits and pants till Robert Darcey became a useful and desirable ally—all the way from the boardroom to the bedroom!

Tonight, Suzue had every reason to be happy. She fully anticipated another memorable night with Robert and God knew that she needed to unleash all the pent up passion and sexual energy that a week of corporate wheeling and dealing had built up. At their intimate birthday dinner, Suzue excitedly shared with Robert how the three pillars had finally managed to wrangle a three-day holiday together and would all be taking a long awaited trip to a nearby onsen or hot spring resort the following week.

"Plus, over and above everything else," she continued over a dinner where not only the steaks were sizzling but where their "socially restrained animal lust" was also sizzling twice as hot, "Emi is coming home in a couple of months! You haven't met her yet but she's the sweetest of all the pillars! However, don't get her wrong—underneath all that honey is a determined woman who can run through all social barriers like a bulldozer! Well, what do you expect, after all, she is one of the pillars!"

"That's the one from the hoity toity family who threw all

the carefully-laid plans of her parents to the wind to wallow in the muck of us working mules, right?"

Before Suzue could reply, Robert threw his napkin on the table and signaled for the check.

"You know what? I give up this pretense of enjoying a slow dinner when both our hormones are raging and what we actually want to do will be rated adult plus 18 in Japan!" Robert said. "So let's get out of here before our hormones take over and both of us end up in a police lock up for performing indecent and lewd acts in public!"

From the next table, a man watched them. His face was obscured by the shadows of the dim corner table light and but his eyes followed Suzue as she grabbed her purse and tried to walk as nonchalantly as she could out of the restaurant.

# CHAPTER 10

It was a busy week and Suzue was rushing to meet a deadline, so she was irritable when Fumiko buzzed her a second time to say that their newest client was insisting she be present at their first agency client dialogue later that afternoon.

"Just tell him I'll be engaged with a prior appointment and we'll send our team manager to handle the introductory details," she said without looking up from her work.

"That's what I already told him, but he insisted he wants you to be present—and Tanaka san, I checked up on Mr. Mori and he's a corporate voice and power that cannot be ignored," Fumiko replied. "Shall I pencil you in for the meeting this afternoon?"

Suzue sighed, "Big Echo is a high value client so I guess you have to pencil me in. God knows why, though, this Mr. Mori is so insistent I be there; most of our clients couldn't care two tails as long as we send a senior level manager or any director! But I guess they pay our bills so we have to run when they crook their fingers."

Big Echo's offices were in a swanky part of Roppongi Hills and even Suzue, used to the glass and glamour of some of their most 'branded' clients, was surprised at the foyer and designer suites she saw as she stepped off the private lift at the company's executive floor.

Suddenly Suzue wished she had put on her better Armani suit that day so that she would not feel so "dwarfed" by the large expanse of shining white marble floor that led to the chrome and glass reception counter. It was clear no one was worried about wasting space in this office building that was located in one of the most expensive areas of Tokyo.

Suzue shivered at the sheer strength and power the offices of Big Echo exuded. She didn't like the way it made her feel tiny and vulnerable, like a small ship rocking in a temperamental and unpredictable ocean. With a confidence she didn't really feel, Suzue let her stilettos tap firmly across the huge span of marble floor and down to the conference room to which she was being shown.

Perhaps that was what all that empty space was supposed to do—intimidate Big Echo's clients, suppliers and competitors in order to wrench cut-throat deals from them. Suzue had read up a little about this Mr. Mori and not all of it was beautiful! His name faintly jolted her memory but she was too busy to go beyond a mild interest.

The minute the frosted glass door of the conference room swished open, Suzue had the uneasy feeling that something was wrong. Call it her survivor's instinct but there was that strange energy in the air, like a tiger waiting in the wings to spring on her. She chided herself for being paranoid and placed her folder with a self assuring bang on the highly polished oak table, the only concession to the chrome, steel and glass fittings in the room, before looking up to face her client already seated at the head of the table, watching her.

Suzue's heart turned to ice as her eyes met Mr. Mori's and the automatic words of greetings and introduction she had uttered countless times to countless clients froze in her throat. The blood drained from her face and with a great effort and iron clad self-discipline, she collected herself, gripping the edge of the table fiercely to prevent herself from falling.

*Get a grip on yourself, the room is filling up and people will notice and wonder what is wrong with you. Remember how hard you fought to be here; it's not all going to come tumbling down like a pack of cards!* The words beat into her head like a drum and Suzue quickly recovered from the terrible shock of finding out the identity of her influential client, Mr. Mori.

In the end, the survivor in her took charge and somehow she was able to get through the afternoon and avoid meeting Mr. Mori's eye. To her credit, no one who saw and heard Suzue Tanaka deliver a brilliant presentation of the project at hand, complete with her trademark acerbic sense of humor, would have had an inkling of the turmoil and ice cold fear that was churning inside her at the prospect of a very dark period of her past coming back to haunt her.

As soon as the meeting ended, Suzue excused herself and bolted for the ladies' room where Mr. Mori could not follow her. Although he might be waiting for her when she came out, at least for those few minutes she would have time to collect herself and walk out eventually with a cool and calm head. The one time she had made eye contact with Mr. Mori, Suzue had seen the way he looked at her and realized, with a sinking heart, that he remembered. She had hoped he would not connect the two Suzue Tanakas but no such luck; it was clear he remembered!

Her face looked ghastly in the mirror, pasty except for the gash of red lipstick she had applied so carefully that morning without a clue as to what was coming! Suzue had been in control of her life and all its attendant problems for so long that she found it hard not knowing what to do. But even now, her first thought was damage control and how to challenge and contain a man who was as powerful and invincible as Mr. Mori—both as her major client and in the business community.

In her jacket pocket Suzue's cell phone, which she had put on silent mode for the meeting, started to vibrate, sending little waves down her thigh and shaking her out of her moment of despair and weakness.

With a firm tweak of her crumpled skirt and a fresh application of rouge on her cheeks, Suzue pushed open the heavy tempered glass door and walked out of the ladies' room. Mr. Mori was nowhere in sight and Suzue heaved a deep sigh of relief. She could probably get out of the building and back to her office without confronting him and her past after all.

But as she hurried across the large imposing reception room to the main entrance, he called out to her, a familiar voice echoing across the years to a high class social escort Agency's 'office' in a deceptively quiet part of Ginza. Suddenly, the veneer of sophistication and supreme confidence fell away from her like peeled onion rings, layer by layer, and Suzue was, once again, that lonely young girl, lost and bewildered, who had just landed in the vibrant, pulsating city of Tokyo.

*****

**81**

She was 19 years old and flat broke. Her mother had stopped working in the hostess club because, at 44, she was considered too old to charm and pamper the stress from the high-value patrons who responded better to younger women. Japan was facing an economic downturn and the club's patrons were not as generous as before and younger, more attractive women were needed to keep the rich and famous coming back to leave more bottles of expensive whiskey and liquor labeled with their names.

It was really a bad time for Rumiko to be suddenly tossed from the high paying job they had all been relying on because Suzue had just been accepted by one of the country's most prestigious yet horribly expensive private universities. It was an ambitious girl's dream come true.

But soon, in order to survive, Suzue's mother used whatever savings she had to start a grooming and social deportment school for young ladies. Although it was enough to support a simple lifestyle in their suburban town, Suzue knew she was on her own if she wanted to pursue her dreams and studies in Tokyo.

There had been tears in Rumiko's eyes when she told Suzue what she already knew — that they simply didn't have enough funds to send her to the university in Tokyo. And although her heart was breaking, the young girl kept her cool and disclosed nothing of her determined decision that by whatever means, when the school year started in the spring, she was going to be there.

"No, I will not accept it," Suzue cried into her pillow that night as she remembered her grandmother's resigned philosophical words that thanked God Suzue was a girl and had the option of getting married and being a home-maker.... So not being able to pursue her studies at a blue blooded university was really not the end of the world.

"Don't they see it? That I am no ordinary Japanese girl — my skin is darker, my hair is curlier, I am angrier and because of that, I will always be sitting on the fringes of society looking in unless and until I become somebody in life! I will make people respect me and even if they disapprove of me, they won't be able to ignore me!"

At that moment Suzue hated her father with renewed vigor. How dare he mess up her life by injecting his foreign genes and blood into her and then disappearing without a trace? Did he ever wonder what the little baby he walked away from had become and whether she was coping, being different and living in Japan? God, how she hated the cold, calculated callousness of men and what they considered their God-given right to hurt women since time immemorial!

When Suzue first arrived in Tokyo with just enough money from her grandmother's meager savings to rent a 3 tatami mat room in a dingy wooden rooming house for poor students and permission to defer tuition fees for three months, she knew she had to find a job—or even two—as soon as possible. Daily scanning of the university part-time employment board finally produced an afternoon job at McDonald's, which she stuck to despite being appalled at the fact that female employees were paid less per hour than male employees performing exactly the same duties. But working part time at McDonald's was not enough to pay her rent and meet even her most basic needs, and after living on a daily diet of McDonald's burgers for a month, Suzue was ready to starve rather than eat another burger. She knew she had to get another better paying job as the deadline for paying her deferred tuition fees drew alarmingly near. At that point, Suzue was prepared to do anything but there was nothing, not even cleaning public telephones and toilets-because- someone was always ahead of her to grab whatever came along.

One night the claustrophobic closeness of her tiny room was so oppressive that Suzue rushed out to the little patch of grass they called a 'garden,' literally gasping for air. She was close to giving up fighting for a dream that seemed impossible to fulfill and run back home. Then her hand closed around a card she had thrust into her jacket pocket a few days earlier and her heart began to beat that unsteady staccato it did whenever she was about to step over the edge and freefall into a place her family would never approve.

In her second month at the university, Suzue befriended a girl from the science faculty who had been pointedly sharing her table at the cafeteria almost every lunchtime. After a few days of skirting around each other, Suzue finally got tired of this stupid game they were playing of who should make the first move and carried her food tray a few chairs up to sit right next to the girl.

"Hi," she said agressively, traces of the down to earth and

brutally direct Suzue of later years already showing. "I noticed you have been sitting at my table during lunch for the past week and looking at me, so I'm wondering whether, perhaps, you have anything to say to me."

"No, no," the girl replied hastily, a little taken aback by Suzue's very unJapanese directness.

Then, as Suzue raised her eyebrows in that piercing way which made people who were lying uncomfortable, the girl shrugged and said, "Oh, OK, I was trying to approach you because you seem, well, different and interesting..."

At really close quarters, Suzue was shocked to discover how gorgeous this new potential friend looked, even with her dyed honey-blond hair scraped back into a simple pony tail and her toned, tanned and obviously much worked-out body clothed in nothing but a severely minimalist sheath.

*Some rich kid I have nothing in common with,* Suzue thought, already regretting her decision to break the ice with this strange girl, as she noted her Louis Vuitton back pack and the Gucci sunglasses perched on top of her head. *Louis Vuitton and Gucci; God, this is disgusting!* she groaned inwardly. *And here I am struggling to pay my deferred tuition fees! What on earth could we possibly have in common?*

"My name is Junko and I've been watching you search the employment notice board daily, so I gather you must be in need of a job," the girl's voice broke through Suzue's slew of thoughts. "I like you so I'm going to let you in on a work opportunity that I think you could take on, make a whole bunch of money and solve your financial distress."

Although Suzue knew she should be skeptical about "too good to be true" offers from total strangers, with a big tuition fees deadline hanging over her head, she was desperate for any chance at all to make money.

"OK, you got my interest but first of all, tell me what I have to do to make this bunch of money," she said after a slight hesitation.

"I'll come straight to the point," Junko said, "You are exotic and attractive enough to entice a lot of high-end men to part with their money. I bet those breasts and that nose are all for real and not the result of subtle trips to the plastic surgeons that the rest of us less-endowed, pure-bred Japanese girls have to make!" The girl called Junko paused, then continued. "Look, I can beat around the bush and call this by any number of polite and sophisticated names but I'm not going to do that. At the end of the day, it is what it is — social escort service — and there's a lot of money to be made there, if you play your cards right."

Suzue was no innocent simpleton and had already gone through two serious boyfriends but even she balked at the nature of the job that was being suggested to her.

*My God, I may be brash, loud- mouthed and prone to giving the wrong signals with my foreign genes but I am no social escort girl material!* she bristled inwardly. The nerve of this girl to insult her with this preposterous offer!

When Suzue did not reply, Junko stood up, pressed a card into her hand and said, "Look, you don't have to decide now, just call me if you change your mind and remember everything — including my obsession with brand name goods — is supported by this job. That's how good the money is!"

She gathered her files and walked off, leaving behind a potent trail of expensive perfume and cigarette smoke from her Virginia Slims. Suzue stuffed the card deep into her jacket pocket as if it was contaminated, then returned to her world of dwindling resources and mounting debts.

That had been two weeks ago and Suzue had forgotten about the strange encounter with Junko and the card that still lay in her jacket pocket until today.

Junko's words *"You can make a whole bunch of money,"* and *"It will take care of your tuition fees and everything else,"* kept pounding in her head, demanding a response. Suzue was particularly down that day because her grandmother had called with the usual rhetoric that there was still time to withdraw because she hadn't paid her fees yet. Yes, she could return home to the easier and stress-free life of helping to run the etiquette school until somebody decent offered to marry her. In fact, it was her grandmother's last bruising remark that finally goaded Suzue to reach inside her jacket pocket for the controversial card and, as she slowly dialed Junko's number, she felt a strange sense of release, as if she was relieved to have reached a decision that was inevitable anyway.

\*\*\*\*\*

The sound of Mr. Mori's voice calling out her name "Tanaka san, can I see you a minute?" brought Suzue back to the present and she retraced her steps and walked slowly back to the black leather sofa set in a corner of the bare minimalist lobby where Mr. Mori was waiting for her.

# CHAPTER 11

Junko didn't seem surprised to hear from Suzue and her voice on the phone was brisk and matter of fact, "I knew you would call because you are like me: Hard, ambitious, we know what we want and we will stop at nothing to get it."

A momentary flash of anger and irritation at Junko's smug, presumptuous assessment of her raced through Suzue, partly because the resounding truth to the remark made her feel bad about herself. But she kept her cool because she needed to make money fast and couldn't afford to offend Junko. There was one question, however, that Suzue couldn't help asking because it had been playing on her mind the whole day.

"Honestly, why are you doing this for me? It can't be because you care—you hardly know me—and I have grown up believing that absolutely nothing is for free!"

Suzue could hear Junko light a cigarette before she replied, speaking from behind a hazy cloud of smoke. Suzue herself would pick up the habit of heavy smoking before long to calm her nerves sufficiently to cope with the brittle and difficult life of a social escort.

"You're right of course, nothing is for free indeed! You might as well know that for every girl I recruit for the agency I get a generous commission, especially if the girl is attractive and exotic. I used to earn big bucks for the agency but the clients, most of whom are regulars, always get bored with the same stable of girls and want some new flesh—like you, for instance. They always joke that if they wanted to eat from the same menu every day, they might as well stick to their wives! But we know it's not a joke at all!" Junko said. Her voice was hard and expressionless.

Suzue knew she ought to be shocked by Junko's ruthless approach to this high-class, high-priced flesh-market, which was what the polite designation of 'social escort and entertainment services' boiled down to. But, beyond the fleeting question of whether she would be expected to sleep with her clients, she didn't feel anything except a bizarre kind of relief that she had lost her virginity to a boy she at least thought she loved at that point in time and not to some rich, aging client for 'a bunch of money.'

Suzue shivered. What was the matter with her? It was as if she expected to sleep with her prospective clients and didn't even mind doing so, an uncomfortable and disturbing replay of her mother's club hostess days. What if the money was so good that she gave up her studies and rode this roller coaster to self destruction? Wasn't that what happened to children from broken families?

The next day, Junko took her to the 'offices' of "The Sakura Escort and Entertainment Services" located in one of Akasaka's discreet little cul de sacs. At this point, even if Suzue was beginning to have some reservations, it was too late to turn back.

The reception room of the agency was anticlimatic in comparison to Suzue's vivid expectations of immediately encountering a world of eroticism, depravity and vice. Once the simple and unassuming frosted glass door swung open to admit them, in a bizarre way she was almost disappointed. The lime green lobby with its classy off-white leather sofas and little coffee tables of gleaming glass and chrome had a zen feel to it, with none of the sexual energy or seduction Suzue expected of such a place. Upon seeing the look of disbelief on Suzue's face, Junko leaned over and whispered, "Amazing, isn't it, this whole false façade! You can't imagine the amount of sexual wheeling and dealing that goes on here behind the second closed door. It is said that some of the most prominent men in the business and bureaucratic circles of Japan have walked through that door at some point or another! It makes you feel that marriage and being a wife or long-term girlfriend really sucks big time, because there's really very little loyalty in men who can afford to indulge!"

As if to complete the whole 'false façade' image, the receptionist at the classy chrome and glass reception counter was dressed in a grey suit and looked like any other receptionist in Tokyo's many high end corporate offices. She announced their arrival through the white telephone system on her table to someone inside, and within minutes, Suzue found herself walking down the short carpeted passage to another room inside, feeling more like a corporate job applicant than a woman who was about to commit to selling her flirting skills and perhaps her body to strange men for "a whole bunch of money."

She breathed in the cool, soothing lavender scent that filled the whole place and felt strangely at ease and euphoric. But later, when she thought about it, Suzue realized that the whole set up — including the heady lavender scent — was probably to put both escort girls and patrons at ease, take the clandestine effect away and make them feel that they weren't doing anything wrong or immoral, until the real work started and things got hot, heavy and sometimes nasty.

The hard and ruthless nature of the business showed on the heavily made up face of Mizuko Kan, the forty- something year old woman owner and founder of the chain of four escort agencies spread out all over the posh Ginza, Akasaka, Roppongi and Shibuya areas of Tokyo. Her sharp, appraising eyes looked right through Suzue, undressing her and taking in all the details of her body with fuller breasts and hips than the standard Japanese girl, before giving her nod of approval as if to say, "Yes, with that sexy body and those full breasts, she should be a good playmate for our fabulously rich, bored and restless patrons."

Suzue decided her new boss did not have the classic 'mamasan' look apart from the hardness of her eyes. In fact if she walked down the tree lined up market streets of Harajuku and Aoyama i-chome, with their Louis Vuitton and Gucci boutiques, Mizuko Kan with her expensive clothes, trim elegant figure and Hermes bag,would look every inch the well-brought-up daughter or wife of one of Japan's rich, blue-blooded families.

*"Oh my God, how can a woman look like that and be in this nasty flesh business?"* she thought, remembering her determination, as a child, to try and fix the pieces onto a wrong puzzle. That was how Mizuko Kan made her feel — safe and trusting because she looked so classy.

Two weeks later, Suzue would eat her words when she discovered how shrewd and hard Mizuko san could be. Although privately contemptuous of the spoilt, rich men who threw indecently large sums of money at her agency, it was all sweet smiles and fluttering false eyelashes in public and Suzue watched, fascinated, the way she drove very hard bargains with the softest, most velvety kid gloves that could break down any man's defenses.

*In a bizarre twist of my life thus far, watching how Mizuko Kan worked was my first lesson in PR,* Suzue would admit in later life.

The first time Suzue spent a whole night in an upscale luxury hotel in Akasaka with one of the agency's die hard regulars, the founder and president of a major pharmaceutical company in Japan, she surprised herself by feeling nothing beyond a growing contempt for the men who cheated repeatedly on their wives and even girl friends and fiancées to dally with girls half their age.

She learnt too that men were clinical and methodical and everything was properly compartmentalized. The powerful icons of Japan's money and industrial world could stagger or swagger into the agency, depending on how much alcohol they had consumed, to select their girl for the night or have the girl 'delivered' to them in swanky hotel rooms. Then they would make complete fools of themselves, slobbering over the agency girls who were well trained to seduce and entice.

But come morning, as soon as their ties and business suits came on, the roles would be reversed and the sex goddesses of the previous night would be put in their proper places and dismissed coldly and impersonally with hardly a backward glance. That suited Suzue and the other girls fine because all that mattered to them was their cut from the agency and the generous tips their patrons usually left behind for the night's trysts.

Mizuko worked her girls hard and Suzue, the new darling of the agency with her full sexy figure and 'foreign' looks, found herself having to balance her studies at the university with being 'on call' almost every night. But the money was fabulous and she was making more of it than she had ever seen in her entire life.

Once she had settled into the routine of another wine and dine fine restaurant, another expensive luxury hotel suite, another man to cajole and please as a prelude to ultimately undressing for him, social escorting became another job for Suzue to churn out the money for her tuition fees, living expenses and gifts for her mother and grandmother. She had to be careful because her mother had started to ask questions about what kind of work she was doing that brought in so much money, but, thankfully, so far she had managed to lie her way out of this tricky situation.

"Modeling, I got a very good modeling contract," she lied, and they seemed to buy it. After all, foreign models were in great demand in Japan and it was very easy to believe that Suzue, with her exotic looks and the added bonus of being Japanese with no language barriers, would be well sought after.

Although she appeared outwardly nonchalant, even defiant, about her new job, there were some nights when Suzue would wake up in cold sweat, frightened and wondering who she was and why she could undress and have sex with strangers so coldly and dispassionately. Some were inebriated, middle-aged men whose alcohol sodden bodies refused to function and Suzue could push them aside and have a good night's sleep and the next morning coo to them, tongue in cheek, about the night of passion they had shared.

Men could be so dense and easily fooled by women and no matter how iconic they were in their own world, they were all the same in bed. Suzue had nothing but contempt for the cheating, lying men she slept with. Most of the time she managed to keep her cool but she nearly lost it one night when a client, who Mizuko had earlier whispered to her was some big car industry name with very deep pockets, told her, almost with loathing, that he needed her services because his wife was pregnant and did not satisfy him anymore.

"The sight of her clumsy figure and protruding stomach really turns me off," he grumbled, and it was only the deep pockets that prevented Suzue from spitting in his face and walking off.

Suzue loved her drink-sodden patrons best and made it a point to ply them with more drinks during the wine and dine prelude to sex. Sometimes she wasn't so lucky and would be assigned a patron hellbent on making his money's worth in sexual favors and Suzue would have to work harder for her money. She got through these long nights by thinking of her research papers while going through the motions of stroking her client's ego and getting an A for her performance in bed. Everyday, Suzue told herself that she would quit after one more month but every time she tried to leave, Mizuko would up her cut and the money was so good she would agree to stay on.

It had been a trying day at the university where she had been warned about missing too many assignment deadlines, and Suzue had just decided to take a break from her escorting work when a call came through on her cell phone from Mizuko. She considered not answering but knew that Mizuko would keep calling till she answered, so with a deep sigh, she took the call at the third ring.

"Suzue, you have to come down to the agency tonight," Mizuko said, abrupt and to the point, as usual.

"But I thought I told you I want a few days off," Suzue replied. "My university grades are plunging and I really need this break."

"Yes, I know," Mizuko interrupted her. "But we have a client who has asked specifically for you. He is a very important man and prepared to pay very generously for your company tonight."

She named a sum which made Suzue suck in her breath. She knew she ought to stick to her original plans and say no, but it was a figure that no financially-strapped girl could turn her back on. Against her better judgment, within the hour Suzue found herself dressed for work and riding the elevator to the presidential suite of a top-end hotel in Ginza.

*Another depraved tycoon or another lonely heart, but by morning it will be over and I will come away with much more than the usual amount of money,* she thought as the plush private elevator whispered to a stop. It did not occur to her to wonder why a total stranger would ask specifically for her.

When the heavy door of the presidential suite swung open, Suzue almost gasped, for standing in front of her was a face she had seen countless times on TV forums, business magazines, newspapers and gossip magazines. Kakuei Mori, steel, shipping and property magnate, said to be one of the richest and most influential men in Japan, had actually asked for her!

\*\*\*\*\*

"Well..well..well, Suzue Tanaka, you have certainly come a

long way from the last time I saw you!" Mr. Mori's voice cut through her thoughts and brought her back to the present. She stared at the lazy smile that was playing on the lips of the man who sat on the black leather sofa, legs crossed, watching her.

# CHAPTER 12

For the next week, Kakuei Mori asked for Suzue almost every night, and each time she met him at his swanky hotel presidential suite. Even to Suzue, by now used to 5 star hotel dalliances, the suite was so luxurious that it took her breath away. It added to the intimidating and yet irresistible aura of energy and power that surrounded Mr. Mori, and Suzue was both fascinated and terrified of him. If she really didn't want to "do" him, she could have called in sick or been in her menstrual week but if the truth be known, she was drawn to this cold, haughty man with a cruel streak which both chilled and thrilled her.

That first night had been bizarre and like nothing she had ever experienced in her escort work thus far. All Mori wanted to do was talk and find out about her, and although his eyes savaged her, undressed her mentally and seduced her mercilessly, he did not make any move to touch her. It left Suzue strangely unfulfilled and fuming at the way he deliberately refused to have sex with her.

He wasn't impotent because she had tried to seduce him back by staring pointedly at the bulge in his pants and watching it grow, all the time telling herself that she couldn't be panting for a client; it was just that the more times she could get into his pants, the bigger the tips she would get the next morning. Surely, that was the only reason she was lying under the silken sheets completely peeved that he had refused to touch her.

On the second and subsequent nights, Mori made up for his sexual "misdemeanors" tenfold, and Suzue discovered that he had sex the same way as he was rumored to rule his business empire—powerfully and ruthlessly, taking what he wanted and discarding what he did not. He had an animal energy that was both fascinating and repulsive and he made sexual demands on Suzue that she never knew existed!

Most of the busy executives who used her only wanted sexual gratification and variety, away from the boredom of their wives or constant companions, emphasis, as one of them had derisively put it, on the word 'constant.' They had neither the time nor inclination for any length of foreplay and their sex was direct and to the point, which suited Suzue fine.

But Mori was different; he treated sex as an art form and was unhurried and creative.

"Take off your clothes and dance for me," he would order Suzue, and then spend the whole dance number studying her beautiful, naked form, taking in every detail with such intensity that, notwithstanding her having become a seasoned social escort, Suzue still couldn't help wishing that the floor would open up and swallow her into its merciful oblivion.

Mori was the first and last client for whom Suzue broke the most important rule of the professional escort industry: Never ever, under any condition, develop feelings for or interest in a client. She had never seen a man who was so controlled. He could be tearing down the defenses of an escort girl with one hand and conducting business on his cell phone with the other. She found herself listening to his conversations and although she didn't know it yet, it was beginning to shape the hardnosed business acumen that was to propel her in later life to the heights of a successful career right alongside her unlikely guru—Mr. Mori himself.

"You're crazy," Junko scolded when Suzue confessed a few days later that she found Mr. Mori intriguing and enjoyed having kinky sex with him. "We're not supposed to enjoy sex with our clients but to treat it as just a job. You're asking for trouble when you start enjoying it because to our clients, we're just the pound of flesh they bought at the meat market.

"But what kind of kinky sex though?" Junko couldn't help asking. "Just curious, that's all!"

"He likes to be whipped and blind folded while having sex," Suzue replied. "In the beginning I felt bad whipping a client, till he reminded me that he was not asking but ordering me to whip him! And when I just tapped him lightly with the whip, he screamed, "Harder, faster!"

"Then another time, he told me it turns him on to watch me pee and then rub my pee all over his genitals!"

"Revolting!" Junko shuddered. "He must be sick—but we can all live with that as long as he leaves generous tips. Hell, who would think, watching him on TV, so debonair and an authority unto himself, that he could be so depraved and lewd in bed?"

"But despite the fact that he can be a real sex animal, I admire him, " Suzue continued. "And what really draws me is the fact that he is successful and powerful, a maverick entrepreneur who isn't in his place in society now because of birth or heritage but through sheer hard work, lots of luck and tough, daring business decisions. It makes me think that if he can do it, maybe I can too!"

"Being a woman makes it harder, doesn't it? After all, this is Japan and it's standard fare here to think that "what a man can do, a woman cannot do." Anyway, I'm lazy and if I can find a rich man to latch onto for a good life, I'd much rather do that than work!" Junko replied. Years later, when they met and Junko had become a successful branded goods boutique owner, they laughed about their dark secret past and concluded that Junko hadn't been able to find her "rich man to latch onto for a good life" after all, and been forced to work.

Suzue was down because Mori hadn't asked for her in a month and she missed his powerful presence and the business conversations she secretly listened in on, and from which she was learning a lot. She had found her goal and purpose in life at last, and was starting to build up a secret cache of information and business practices. She'd learnt some arm twisting and what Mori called "ball squeezing" maverick moves that would stand her in good stead in later dealings with competitors, corporate "dissidents" and the men who tried to write her off as female and therefore easy prey.

Mori's absence coincided with a short university break, so Suzue took a week off to visit her family, careful not to flaunt "the whole bunch of money" she was earning. Even so, she caught her grandmother looking surreptitiously at her well-manicured hands and trendy, above average clothes, but the older lady didn't ask any questions. When her mother lamented over how much they needed a new washing machine, Suzue had to bite her tongue to stop herself from offering to get one for them. She was, after all, supposed to be a cash-strapped student living from hand to mouth on odd jobs, and it would break her mother and grandmother's hearts to know what she was doing to support herself.

Suzue sighed as she thought about how proud her mother was of the fact that her only daughter was putting herself through one of Japan's most prestigious universities and she wondered, not for the first time, whether it was wrong for her to have taken so easy a way out of her financial predicament. And all the time she thought of Mori Kakuei, and the farfetched daring ambitions he had initiated in her. Perhaps he had stopped booking her simply because he had gotten tired of the "same menu" and moved on to other girls, something escort girls had to accept all the time. The years had passed so fast that Suzue was shocked to realize that she had been a social escort for three years, almost her entire university tenure, and it was a miracle she had managed to get through her exams every semester.

Thank God Japanese universities were generally very difficult to enter but also very hard to fail or drop out of.

After the visit with her family ended, Suzue had a long talk with herself. Three years of living the fast and hard life was beginning to take its toll and when Suzue looked at her face in the mirror, she was shocked by what she saw. Gone was the fresh face framed by a riot of arresting curls and in its place was an attractive but tired looking face, its slightly rounded cheeks now hollowed out, giving her a haughty yet distant look, necessary armor against what Junko called "occupational hazards" of the industry.

Suzue grimaced at her face in the mirror. Why would any man think this skinny, chain-smoking, neurotic woman exotic and sexy was beyond her! It was really time to return to the world of sanity and pray that no one would ever find out about her past. After serious reflection, Suzue decided that it was time she stopped working as an escort. She had enough money to finish her courses and there was no reason for her to stay on in this high paying but degrading job. Tomorrow she would tell Mizuko Kan that she wanted out immediately and would not be available for bookings any more.

The enormity of what she had been doing for the past three years and the number of men she had slept indiscriminately with for money hit her like a rock and Suzue started shaking. What if someone found out about her dark secret one day? If she ever became a career woman of consequence, such a scandal would destroy her! What if someone tried to blackmail her in the future?

She slept fitfully that night as she waited for morning to come and the showdown with Mizuko Kan, who would be very unhappy to lose her highest performing escort and would probably go into one of her famous tantrums.

The next morning, Suzue looked and felt terrible. Her tongue was thick and furry and her eyes bulged out, red, angry and swollen. "Certainly nothing sexy or exotic about me this morning," she said grimly as she patted on heavy make up to hide the dark lines on her face. She dressed down in a simple T-shirt and jeans and began waiting till noon for Mizuko to show up at the agency's office in Akasaka.

But at around 11 a.m. her cell phone beeped and Suzue's heart started beating furiously. It was a message from the agency's receptionist, and even before she read the text—call it intuition or telepathy—she already knew that Mori Kakuei had asked for her. He would be a difficult man to resist, given his lure as the unwitting mentor of Suzue in her ambitions to make it big in the communications industry. But she had to be firm and stick to her decision or she would be sucked deeper into this unholy alliance with a man who saw her only as a professional sex worker. It would take a supreme effort to turn down his request, but she was leaving the agency and escort services work altogether.

To her surprise, Mizuko Kan took Suzue's termination well and merely said, "To be honest, I was surprised that an intelligent and well-educated woman like you stayed as long as you did. Although you are my most sought after escort, a girl like you should do something better with your life."

Suzue swallowed, too taken aback to say anything and Mizuko Kan took the opportunity to continue.

"You know, of course, that Mr. Mori has asked for you, this

time for two weeks. He's making a business trip to Singapore and wants an escort to accompany him— a smart one like you and not some bimbo, that's what he told me," she said.

Suzue opened her mouth to decline but Mizuko did not give her the chance as she continued. "You also realize, of course, that you are leaving me without much warning at a busy time for the agency and I've graciously accepted it. In return, I am asking you for a favor—that you agree to take this booking from Mr. Mori for the last time. It'll be only for two weeks and you will be very well rewarded for it, plus you get to travel and see a new country. Will you at least think about it today? I need to give him an answer by tomorrow."

That had been a few days ago and within a day, Suzue found herself agreeing to go with Mr. Mori to Singapore against her better judgment.

*****

The room began to spin and Suzue realized that she was still in the gleaming marble and glass lobby of Big Echo's building and Mori Kakuei had stood up and was walking towards her, one lazy hand stuck in his trouser pocket, a habit she remembered only too well. Mercifully, her cell phone beeped and Suzue had the few minutes she took to check the text message for a deep breath, which calmed her down sufficiently to get her act together. It was a "Go show them what stuff we girls are made of!" message from Sachi, and it made Suzue smile and feel energized because she was reminded that she was not alone. She had the other pillars, and together they could take on Mori Kakuei, anytime, anywhere.

# CHAPTER 13

*The soft purring of engines and the luxury of expensive leather caressing her skin was luring Suzue into slumber, but she refused to sleep because she wanted to savor every moment of this new and exciting adventure.*

*After just two hours of pitching the pros and cons to herself, Suzue had agreed to take this last "assignment" of being Mori Kakuei's escort on his business trip to Singapore. The chance to travel out of Japan for the first time in her life, the amount of money offered and the opportunity of observing and learning for the last time the business practices and manipulations of a prolific entrepreneur up close and personal had proved impossible to resist, even though her "work" would be more in the bedroom than in the boardroom. Still, she would be near the man who had given her a passion and goal to work for and even if she had to kill herself by clocking in 18 hours of work a day, Suzue knew she would someday claw her way to becoming Mori's equal if not more.*

*It was a daring vision for a girl whose feet were barely on the bottom rung of the very celebrated business wizard's ladder. The social and situational divide between them was so wide it seemed totally insurmountable, but the young Suzue, leaning back against the plush leather seat of Mori Kakuei's private corporate jet, swore that her time would come someday. After all, she had the time, energy and burning determination of youth on her side.*

*Singapore was a wonderful place, modern and sophisticated and yet with enough local culture to intrigue and charm. The well-planned infrastructure and sparkling clean subway system were beyond reproach and the many glittering shopping malls were every woman's dream of* retail therapy, be it high-end branded goods or the amazing bargains of never-ending sales.

But Suzue had a different agenda, and after the initial excitement and euphoria over a new country, new cultures and a few days of shopping mania, she summoned enough courage to ask Mori if she could accompany him to some of his business dinner meetings. One night, after a particularly memorable massage in bed, he agreed and she found herself sitting in on several meetings involving an important takeover bid, gripping the edge of her chair, watching and absorbing the discussions and clever manipulations of the day with emotions ranging from deadly calm to nail biting nervous energy.

The participants were a group of men – acquaintances, strangers and even foes – brought together by their common quest for success, wealth and dominance. They paced the conference rooms of their hotels, suits awry and shirt sleeves rolled up, brows knitted in deep concentration, voices raised for emphasis and control. In such intense meetings, no one cared about the smoking ban observed by almost every hotel or conference room in Singapore and cigarette smoke flowed as freely as the beer and whisky supplied as ice breakers.

In a particularly intense and heated discussion session, one of the chain smokers in the room absent mindedly offered Suzue a cigarette, forgetting she was not one of them but just a decoration piece. She took her first puff and was hooked for life.

In the years to come, whenever Suzue suffered from low self-esteem, lighting up made her feel sophisticated, confident and aloof. Behind the billowing smoke, no one could touch her and in sticky situations, she used it as a shield to think and collect herself. Little did she know it at the time but Suzue herself would eventually become one of the powers that be, pacing numerous conference rooms, suit sleeves rolled up and smoking up a storm.

But for now, this profile seemed highly unlikely for the 22-year-old playmate of a prolific business personality, who was being treated to candy like a little girl – except that in this case, the candy was not some mindless shopping spree but a strange request to sit in at her patron's business and boardroom meetings. She caught Mori looking at her quizzically several times and wondered what he thought of a high-class call girl who was more interested in learning the ropes of business than shopping at Singapore's many fabulous malls.

*One afternoon, two days before their return to Japan, Mori wrapped up early and took Suzue with him shopping. They ended up at the Louis Vuitton boutique where he urged her to choose a bag and put it on his account. Her life had always been about making ends meet and being frugal and splashing an indecent amount of money on brand name goods was something she did not do easily. But the feel of having so much money and being able to spend without a conscience was tempting and in the end, Suzue chose an LV Speedy 30 – the kind she had admired on Audrey Hepburn's arm in Hollywood movies but never thought to ever possess.*

*In later life, when she tried to identify the exact point in time that her career ambitions together with a lifelong addiction to heavy smoking and brand name handbags took form, Suzue would remember her first memorable trip to Singapore riding on the back and arms of Mori Kakuei, no less!*

*Some days and nights it was a rough ride, because the harder Mori worked during the day, the harder he wanted to play at night and his sexual demands were raw and rough. In fact, it started Suzue's penchant for the wild, savage and uninhibited sex that was to drive her future lovers and partners crazy. She also acquired some of Mori's ruthlessness and arm twisting tactics but mercifully stopped at her bizarre mentor's sadistic methods of eliminating and destroying anyone who crossed him.*

*****

A cold sliver ran like ice down the back of a sophisticated Suzue years later, as she sat across from Mori Kakuei, on his turf, waiting for him to speak. She had achieved her youthful dream of being his equal, and yet, here she was, sitting on the edge of his chair, her professional life in his hands once again.

God, the man had not aged at all! He was still as suave and trim as ever and the years had not dimmed the air of lethal energy that flowed from his heavily lidded eyes. How frightened she had been when she fell under the spell of those eyes and found herself hopelessly attracted not so much to the man himself as to the great power and respect he commanded.

After all those years and great change of fortunes for her, Suzue was surprised at how much Mori Kakuei could still affect her, but now mostly with anxiety because he was the only one in their circle who knew about her past and, somehow, she felt that

Mori would capitalize on that knowledge if he did not get what he wanted.

"Never let an opportunity pass without making use of it and if you find out anything negative about a person, store it in your cache of bullets—you never know when you may need to use them!" Suzue was thinking of Mori's chilling words now as her hands involuntarily gripped the edge of her chair.

Everyone in the business circle knew that Mori Kakuei was a dangerous man to cross because he never forgot or forgave. It was just Suzue's luck that she had won a major account with one of his companies and their paths were crossing again. She remembered his last words to her more than a decade ago: "I don't take the answer "no" easily, and I'll find you someday." Those words spooked Suzue so much that she had taken the Louis Vuitton bag and shoved it in the deepest corner of her cupboard and in later years, when she became successful beyond her dreams and could afford any designer bag she wanted, she never looked at another Louis Vuitton again. It reminded her too much of Mori Kakuei and her involvement with him in her past life.

*****

*After their Singapore trip, Mori had made her a proposition: The "full time" job to be his mistress with all the perks of a life of leisure. She'd have her own apartment, car, a generous allowance and any number of credit cards she wanted. Suzue had been outraged and hurt that he thought she could be "bought" so easily, till Junko pointed out bluntly that weren't they all for sale, trading their bodies and company for "a whole bunch of money?"*

*"How do you think men look at us?" she asked. "We are, after all, social escorts, for God's sake. Did you expect him to offer you a job as a suit in one of his companies?"*

*"And why would that be unattainable?" Suzue retorted. "I will be graduating soon with a degree in mass communications, after all!"*

*"Well, smart women never put themselves in vulnerable positions by working for men who have shacked them in such circumstances. Instead, they cut off all ties and association with anyone from their sordid past and rejoin high society as self-respecting professionals with a blank slate," Junko replied.*

*Later that day, Suzue sent a text to Mori declining politely but firmly his offer to turn her into a "kept woman" as mistresses were called in Japan. He kept her waiting for almost three hours before replying with a cool reminder that he was not used to being rejected and would not forget that easily. For the next two weeks, Suzue compounded Mori's intolerance of rejection by turning down further bookings because she had left the agency and no longer worked as a social escort even on a freelance basis. She thanked her lucky stars that he had never been interested enough to get her personal cell phone number and that they had communicated on the cell number provided by the agency. Mori had never regarded Suzue as anything more than a woman he paid for to amuse himself; it was only when he could no longer "buy" her that he was piqued and interested enough to really notice her as a person.*

*As it turned out, Suzue could not forget Mori Kakuei easily because he had been the bullet that fired her up the path of a brilliant career. She was both admired and resented for her skillful manipulation of people and situations, tricks of the trade she had picked up from Mori. In the beginning, when pushed for spot action or a decision, she would even ask herself, "What would Mori do or decide in this situation?" But thankfully, over the years, he had faded away and sometimes, when she opened a newspaper or switched on the TV and his face appeared, it was just another familiar face that no longer frazzled or worried her.*

*And just when Suzue thought she was invincible and had reached the point in her life where no one could touch her anymore, this unwelcome ghost from her past had resurfaced to haunt her again. Well, whatever Mori wanted, she wasn't going to give in without a fight.*

\*\*\*\*\*

With a sudden surge of anger, Suzue drew herself up to her full height and asked in the cool detached voice she always used when facing an adversary, "What exactly is it, Mori Kakuei, that you want from me?"

"Meet me for dinner any time you want and you will find out! I can wait so you call the shots — but don't leave it too long!"

"I don't owe you anything, you know, Mori, not anymore," Suzue replied, throwing caution to the wind because she was so angry. "So I'll call you when I'm ready. Remember, I'm as busy an executive as you are."

After a few days' deliberation, Suzue delegated the Big Echo group accounts to a new but experienced director. She had selected a man, Takao Hirata, so that Mori would not have another woman to flirt with and impress. She took an almost sadistic delight in doing that but Hirata was surprised that Suzue so readily gave away a prestigious account. It wasn't like her because usually Suzue wanted to be in control of a large account like Big Echo. But if the lady had grown soft in her mid thirties or pre-menopausal stage and wanted to distribute her goodies around, Hirata could definitely live with that! He admired and respected Suzue although he thought she was weird and totally out of his league.

Elsewhere, Sachi and Tomoko had also noticed a change in Suzue. It was as if someone had taken the wind out of her sail and she couldn't roam the high seas fearlessly any more. Tomoko, ever the direct lawyer, was the first to tackle Suzue about her sudden worrying inertia.

Suzue had just given Tomoko a client and they were meeting at a coffee shop for a quick discussion. Suzue was chain smoking again and Tomoko removed her friend's third cigarette in less than 30 minutes and snuffed it out in a pretty stained glass ash tray.

"They should really ban smoking in every coffee shop and restaurant in Japan," Tomoko said waving away the dense cloud of smoke that was hovering in front of her. She took Suzue's hand in hers and absent mindedly massaged it, oblivious to the curious side glances from the next table, thanks to the recent surge of gay and lesbian couples among the young in Japan.

"What's up, Suzue? You haven't been yourself for the last few weeks and I know something is wrong. Why, last week when we were at this bar in Roppongi and some slimy guy gave you 'the eye,' you didn't even do your usual thing of walking over and frightening the life out of him by sitting on his lap and whispering, 'I'm actually a guy—do you want to take me home, doll?'

"You actually passed over something like that, Suzue! Is it your mother or grandmother or something terrible has happened at work? Or worse still—you're in love and it's pissing you off?" Tomoko persisted. "I miss you, Suzue, the *real* you."

"You're right, a lot of things are pissing me off right now but I'm not ready to share them with anyone yet," Suzue replied.

"'We're not just anyone, Suzue," Tomoko pointed out.

"We're your pillars, in fact, we're each other's pillars! But we always said we would respect each other's privacy and need for space, so just share when and if you want to. In the meantime, can we have our Suzue back? What would we, the marginalized women of Japan, do without you to make a point for us?"

Suzue laughed and ruffled Tomoko's freshly coiffed hair till every tight curl was loosened from its sophisticated chignon.

"Do you know how many times I've wanted to do that to you?" she laughed again. "Just seeing your hair all messed up like that actually makes me feel better! I can't stand it when your hair is so perfect!"

"Thanks a lot for sending me back to court this afternoon looking like Albert Einstein, no less!" Tomoko protested, but she was pleased that Suzue had recovered a little of her feisty spirits — even if her hair had to suffer for it.

"But you do understand, don't you, it's not that I don't want to share my current concerns with you but I just need to think things through first," Suzue said, sobering up a little.

"Of course I understand, what a silly question to ask! There's one thing though; it's not anything to do with Robert Darcey, is it? You two are still together I presume? It's not two years yet, you know!"

"No, nothing to do with Robert at all, we're still great together," Suzue laughed again at Tomoko's allusion to her famous two-year boyfriend expiration date. She was laughing a lot these days — as if the sound of her own laughter made her feel confident and in charge again.

In fact, the Mori threat was drawing Suzue closer to Robert and if he noticed that in recent days, she held him a little longer, a little tighter and that their love making was becoming not just pure sexual gratification but was acquiring new meaning, he did not say anything to her. It almost seemed as if, for some strange reason, Suzue actually needed him for something more than sex! One night, two uncharacteristic things happened: Suzue agreed to spend the whole night in Robert's apartment so that his face was the last she saw when she went to sleep and the first face before her when she woke up the following morning. Plus they didn't have sex the whole night but spent it cuddling and holding each other.

# Onna Rising

Suzue was perfectly aware of the direction in which what was supposed to be a purely physical and sexually-beneficial relationship was going, and she blamed it angrily on Mori and the web of insecurity and fear he was weaving around her. Robert and his solid body and mind stabilized her. She had started to spend more nights with him because he energized her for work the next day and helped her deal with the inevitable phone call or text message from Mori, demanding her reply to his request for dinner with him.

As she looked at Tomoko's attractive but angular and determined face and felt the solid bonds of friendship that held them together, it was on the tip of Suzue's tongue to spill out everything to her.

"Just spit it all out—keeping everything inside is killing you she told herself. "Tomoko won't judge you and sharing with someone so close will take the load off."

But just then, Tomoko's cell phone literally shrieked, and the moment was broken. Suzue said lightly instead, "I still can't get over why you put such a ring tone on your cell phone; it's fit to freak anyone out!"

"Because," Tomoko replied, pausing for dramatic effect. "It shrieks like a woman in climax and that stimulates my mind!"

"Now why didn't I think of that first?" Suzue laughed. "You must be the singular woman with the dirtiest mouth and mind in the whole of Japan!" She gave Tomoko's hair another ruffle as they said their goodbyes and watched her friend hurry back to court, frantically trying to pat her hair back into some kind of order.

Her own cell phone beeped and still smiling, Suzue took it out of her pocket to read the text message. Her smile froze and she felt the familiar staccato beat of her heart. It was Mori asking very politely when she might be ready to meet for dinner and a chat about old times.

Suzue sat down again on the coffee shop chair she had just vacated, needing time to compose herself before heading back to the office to face the barrage of publicity campaigns she had organized to launch a client's new product. Once there, she would have to be the dynamic team leader and boardroom hotshot, always one step ahead of the other players on the chessboard. But here, in this anonymous coffee shop, she could crumble a little, even cry a little and just be herself.

She read Mori's text again and a raw wave of anger flooded her body. Why the hell was she afraid of him anyway? He was just a big bully and in 21st century Japan, there were laws against such people, no matter how important they were.

"He wants to have dinner with me? Fine, let's see what Mr. Kakuei wants, and never let it be said that Suzue Tanaka ran away with her tail between her legs! Just remember you are no longer that social escort girl any more, but every bit the social and professional equal of Mr. Kakuei!"

She picked up her cell phone and punched in a reply. "Tomorrow, 7 p.m., Keio Plaza Hotel coffee shop. Let's have it out!"

# CHAPTER 14

Somehow Suzue managed to get through the next day at work. She was in total control of herself, buoyed by the anger that had followed her to bed and had awoken her in the morning. That anger had sparked a passion and sexual appetite that was savage and raw, and Suzue had shown up at Robert's apartment and declared without preliminaries, "I need you tonight, Robert Darcey. Just love me!"

"My darling, I thought you'd never ask!" Robert tried to be flippant but the sight of her flashing eyes and the sensual curves that she had stuffed into a barely there micro mini dress aimed to seduce and conquer, drove him mad.

They almost didn't make it to the bedroom and although he wasn't going to look a gift horse in the mouth, Robert did wonder very fleetingly what had driven Suzue so hard and so furiously that night.

Later when they lay together, sodden with sweat, their passion spent at last, Robert stroked her damp curls with a tenderness she had never found in any of the men in her life thus far, and it almost broke her defenses. Suzue felt a twinge of guilt because she had used Robert shamelessly to vent her anger against all the men, including Mori, who had ever violated her body and humiliated her. God, she was sick!

In the sliver of moonlight that was streaming into the room, she saw him looking at her with a kind of wonder and Suzue closed her eyes and prayed, "Please don't say it, don't say those words and spoil everything. I'm not ready for anything emotional and if you say those words, it'll make things awkward for us and I'll have to distance myself from you so please don't say it!"

To her relief, the moment passed and they continued to hold each other, both knowing that there was something special but better left unspoken between them for the moment. Suzue ended up spending the whole night in Robert's apartment but she had to return to her own place early in the morning to change into her work clothes.

"Look at how inconvenient this is! It makes sense for one of us to move in with the other!" Robert had commented, watching Suzue slip a light coat over her micro mini dress to walk the few blocks back to her own apartment.

"Good try, my darling," Suzue laughed but there was a catch in her throat. Robert looked so wholesome with the glow from the bamboo lamp they had bought together at a flea market a month ago catching the golden glints in his tousled hair, she wondered for a moment what he would think if he knew about her past and how many men she had slept with for "a whole bunch of money." Maybe that was why she didn't want Robert to love her and see that love turn to disgust if he ever found out about her past and, in particular, her very intimate involvement with Mori. If any of that happened, one of them would come out limping and it had better not be her!

"Will I be seeing you tonight?" Robert asked and it reminded Suzue of her dinner appointment with Mori Kakuei.

"I'm afraid not because I have an obligatory dinner meeting with a client," she replied, feeling a little rush of guilt again because although he was obviously disappointed Robert believed and trusted her without question. The most endearing thing he had ever said to her was that every woman should have the right to choose, to marry, to have babies, to have a career and, in short, to have a life! That meant more to her than a whole litany of romantic declarations.

It was a new emotion for Suzue, caring about what a man felt or thought about her. Ever since she could remember and certainly as soon as she was able to form her own opinions and act on them, the lack of respect for a father who had shirked his responsibilities and dumped his family had always given Suzue justification to use men either to further her ambitions or just for pleasure or entertainment.

One day, when the pillars were sharing stories about their childhood, Suzue recounted one when she was just six years old and a classmate from her primary school had declared his love for her. Even at that age, she shrewdly accepted that "love" and thereafter made use of him shamelessly, to fetch and carry for her, do her homework and spend almost all his pocket money on her. "Poor little boy, by the third week, he decided being in love was too tough on a six-year old and he was better off playing the field! Do you know he's a doctor now, father of a pair of twin girls and we still stay in touch? Whenever we talk about old times, this always makes for a good laugh!"

It was ridiculous but Robert reminded Suzue a little of that really good and sincere little boy. She had always been with bad boys who intrigued and excited her because they were hard, commitment shy and selfish like her. Good men bored her with their need for commitment and long term togetherness. In fact, Robert was the only "good boy" she was still with after ten whole months, and far from being bored with him, their sex was getting better and more intense and they were even starting to do what she had always scoffed at as "couple" things. But there was one thing Suzue was still adamant about and that was they would maintain separate apartments.

From the tiny kitchen of Robert's bachelor pad, she could hear him moving around, obviously preparing breakfast for them, one of the "couple" things they were drifting into and somehow, those little domestic sounds were soothing and safe in their crazy world of corporate back stabbing, bad mouthing and constant hits below the belt—especially the female belt.

"Oh my God," Suzue thought. "Is this....am I.....no..no...I can't...I shouldn't...it's just this Mori thing that is making me vulnerable, this nesting instinct, it's just like temporary insanity!"

She knew that she should just hurry back to her own apartment, but the smell of Robert's English breakfast of crispy bacon, fried eggs, tomatoes and mushrooms and the aroma of strong, life-infusing coffee from the kitchen was too great a temptation to resist.

Suzue sighed. Leading the life of a high-flying global brand director, eating out most of the time and leaving a kitchen her mother had so excitedly fitted out, shining and practically unused, made her hungry for home-cooked meals. One of Robert's greatest attractions was that he was a great cook and loved to mess around with culinary experiments in the kitchen— and Suzue loved home-cooked meals provided she didn't have to cook them herself!

"Maybe that's why I'm still with him! Because he feeds me!" she thought, half amused as she walked the four blocks back to her apartment forty-five minutes later, the chilly early morning air raising goose bumps on her arms. A delivery truck screeched to a stop just in front of her, splashing a puddle from last night's rain on her legs and Suzue swore at the scurrying delivery boy under her breath.

It was going to be a very long and tempestuous day, with two challenging and unforgiving pitches just one hour apart to get through, and the confrontation with Mori Kakuei as a grand finale to end the day with a huge bang!

# CHAPTER 15

Suzue was feeling really lousy as she rode the Yamanote subway line to Shinjuku for her controversial dinner meeting with Mori. It had been a bad day, nothing seemed to go right for her and for the first time, she had picked on her assistant, Fumiko, and made her cry.

"Oh God," Suzue thought. "I've become a monster!"

But when it came to work, she did not allow her emotions to get in the way. The day's two pitches went through without so much as a hiccup, much to the chagrin of her arch enemies in the company and in the industry, who were just waiting for her to lose her shine. But somehow, Suzue always managed to get her act together when it came to work and her clients bought her confidence and professionalism enough to give her the two accounts.

"I don't know how the bitch does that," her pain in the ass immediate subordinate, Noboro, muttered, peeved because the clients hadn't even looked at him. It was as if when Suzue was in the room, she shone above everyone else. How Noburo hated Suzue and wanted to see her fired — in large part so that he could get her position — but that might never happen because Suzue was just too good with the clients who called the shots.

As the train pulled into Shinjuku, Suzue made a mental note to get something small for Fumiko by way of a silent apology for her boorish behavior. The Friday night dinner crowds pushed her out of the train and straight into a queue snaking down the escalator to one of the station's many exits.

She was almost thirty minutes late, which was intentional

because Suzue was very Japanese and punctuality was like the Bible to her. Suzue even hoped that Mori would get tired of waiting and go off, but there was no such luck. As soon as she got through the heavy glass revolving door she saw him in his classic lazy lounging position, draped over the most comfortable chair in the hotel lobby.

Suzue had purposely chosen the Keio Plaza Hotel, a good but quite standard four-star establishment, because it was nothing like the mega luxury hotels they had used for their trysts in the past. Somehow it widened the space between them and made him feel more like a stranger whom she had just met.

*Keep your head up high, Suzue. Remember you are no longer that escort girl, but the highly respected global brand director of one of the most prestigious agencies in Japan, and you rub shoulders socially with the likes of Mori Kakuei and his circle in your own right,* she told herself as she walked across the bustling lobby to greet Mori with a small bow and a hand extended for a handshake that he ignored. Instead, he took her arm, again ignoring her withdrawal at the physical contact, and steered her towards a Japanese restaurant.

Suzue had hoped for a quick coffee-house dinner and coffee but it was clear that Mori preferred a long, drawn out dinner at an upscale Japanese restaurant where there were serving rituals, food presentation and impeccable personal service for an important guest like him. It would be hours before they called it a night. As soon as they were seated and had ordered everything their personal waitress recommended, Suzue leaned forward and asked directly, without mincing her words, "What do you want from me, Mori?"

Although her voice was steady, Suzue's hands were gripping her thighs under the table so hard that she could feel the dampness of blood. Looking at the face before her at such close quarters brought back disquieting memories of a time when all she thought about was how to please this man as his sex toy so that he would leave her a very generous tip. It was demeaning to remember how intimately she knew this man's body and all manners of sexual acts he had demanded she perform on him.

Her feet wanted to take flight. *No, she couldn't do this. She just couldn't take him on—remembering all the hedonistic passion she had unleashed on that body which still looked so good after all these years!* But her feet had turned to lead and refused to move, so Suzue had to stay put to face her tormentor and try to build up enough anger to fight him.

"Well, well, Suzue, isn't it? You've done very well for yourself and I can hardly recognize you! I just wanted to see you to be sure it's the same Suzue!" Mori spoke at last and his voice was mild and conversational, an anticlimax to the defense mechanism Suzue had put in place.

"Thanks for saying that," she replied cautiously. "I"ve worked very hard and kissed a lot of asses to be where I am." As soon as she said that, Suzue could have bitten her tongue off. Her allusion to kissing asses was too uncomfortably reminiscent of the very dark past with Mori that she wanted to keep the lid on. *Oh God, what have I just done?*

Their main course arrived and in the flurry of the gushing service from their personal waitress, Suzue managed to get over her blunder and compose herself. By the time the waitress glided off in a wave of discreet perfume, bobbing obi and rustling silk kimono, she was in control of herself again.

To her relief, Mori seemed either not to have heard her remark or had chosen to ignore it for the moment. "You know, I always knew you asked to sit in at my business meetings for a reason and I see you have learnt some really useful things. I was a bit surprised because my...you know.. girls normally ask for shopping sprees or some beauty therapy or other. I never had one who insisted on sitting in at boring business meetings," Mori said and Suzue knew he had almost used the words "social escort girls" before stopping himself just in time.

*At least he had some respect for her,* she thought. *Maybe all he wanted was an innocent dinner with her for old times' sake and she was just making a mountain out of a molehill.* Suzue relaxed and even managed to enjoy the fabulous kaiseki dinner Mori had selected for them, talking mostly shop and studiously avoiding any references to their past connection.

It had become such a pleasant, normal global brand director and client dinner meeting that Suzue couldn't pin point exactly when Mori steered the conversation towards their shared past.

"You know, Suzue, I'd always found you very attractive in the past and that's why I always ended up booking you. And now that you are this successful, self-assured woman, I find you even more attractive," he said suddenly, in the middle of a conversation about their new project.

"Pardon me?" Suzue replied, her heart was thumping. She knew exactly what Mori was getting at but was playing for time to think. "I thought we were talking about your new project."

"I offered you a life of luxury as my mistress. You could have had all you have now and more without having to work a day for it, but you turned me down," Mori continued as if Suzue had not spoken and that made her blood boil. "Even if you wanted to work for some reason, I could have put you in any of my companies."

*God, the arrogance of the man,* she seethed inwardly before cautioning herself. *Cool it, Suzue. This man can be a dangerous adversary so hear him out calmly first. No tempers to antagonize this crouching tiger yet!*

"Yes, I did turn down an easy life," Suzue smiled, trying to play down the sudden tension between them. "But it didn't have anything to do with you, Mori san, it was me. I have always wanted to work hard for what I have and not get it the easy way. I guess for me, it is always about seeing my hard work bear fruit rather than the fruit itself."

"Well, you know it's not too late for us to continue where we left off."

Suzue could not believe what Mori was saying. Had he forgotten that she was an award-winning global brand director of one of the biggest agencies in Japan?

Aloud, she tried to keep her voice calm and composed. "I think, Mori san, the past is over and as we stand socially and professionally today, it's quite inappropriate for you to make such a proposal to me—flattering as it is."

"Ok, if that's the way you want it, I shall not mince my words, Suzue," Mori replied. "Let me ask you a question. How important is this career and your position and reputation in the industry to you?

"It means the world to you, doesn't it?" Mori continued when Suzue did not reply. "It wouldn't do, would it, if word were to get out that the industry's prized creative and branding whiz kid was a high-end social escort, just to put it politely, with an impressive track record? This is Japan, remember!"

# Onna Rising

For once in her life, Suzue was so furious she did not trust herself to speak because anything that came out of her mouth would be completely unfeminine expletives and she couldn't push Mori over the edge until she had come up with a defensive strategy.

She took a deep breath and held it till her lungs almost exploded but the pain helped to calm her down and when she replied, it was in a tone that was smooth, flippant and almost condescending, showing not a sign of the anger and fear with which she was grappling.

"Mori san, am I hearing things or are you actually trying to blackmail me?"

"Well, I am not a man to be queasy about anything so let's be direct. If you'd like to call a proposition to an attractive woman blackmail, so be it." Mori's voice lowered to a softness that Suzue didn't like at all as she remembered incidents from the past when, the softer his voice got, the more determined he was to pursue and close in on his quarry.

"You rejected me once, Suzue Tanaka, and I let you go — but not this second time round, I'll make sure of that. I'm not asking too much: Be my woman till we get sick of each other and I'll make sure that you get all the biggest contracts with all the big name companies I either own or control or that owe me favors, that's all. It's as easy as that! And if you don't want anyone in the industry to know, we can even keep it under wraps."

Suzue looked at Mori and it was almost on the tip of her tongue to retort, *Yet I will know and I can't even bear to touch you!* But she had not become what she was by losing control and being outmaneuvered in life's perpetual chess game. She had got where she was by gathering her ammunition and firing it at the right time, in the right place and at the right people, and she would do just that with Mori Kakuei. *Calm, she had to stay calm, in the face of this latest challenge. As her grandmother always said, it was easy to know what a snarling woman thought but difficult to ascertain what lies behind a smiling face.*

Putting on her best act, Suzue replied smoothly, "Just give me a few days and I'll sort it out. Coming from a man in your position and of your caliber, this is very flattering! It's late so we should call it a night. But I'll be in touch in a few days' time, all right?"

Suzue declined a ride in his chauffeured limousine and took the subway back to her apartment. *The cheek of that man to blackmail her into sleeping with him!* The thought of it made her sick and although she would rather die than admit it, Suzue knew the hurt went very deep because to Mori nothing had changed except that this time round, she would be selling herself not for a whole bunch of money but for contracts and accounts with all the big corporate names. Call a spade a spade, he had said. Selling one's body for money or for professional favors, it was nothing more than prostitution!

Yes, to Mori nothing had changed, because she was a woman.

# CHAPTER 16

Suzue paced her apartment the whole night, not picking up any of her calls, not even those from Robert and two from Tomoko and Sachi.

The last call from Robert left a worried message. "Suzue, it's Robert. Are you O.K.? You haven't given me your usual good night buzz! And it's not like you not to return calls because you always want to know why people are calling!"

"It's me Robert," — as if I could possibly not know his voice after shagging him in as many kamasutra positions as we could manage! Suzue thought, half amused. Men — always demanding! Be my girl friend, be my wife and housekeeper, be my mistress, dress like a slut yet be intelligent, give me a good night buzz — God, the list just goes on and on!

Who did he think was there to find out whether I got home safely before he came into my life, anyway? God, why do men think that women become instantly helpless once they have a man in their lives?

In a fit of angry frustration, Suzue picked up the offending telephone and flung it across the room. Then she thought of Robert's earnest, worried face wondering why she hadn't buzzed him and she softened up. He was really a decent guy to put up with all her eccentricities, and all he asked was that she give him a goodnight buzz whenever they were apart. If anything, it was she who made demands on him all the time. She needed space so there was no question of moving in together — just the occasional sleepover and weekend getaways — and no mention of sensitive subjects like love and marriage because she was not ready for that. Also, there was

**119**

no meeting of families yet because that would be too much like being a "committed couple." Good Lord! In fact, her list went on even more!

Poor Robert. Why on earth did he stay with her when there were any number of more beautiful and definitely less complicated Japanese girls he could have?

Suzue took out her cell phone and punched out a text to Robert. "One good night buzz coming your way! I'm fine and I think I might even love you! P.S. This is a drunk and irrational Suzue talking—so don't take me seriously!"

She smiled as she read Robert's immediate response. "A relieved kiss coming your way on two counts: That you're safely home and for your drunken declaration of love—God forbid—that forbidden word! I might even hold you to it in the morning when you return to sober sanity!"

Sometime in the early hours of the morning, Suzue made a decision: Mori was one problem she couldn't handle alone. She would have to involve the pillars and, maybe, even Robert. Yet her body and mind protested violently against this invasion of a part of her life that she had been too ashamed to expose to anyone, even to her closest friends and the man she had just made a drunken declaration of love to.

*No, no, no,* the words were throbbing in her head and Suzue swallowed a painkiller to ease the onset of what promised to be the mother of all headaches. *I can't let them know that I put myself through university by prostituting myself!*

*What will they think of me? What will Robert think of me? Will it play on his mind how many men I have slept with in the past, not for love but for money?*

*I can't...I can't let them know that the Suzue they admire and respect as a role model for aspiring young Japanese women professionals is fake. And all the talks I have given and the workshops for empowering women in Japan I've conducted are a sham because I did not struggle to get the education I needed to achieve my goals. Instead, I took the easy way out and sold my body over and over again without dignity and self respect. If Mori splashes this all over the news and in the industry, I'm finished. From a Skirt in the Boardroom, I'll be labeled Slut in the Boardroom. How ready society is for any excuse to judge a woman in Japan!*

# Onna Rising

Suzue closed her eyes and imagined the Japanese tabloids and gossip magazines getting her story and tearing her apart.

"Sordid past of award-winning global brand director of top advertising agency, Suzue Tanaka!"

"Suzue Tanaka, well-known champion of empowering professional women in Japan—exposed as a sham!"

"Woman activist, Suzue Tanaka's own degrading and shameful past!"

And the look of horror and disbelief on her grandmother and, ironically, even her mother's face!

She could see all the bold merciless headlines of the gossip vultures as they flashed before her mind's eye, and the years of building up a sterling reputation and career crumbling within days. Suzue shuddered.

*No..no..this is not going to happen, not now, not ever!* she swore, leaning against the cold glass of a display cupboard and letting its sharp edge cut into her back. She needed to feel pain to get her blood flowing and revive her numb body and soul.

*You know you can't fight this alone, Suzue. You need help and the only people you can count on to rally round you are the pillars and perhaps Robert.*

She added Robert as a "perhaps" because she was still wary of men and their fragile loyalties towards the women they slept with. Still..the question popped up: "What if Robert can't take it and leaves you?"

*Well, then, he was never worth it! You were never bothered about your bedmates' feelings anyway! Remember your old rhetoric: Men are for playtime and you need to just take what you want from them! My goodness, what happened to your golden rule that men are to be used as and when it suits you?*

"I know…I know…but Robert is different…"

*He'll only be different and worth fretting over this way if he proves himself by sticking by you now and not holding your past against you!*

*For God's sake, Suzue, don't be so hard on yourself! You were only 20 years old at the time with a burning ambition. You wanted to climb and the only way to reach even that first step was a sterling university education which you couldn't afford. You succumbed because you were tired of being poor and living from hand to mouth, and you didn't harm anyone in the process — only yourself. So come on, Suzue, don't be so hard on yourself!*

The internal debate had gone on the whole night and when the first light of dawn began to filter in, Suzue gave up trying to grab the last couple precious hours of sleep. She got up and padded over to the kitchen to make herself a strong cup of coffee.

The steaming coffee with its potent caffeine content immediately infused her with alertness and energy. She got out a piece of paper and a pen and drew two columns, one for the pros and the other for the cons of involving the pillars and Robert in her dilemma over Mori.

In such "hovering on the edge of indecision" moments, Suzue preferred the good old traditional paper and pen method over her collection of ipads, iphones, netbooks and all the other high tech gadgets she could never resist buying but then left to clutter her table. It was always amazing how writing everything down by hand on a piece of stark white paper helped her think and see things with greater clarity.

*And that's why pen and paper will never die no matter how high tech the world gets,* she smiled grimly as she began to write.

For the next hour Suzue wrote furiously, inspired by the calming effect of the written word and a black ball point pen against white A4 notepad paper. At the end of the hour, she totaled up the pros and the cons and was relieved that the pros far exceeded the cons. It was decided then! Feeling much lighter, as if a heavy load had been lifted from her shoulders, Suzue started to dress for the day, opting for the most severe and sober one piece dress in her closet — the one she called her "funeral dress."

Sachi was still sleeping when Suzue's call came through and she answered with a slightly irritated, "For goodness' sake, Suzue, it's 7:30a.m. Who wakes up at this hour on a public holiday?"

"Oh my God, is it a public holiday? I'd forgotten and even got dressed for work!"

"Seriously, Suzue, is something bothering you?" Sachi was fully awake now. "You seem very unfocused these days and frankly, Tomoko and even Emi, all the way in Africa, are worried about you. You know, don't you, that you only need to make a major mistake and cost the company a big loss to find yourself sitting outside the boardroom and not inside. We don't want to see this happening to you so if there's anything wrong, can you let us in?"

"I'm glad you asked, Sachi," Suzue replied, and her voice was strangely small and subdued.

"What is it? It's not like you to talk so humble and you're freaking me out! The Suzue I know would not have taken what I just said sitting down, for God's sake!"

"Chill! Admittedly, I have a bit of a problem but it's nothing that we can't fix together!" Suzue replied. "Because it's quite big in details, we really need to meet up for a discussion as soon as possible — so can you and Tomoko meet me for lunch today? It's actually quite urgent otherwise I wouldn't drag the two of you out on a public holiday."

"Don't say that, Suzue," Sachi replied."If you're in some sort of trouble that you need to talk about, we'll not only have lunch with you, but be there with you as long as you need us."

"Thanks, Sachi. What would I do without you girls to prop me up every time I go too near the edge? Have I ever told you I love all three of you? You never judge, you never comment, you're always just there to help," Suzue replied, her voice cracking.

"Suzue? Are you about to cry?" Sachi asked in a gruff voice . "For as long as I've known you, I've never seen you cry! You should, you know, if it will make you feel better, have a good, long and even loud cry. Get it all out of your system like a really good detox!

"Let it all out — no one will think any worse of you because that's what women do. We cry to get all the pain, hurt and suffering out of our system. That's how we've survived all kinds of abuse and discrimination since time immemorial and come through it all actually stronger than men!"

"Thank you, Sachi, but you don't get it. I'm told I actually have dysfunctional tear ducts and I can't cry even if I want to!"

"Ok then, you hang in there. I'm going to poke that pile of lazy bones, Tomoko, up and we'll meet at Suehiro in Harajuku at 12 noon. I think Tomoko's current boyfriend is sleeping over but this is important so I'll drag her out, even if I have to break up their relationship in the process!"

After she'd hung up with Sachi, Suzue sat for a long while

fingering her cell phone, knowing that she should call Robert, but wanting to delay involving him for as long as possible. She wanted to delay the moment when his respect and admiration for her turned to disbelief and perhaps hurt and pain.

Why is it, she thought listlessly, that a woman always runs to her girlfriends when she's in real rock bottom, kick-ass trouble — especially when relationships, sex and her body are involved?

A man may profess undying love for a woman and she feels the same for him, yet it's her girlfriends that she runs to for support and resolution! Perhaps we know instinctively that a man will never understand a woman's needs completely. How can he when his perception of life is so different? Only a woman can understand the need to analyze, dissect, go into endless unproductive "what ifs" before getting into the practical solution stage.

And yes, as Sachi said, it was a woman's birthright to cry away her anger, pain, hurt and suffering. God probably gave women this birthright because he knew that women would get short changed in life much more than men!

But it really wasn't Robert's fault in this case because he really had no clue what was happening and was no doubt waiting for her to call him. Still, Suzue couldn't handle him till she had spoken to the pillars, and right now she needed them more than she needed Robert.

"This had better be important," Tomoko grumbled as Sachi pounced on her at the Harajuku station and they melted into the jostling holiday crowds and tourists to walk the short distance to the Suehiro restaurant. "I gave up a perfectly good holiday sex therapy session with Michael Takeda to rush over here!"

"Michael Takeda? I thought not too long ago it was Shintaro, that suave, too-handsome-for-his-own-good banker guy!" Sachi raised her eyebrows.

"Oh, that is history now," Tomoko laughed. "Michael is an American Japanese doctor and his specialty is, would you believe it, physiotherapy! He gives heavenly and sensual massages and I'm becoming addicted to him *and* his massages!"

"Sorry to deprive you of your holiday 'physiotherapy session,'" Sachi rolled her eyes in mock despair. "I hope dear

Michael wasn't pissed off by the interruption and didn't throw a tantrum as all little boys do!"

"No, Michael is sweet about such things. He's a physiotherapist and a healer of broken body parts, for God's sake!" Tomoko replied a little too nonchalantly and Sachi raised her eyes brows again. "He was like, 'Go, your best pal needs you,' and that gave me very good vibes. Mike's very good natured and that's why we're still together after four months! You know, Sachi, I made a decision after my last committed relationship to date only good natured and easy going men. Forget about that macho crap! Michael knows I'll drop him like a hot potato if he stresses me out — but the way things are, we could be in for at least a medium-term haul!"

"Well, it's convenient to have a guy around — ready and available when you need, shall we say, 'massage therapy' sessions," Sachi replied and her eyes twinkled despite her worries over Suzue.

"You're disgusting!" Tomoko said good naturedly. "But you're right, of course — and let's acknowledge it for what it is. Women who work as hard as we do have needs but you know, when all is said and done, the sex is always better if you feel something for your partner."

They were both laughing as they pushed open the heavy wooden door of the traditional Japanese restaurant where Suzue was already seated, waiting for them.

"Suzue, you look awful! What exactly is going on?" Sachi said as soon as the kimono-clad waitress had taken their coats away to hang.

"Thanks a lot! It's only my pillars who will be this honest with me!" Suzue quipped, but her smile was tired and lackluster.

Tomoko's eyes darted from Sachi to Suzue and her heart sank. All the asa nebo — morning sleepiness — and flippant thoughts about Michael and their bedroom antics were gone in an instant. Something had happened to Suzue and by the look of things, it wasn't good.

All around them, was the cheerful buzz of relaxed conversation and laughter. Even the babies in their strollers gurgled and smiled, but the three friends silently went through the motions of cleaning their hands with the hot towels and trying to enjoy the delicious and horribly expensive beer-fed Kobe beef they had ordered. But they tasted nothing.

"What a waste—everything tastes like sawdust to me right now," Sachi thought. "I wish Suzue would speak out soon. This silence is really killing me!"

But it was only when they had finished most of their main dish that Suzue started talking. She didn't give them any warning of the subject of conversation or that it was about her, she just started telling the story of a girl and her life in the shady world of social escort services and prostitution, a world none of the other pillars had firsthand knowledge about.

Tomoko, always one of the more emotional of the pillars, started sweating. Why was Suzue telling them all this? Had she been pitching for an account with Japan's infamous underworld, the yakuza, and had gotten into a run in with them?

"I'm hopping mad! I've always told you to hold that tongue of yours and not to mix with people you can't handle!" Tomoko shouted, unable to control herself. "And stay clear of the underworld, no matter how good the money is! You're in some sort of trouble with them, aren't you?"

"Please, Tomoko," Suzue put up her hand. "I appreciate your concern but you must let me finish my story first and then I'll tell you who that girl is."

"Sorry," Tomoko mumbled and then her heart began to beat unsteadily as Suzue continued with her story and a horrifying thought began to dawn on her.

Did Suzue just mention Mori? Mori Kakuei? The very client that Suzue's company had just landed a big account with?

"What is Suzue trying to say? Why is she telling us all this? Was she…could she be…..no..no…I must be hallucinating!"

Sachi shook her head even as Suzue looked her right in the eye and said, "No, don't shake your head. I know what you're thinking and you're right. I was that girl and the Mori connected to her is Mori Kakuei, the revered kingpin of the industry and one of my most important clients. It's funny, isn't it, how life travels one full circle to finally meet?"

No one said a word and as the silence at the table lengthened, Suzue sighed and said resignedly, "I know what you think of me now. Your dynamic and adored Suzue rose from nothing but being a big time slut. That's what you think, isn't it? And you know what? I don't blame you. I deserve it because no one forced me to do it. I took the easy way out and chose that life myself!"

There was a flurry as both Tomoko and Sachi got up from their seats and wrapped their arms around Suzue, as if by doing so, they could protect her from forces like Mori Kakuei and those who wanted to harm her.

"Hush, Suzue san, don't say a word. You don't owe us or the world an apology for your past," Tomoko said as her eyes glittered with the tears she tried hard to suppress. They needed to focus, and tears could not be on the agenda. There would be plenty of time for that later.

Sachi could not say a word. She just held Suzue silently, letting her know that the pillars were right with her, propping her up so she would not fall.

"Thank you, girls, for giving me your support without judgment or recoil. I don't know what else to say!" Suzue said, blinking furiously because something strange was happening to her. She lifted her hands to her eyes and whispered, "Sachi, Tomoko, wonders will never cease! My eyes are wet; I think I could actually be crying at last!"

"Let go," Sachi replied. "Let the tears flow, freely and unrestrained, and after you wipe away the last drop, believe me, you'll feel much better."

"Through the years I wondered why I couldn't cry like other girls," Suzue said. "Now I know that there was only one thing that could cure me. It wasn't love or sex, not loneliness, poverty, money or even success—the only thing that could make me cry is the love, loyalty and unconditional support of my pillars. From now on, I don't have to keep everything inside me, corrupting and poisoning my body and my mind—I can cry it all out at last! Maybe, just maybe, I'll become a more peaceful and better person from now on."

They were interrupted by the arrival of their waitress who had waited at a discreet distance till the storm at her table had settled before gliding over to take their orders for dessert. It lightened the gloom at the table and by the time she had taken their orders and left, politely averting her eyes from the troubled, tear-stained faces of the three women, they had recovered their equilibrium.

Tomoko took charge and, producing a notepad and a pen from her bag, began to write. "Problem at hand, Suzue versus Mori Kakuei," she wrote. "Time is of great essence in this case."

Then she drew a line across and entered the word "Resolution" in big bold letters. She paused her writing to say, "I've an idea from a high profile celebrity divorce case we did a few years ago. Listen very carefully and let me know whether you think it's viable in this present case."

Tomoko was handling the matter like a legal case: first identify the problem, next build up defenses and then execute, and Suzue was glad they had a legal mind in their midst. Finding a solution to a very sticky problem was certainly helped by a more methodical exercise without all the drama and emotional baggage that might have otherwise clouded their judgment.

"Think, Suzue, think: Is there anything at all you can use against Mori Kakuei and play him at his own game?" Tomoko asked. "This guy can only be defeated if he faces imminent destruction himself and right now, he's riding high because he believes he's invincible."

"Off hand, I can't for the life of me think of anything that could be used against Mori," Suzue replied. "He has a lot of enemies but he also has a formidable legal and PR team plugging all the holes he creates and no one dares to cross him."

"There has to be something! You know what, I don't believe that anyone who has lived the life of Mori Kakuei can be that clean," Sachi said. "Look, if all else fails, can I give my two cents' worth? Why don't we engage a P. I. to dig into Mori's past and all his affairs, sleaze related or otherwise. The P.I.s are the best people to dig up all the dirt and filth!"

"Excellent idea!" Tomoko agreed. "There's one P.I. my law firm uses and my God, when he digs, he really comes up with such scum that even my hardcore senior partners' hairs stand on end! He's our man and if we all agree, I'll make an appointment to see him tomorrow. You OK with that, Suzue?"

# Onna Rising

"Brilliant idea, ladies, I feel vindicated at last!" Suzue replied. "Let's dig as deep as we can go into Mori Kakuei's putrefied body and soul, cut right into his jugular vein and essential arteries, and choke the life out of him as he has done to so many people to get to where he is!

"How dare he blackmail me into sleeping with him? Tell me this didn't just happen in the 21st century and not sometime in Japan's dark history of female disregard and abuse! In any event, why does a man, even one as powerful as Mori, think that he can insult a fellow professional—female of course—who dented his ego years ago, and get away with it?"

"Don't worry, Suzue. By the time we are through with Mr. Mori, he will be reminded of the time-honored saying "Hell hath no fury like a woman, in this case, blackmailed!" Sachi declared, giving the table such a hearty thump that a pair of chopsticks jumped and rolled to the floor.

"And remember the golden rule of survival, especially if you're a woman: Even if you're shit frightened, never ever show it. The person who stays cool and in control wins the day!" Tomoko added. "That's how I survived the early days of legal practice as a skirt prowling the corridors of my blue- blooded law firm."

"Yes I remember those days; you used to vent your frustrations on us! What was the name we had for you—'Rollercoaster Tomoko'?" Suzue laughed.

"But what do you know?" Tomoko continued. "From "We've got a skirt on the other side, no sweat, we'll tear down her defenses in no time!" it became "Oh no, Tomoko Akita is our opposing counsel today—it's going to be a tough fight!

"And you know what? We've done all that and never really lost sight of our femininity. We still wear skirts, put on makeup galore, flirt and sleep with men we like—and wear the occasional killer stilettos!"

"But because we stuck to our principles of skirts in the boardroom—and not pants-strutting amazons trying to be men—those who think we should be aprons in the kitchen can't stand us. God! Wouldn't they just love to see your story fed to the paparazzi and gossip magazine vultures and celebrate your demise and departure from the industry!"

Suzue grimaced. The very thought of her career falling apart publicly, for all to see, made her sick and she almost threw up the horribly expensive beef they had just eaten.

"Visions of that happening have monopolized my every waking moment since I met that wretched Mori; not even sleeping pills help!" she said. "I don't even need my diet pills to stay in shape these days! As if that is not enough, there's this tiresome fallout gnawing at me, this problem of what do I do with Robert? Do I tell him everything or keep it at our usual "It's-none-of-your-business-and-I-don't –have-to-tell-you-anything-if-I-don't-want-to rhetoric?"

"Remember, when in doubt, always go back to the pros and cons list," Tomoko suggested. "Just think: what is the benefit of telling Robert anything at this stage? Do we need him involved? Will that help you or create more problems for you?"

"Definitely create more problems for me because then I would have to deal with the emotional backlash," Suzue replied. "Hell, the guy's human, after all, and he's bound to be affected if his adored girlfriend tells him she was a social escort who shared her body with strange men for money!"

"Then it's settled. The cons outweigh the pros so Robert shall be kept in the dark," Sachi said. "And, Suzue, don't you dare go into those guilt trips and let him start bossing you around. Remember, the strength of your relationship is based on you being you and not some simpering 'yes woman' he can get plenty of elsewhere!"

"Not a chance in hell— can you imagine me as a simpering 'yes woman' anyway? If I'm ever reduced to that, I might as well be dead!" Suzue shuddered.

"Agree totally," Tomoko said. "We are, after all, women of substance, even in Japan, and I think we've earned the right to keep what is private from the men in our lives. They don't own us, the way my mother felt my father "owned" the whole family because he brought the rice home, so to speak."

"Two and a half so the two and a half wins," Suzue declared. "You must be wondering what the half is for. Well, to be dead serious, this little half part of me wants to be honest with Robert, to share some bad times with him, you know, one of those darned "couple things" I've always scoffed about. But God help me, the other half of me asks why the hell do I feel obliged to do so if it is guaranteed to cause me more pain and problems? Wasn't it too much like throwing myself at his mercy — letting him judge me and waiting, heart in mouth, for his Lordship's decision?

"You know what — to hell with that traitorous half! Robert's got to take me as I am, chequered past and all, and if someday, he finds out I didn't share this with him, so what? I had the right to choose and I just didn't want to tell him, period!"

"That's settled then," Tomoko said briskly. Some rambling was good and therapeutic but there had to be a cutoff point; now they should get on with the execution stage. "I'm going to text Yamano san, the P.I., now and hopefully, we can still catch him for a very early morning appointment tomorrow. He's a very busy man but he might see us on such short notice as a favor to me."

She whipped out her cell phone and began scrolling down her list of contacts, undeterred by Sachi's "He would do that even on a public holiday?"

"You don't know Yamano san," Tomoko continued. "Sleuthing is his life — he lives and breathes sleuthing and never takes holidays. Sometimes, I wonder if he ever really sleeps, the way he snoops around! For sure, he's working today — public holiday or not."

Tomoko was right because a reply to her text came moments later. "Why tomorrow? Why not tonight? 8 p.m. at my office?"

"My goodness, you're right, Tomoko! There he is, right where you predicted he would be!" Sachi said.

"This is fantastic! Let's put everything aside and see him tonight. I know Yamano san; as soon he has all the facts and Suzue's signed retainer, he'll start working on Mori Kakuei straight away and if his usual track record is anything to go by, he'll have a dirt dossier on Mr. Mori within a week or even less! I just need to get back home to send Michael off on his way and then I'm all set!"

"Well, it's just a bit after 3:30 p.m., so you have at least three hours to send Michael off on his way — enough time to demand the, shall we say "therapeutic massage" you missed out on this morning!" Sachi chuckled, relieved and happy that they had found a possible solution to Suzue's problem.

"You can still think of such frivolities in a crisis like this?" Tomoko retorted, but her eyes danced with the "Now-I'm-in-the-mood-to-do-Michael!" look. She, too, was happy because she was sure they were on the right track to dispose of the Suzue versus Mori Kakuei case in favor of Suzue.

They arranged to meet at 7 p.m. for a quick dinner at a keisaten opposite Yamano san's office on one of the tree lined side streets of Roppongi.

"Where would a sleuth be working from but under cover of side streets—even one as good as Yamano san," Suzue quipped when Tomoko warned them of the location of her P.I.'s office as they parted on a lighter tone.

"You'll be all right, Suzue?" Sachi asked at the station. "Or do you want me to go back with you?"

"No, no, I'll be fine," Suzue replied. "You go on home and relax for a bit. I got both of you up so early you look as if you didn't even have the time to scrub the asa nebo off your faces!"

But as Suzue rode the subway back to her apartment, she had to admit that she was not really OK. For the first time in her life as Suzue Tanaka, the formidable "Skirt in the Boardroom," she was lost and confused, not able to grapple with the feelings churning inside her—some old, tried and tested and others new, unfamiliar and displaced. Had the whole Mori affair made her realize that she was not as invincible as she thought? It had sliced her open and she was raw, vulnerable and bleeding.

Her apartment suddenly seemed dark, cold and lonely and Suzue was glad when her cell phone rang. It was Robert and she realized how much she had wanted to hear his voice even if it was to tell her about work. Just the sound of his voice talking shop made her feel grounded, secure in herself and alert. Sometimes it was a good thing when you also worked with the guy you sleep with!

On an impulse, she stopped him in the middle of an incantation about a proposed report he was drawing up for a client and said, "Why don't you sleep over at my place tonight? Must be all the Kobe beef I took for lunch but suddenly I have this enormous appetite for you!"

There was a low whistle at the other end of the line and Robert replied, his report instantly forgotten. "I thought you would never ask!"

## Onna Rising

"I have a work-related appointment at 8 p.m., which shouldn't take more than an hour, so let yourself in anytime from nine." Suzue was smiling as she heard Robert growl and this time, the smile reached her eyes.

# CHAPTER 17

"My God, what kind of office does your famous P.I. keep? Are you sure you've got the right address?" Sachi asked later that night as they pushed open the dirty, frosted front door of a rundown three-story building. It rose like a specter from the shadows of a dark side street which ran off the noisy Roppongi dori main thoroughfare that was lined with high-tech karaoke clubs and a big cluster of dining bars, jostling with each other for attention. "I didn't even know Roppongi still has this kind of side street and pre-war building!"

"If you think Yamano san's choice of office premises is odd, wait till you see the inside!" Tomoko declared just as the front door swung open into a room flooded with soft light. "I was floored myself the first time I came here!"

Tomoko was right. Suzue and Sachi's jaws dropped and they stared pop-eyed at their surroundings when they stepped inside. The transformation was so complete and so incongruous that it was impossible to believe that the room and its theme was connected to the same unpainted, dilapidated building they had just entered.

The massive room was fitted out with every form of modern technology that a highly successful P.I. would or would not need for his work. Huge television and CCTV screens lined one wall, there was a recording station in one corner and what looked like a photo developing studio complete with a cordoned off dark room in another corner. On a long glass table were a whole row of cameras of all sizes with powerful, mean looking, intrusive lens extensions and an assortment of equally mean looking binoculars. Yamano san obviously believed in flaunting the tools of his trade and, in fact, the only thing discreet about his set up was the deceptively nondescript façade of his building.

"Look at the walls," Sachi whispered. "Bright blue! And the multicolored armchairs — what is your color today? Take your pick! Is this really an office in Japan? Even my crazy hair stylist is not as daring as this!

"My goodness, who *is* this man?" Sachi continued, her eyes sweeping over the whole room. "With sleuthing devices like this, he has to be good!"

"And I am good," a camouflaged door they hadn't noticed before opened suddenly and an oddly dressed small man with stooped shoulders (probably from so much snooping around) glided silently into the room.

"This man is nuts," Suzue thought, taking in his wrinkly pink shirt and the suspenders barely holding up a pair of checkered golf pants. Still, she was smiling despite the disturbing situation she was in.

Later, they decided that the whole bizarre set up and Yamano san's own eccentric personality were deliberately staged to distract and help ease his clients into a full disclosure of their case and what needed to be done with minimal pain and emotions. If that was the intention, it obviously worked because as Suzue sat down on an orange armchair flanked by her two pillars, who had chosen green and yellow, she was still marveling at Yamano san's bizarre choice of office set up and wasn't even thinking of the unpleasant task at hand.

Yamano san had tagged very clearly to his introductory speech the proviso that he wanted only facts and that meant FULL facts and absolutely no emotional exaggeration. He produced three documents: the first one which discreetly gave his rates, the second one which gave Suzue's consent to have her interview recorded and the third, a confidentiality and client privacy agreement. After going through them together and receiving Tomoko's nod of approval, Suzue signed on the dotted lines and began her story without much ado.

Tomoko's celebrated P.I. obviously knew who Mori Kakuei

was and probably recognized Suzue herself from a very decent number of magazine, newspaper and TV appearances, but he did not display any sign of recognition or even a flicker of interest or emotion and the sense of anonymity put Suzue completely at ease. Once, when she was a child, she had followed a school friend to a Catholic church and been urged to "confess her sins." Suzue had been nervous at first but when she realized that she would be talking to an anonymous priest shuttered behind a thick opaque curtain who couldn't see her, all the nervousness disappeared and there was actually great relief in unburdening her guilty conscious to a stranger in total privacy and anonymity. In later years, whenever Suzue wanted to unload a whole lot of guilt without feeling bad or self conscious about it, she would go to a Catholic Church confessional to "confess her sins."

Talking to Yamano san was oddly like that because his face was so shuttered and expressionless that it felt as if he was behind a curtain. Suzue could not believe how easily she had been able to give every sleazy detail of her social escort days and, in particular, her relationship with Mr. Mori Kakuei, to a total stranger.

When she had finished, Suzue sat back waiting for the barrage of questions but instead, Yamano san merely stood up and said, "Ok, I've got what I need for now. I'll start work on the subject tomorrow and have the profile you want on Mori Kakuei by Wednesday next week, give or take a day or two."

"What, that's all? Aren't you going to ask me any questions?" Suzue protested. Wasn't a P.I. supposed to be more detail orientated? Wasn't he supposed to even badger and squeeze more information from her?

"Yes, that's all for now. I don't need anything else because you were very thorough, Ms Tanaka," Yamano replied.

"Nothing, nothing at all?" Suzue persisted, refusing to be done of the audience the fee she was paying deserved.

"He already said he's got enough, Suzue," Tomoko said, nudging her none too gently. God, much as she loved her, the woman could be a pain. Why couldn't she take no for an answer for once?

"I can understand your anxiety, Tanaka san because for a woman of your position, a lot is at stake," Yamano said soothingly.

"But I'll get your man for you. Mori Kakuei is a very public figure and it's not difficult to get dirt on him. There are just some holes his security and damage control teams can't plug fast enough for him, and we can always get there before them."

The whole meeting had lasted just a little more than an hour but as they left Yamano's office, Suzue already felt much better. She had at least partially transferred some of the burden from her shoulders to someone else and Yamano's pan-faced calmness was so reassuring that not even a text message from Mr. Mori himself reminding her of his proposition could dampen her spirits. The sudden sense of release made her feel like a freed animal and Suzue was glad she had asked Robert to spend the night in her apartment.

He was already there when she arrived, working on his laptop with his reading glasses perched on his nose, the ones Suzue called "old peoples' glasses," and she was straddling him even before he had time to save a glass of Coke from being swept off the work table, narrowly missing his laptop. The brown liquid spread over a corner of Suzue's precious off-white rug but she was beyond caring. There would be plenty of time the following morning to regret and scrub out every offending stain but tonight, God, tonight, she just wanted to work out all her pent-up energy.

"Wow, we're in for a long wild night! Did you have your meeting in a strip club to get so turned on? But I'm willing, able and available so let's started!"

"Shut up, Robert, don't talk so much, just take me!" Suzue groaned. God, did the man have to wear so many layers of clothes?

A loud crackling of plastic told them they had just crushed another pair of his reading glasses and much later, when they had recovered their sanity, Suzue would laugh this recurring destruction off with "it was just old peoples' glasses, anyway!" But when their passion was spent and they lay together, the sweat on their bodies slowly drying on their skin, Robert propped himself up to look at her and said, "That was really awesome but may I say something?"

Suzue reached over to ruffle his damp, tousled hair and groaned again. God, he was just so endearingly British in the way he always asked for permission to speak his mind!

"What? Just say it! You always do this to me—making me

wait to hear what's on your mind! Come on, shoot!"

"Sorry—stoic British upbringing, I'm afraid!" Robert replied. "You know, Suzue, I noticed something different about tonight. You made love not only with your body, but with your heart and soul as well, and I felt I had more of you than ever before."

"Well, for one thing we inflicted more "love injuries" on each other and drew more blood!" Suzue laughed lightly. She was uncomfortable with the "soul searching" and emotional analysis direction Robert's remark was taking them because deep inside, she knew he was right. And no matter how wild and even kinky they got, it wasn't just having sex any more, it was making love.

"No, really," Robert persisted. "You know I'm right, you just don't want to admit that you can feel emotions for another person because you see that as a sign of weakness and losing control of yourself and being dependent on someone else for happiness."

"I don't know, Robert. Maybe and maybe not. But it's something I have to want myself, in my own time, don't you see?"

"Yes, with you I do see," Robert sighed. "You're a very complex person but that's what intrigues me all the time. I can't read you like a book and that keeps me on my toes! We'll never grow old and boring like other, dare I even use the word, couples, do. I hope in time you will get over your allergic reaction to the word "couple" as being too stifling and ownership suggestive!"

"You're impossible to be bored with for long," Suzue laughed. "Tomoko understands but Sachi often asks me how I can find your stoic, pan-faced British wit and sarcasm irresistible and sexy but I do—very much—and that's just my luck!"

She swung her legs out of the bed, threw on a robe and tried to pull Robert up. Suzue was glad she had insisted on a western bed when her grandmother tried to sell her the line that a futon was better for posture and the spine and, besides, Japanese should be Japanese and sleep on futons. She couldn't imagine having to roll up the layers of mattresses and store them in some Japanese oshire every morning and having to unroll them again at night and in fact, every single time she wanted to take even a short nap. Declaring that the futon and its attendant ritual of laborious rolling and unrolling was invented to make life more difficult than it already was for Japanese housewives and women generally, she banned it from her apartment. Although she accepted defeat, Suzue's grandmother was unhappy about how "new fangled western ways were infiltrating their lives" — forgetting that it had already invaded her family with her granddaughter's blood the very day she was conceived!

"I'm suddenly feeling very hungry — courtesy of a dinner that wouldn't even fill a bird's stomach, as my grandma always said — and an eye-popping, mind-boggling and calorie-busting bedroom workout. Care to join me in the kitchen and see what a bachelor girl in Japan has in her fridge?"

The "bachelor girl" finally managed to turn out a delicious fluffy mushroom omelet with a green tuna salad on the side for supper and they were just washing it down with a beer when the conversation turned to work. Suzue always loved that Robert was not only her lover but her working partner as well, and that they shared so many things in common.

She was still basking in the euphoria of a wonderful night when Robert suddenly brought up the subject of Mori Kakuei and Suzue was jolted out of her complacence as if she had been struck by lightning.

Why was Robert talking about Mori Kakuei, for God's sake? Had he found out and said nothing because he was waiting for her to open up to him and she hadn't? Damn it, why did she care what he thought or felt anyway — it was none of his business! But hell, she did care, and that made her angry.

Suzue was about to open her mouth to tell Robert to mind his own business but stopped short when she realized he was talking about Mori Kakuei as a client, their mutual client. She breathed deeply and made a mental note to remember more effectively that Robert not only slept with her, he also worked with her! In fact, to her relief, Robert was bitching about Mori and his impossible, shorter than short deadlines.

"I know he has asked especially for you, but his global account is so big my team and I have been assigned part of it as well — mainly the digital side — and my goodness, the man can be a real bitch!" Robert was saying. "But he's also a real charmer with the ladies and generous to a T! Look at the fees he's paying us and he's got my P.A. and even that witch of a traffic lady, Agnes

Furukawa, eating out of his hands! Tickets to musicals, vouchers to the spa chains he owns—he really knows how to woo the ladies! Maybe I can learn a thing or two from him to win MY fair lady!"

Suzue choked on her beer and didn't trust herself to speak. The situation was so bizarre that anything she had to say at this point would probably have come out in a hysterical squeak or an incoherent splutter. Poor Robert; he had no idea he was discussing a man who had known his roller coaster girlfriend very intimately in the less-than- perfect and degrading circumstances when she was a call girl. It was so bizarre that they would all be working together as a merry trio, against a backdrop of blackmail and counter-blackmail and a P.I. digging for dirt!

How did her life get so complicated? All she had ever wanted was to have a sterling education at a crème de la crème university which would open some doors to reach the upper echelons of the advertising and communications industry. True, she had used a couple of unconventional methods to get her foot in and climb to the top—and now one of those unconventional methods from a long-forgotten and distant past had come back to haunt her.

*"Oh no, you really don't want to learn a thing or two from Mori Kakuei to win your fair lady, especially not this one!"* Suzue thought grimly but aloud she said smoothly, "Yes, Kakuei is known to be a hard taskmaster and ruthless, but I guess he didn't get to where he is by being sweet, kind and nice—except to the ladies when he wants to get them into his bed!"

"Of course not," Robert agreed. "And I hear he has a pretty salacious personal life as well—strings of beautiful women everywhere. It's said that he has a penchant for women with curves and bosoms, not always easy to find among Japanese women and their beautiful but petite and trim figures.

"Someone like you, for example," Robert quipped but it drove a knife through Suzue's heart. "But oh no, he's not having my girl!"

*"This is ludicrous,"* Suzue thought. *"He doesn't have a clue, does he, that Mori Kakuei had me long before he came into the picture and still wants to have me!"*

It was on the tip of her tongue to trust Robert, tell him everything and seek refuge in his strong, broad shoulders. Tonight,

# Onna Rising

Suzue felt, as never before, the burden of decades of driving herself too hard, the heaviness of setting an austere standard for herself, the expectations and the façade.

"*Suzue is strong... indomitable...indestructible...has won numerous industry awards...witty...sassy...attractive.. when she walks into a room, heads turn...,*" glowing words from a recent interview flashed through her mind and Suzue moaned silently. "*Tomorrow I'll be fine but tonight I just want to be human, to be a woman and buckle a little. Tonight I just want to lay my head on someone's shoulders and go limp...*

"*Tomorrow I have to be strong because a lot of people depend on me, most of all the women who look up to me as a role model for their own aspirations and the men who are waiting for me to fall and prove to the rest of Japan that a woman can't keep her skirt in the boardroom....but tonight, let me be Suzue, without the façade, just her bare naked self, vulnerable, imperfect, dented and all.*"

"Suzue....are you all right?" someone was shaking her and stroking her face. She saw Robert hovering anxiously over her and she sat up with a start. "You look really pukey!"

"Oh my God, did I pass out?" she said. "It must have been the potent mix of beer, wine, and great sex!"

The moment of honesty and soul bearing passed and Suzue snapped back to herself again. Robert would be spared the truth, for the moment at least. But she wanted to be near him tonight so she pulled him back to bed and said, "Don't go back, Robert. Spend the night here with me and I promise you won't regret it!"

"Let's see — my girlfriend has to bribe me with promises that I won't regret this very big and difficult decision I have to make to spend the night in her apartment. Oh, my goodness, are you for real?" Robert groaned. "Wild horses wouldn't keep me away from spending the night here with you, tonight, every night and I'll even throw in the offer to move in with you, if you ask me!"

"Whoa, whoa, slow down," Suzue replied, her eyes twinkling with merriment, glad to be back in her own skin and on a familiar turf that she was comfortable with.

"Let's start with tonight first, shall we?"

# CHAPTER 18

Mori Kakuei was away in the United States the following week and just knowing that he was out of Japan brought a kind of normalcy to Suzue's life. At least she didn't have the stress of having to avoid him and, God willing, Yamano san would have some dirt for her by the time he returned.

She spent the whole day closeted in her office with Fumiko, her P.A., going over numbers. She hadn't met her target for the month but that was nothing to fret about—she would just work at a more frenetic pace and catch up. But her company "enemies" must have noticed that she hadn't been herself lately and she could visualize Noburo, her chronic pain in the neck, triumphantly sticking out his foot to trip her and watching her fall flat on her face. People like that made the industry really ugly and she was certainly collecting more enemies than friends the higher she climbed, but Suzue knew she would never give her work up for all the world.

"Our figures for this month aren't very good, Ms. Tanaka," Fumiko said, her face all scrunched up with anxiety. She was upset because earlier, the P.A. of a rival team had commented that her precious Ms. Tanaka seemed to be losing her shine, and Fumiko had stood up for her boss like a lioness protecting her cub. There were, of course, sniggers in the company that Fumiko was so protective of her boss; it was as if there was an unsevered umbilical cord between them and some of the more malicious workers hinted at a lesbian relationship even though Suzue was known to be quite a player in the flirting department until she met Robert.

Internal company gossip didn't faze Suzue at all and she

wrote it all off as "fluff" that a woman who had climbed as fast and as high as she had done should expect and simply ignore.

"Relax, Fumiko! We've just invoiced Big Echo for last month's campaigns, and that's a very big bill which should pull our figures up to even surpass the previous months — so I think we can breathe easier after that!

"Besides, my trip to the onsen last month with my university alumni really paid off," Suzue continued. "I've received invites from three CEOs — one pharmaceutical, the other two steel and minerals and insurance giants — to pitch for their accounts with assurances that unless we mess it up big time — which we shouldn't — the business is ours. If we get those three very big accounts, which we will, that should give us healthy figures for quite a while!"

Fumiko managed a watery smile and for the first time that day, Suzue noticed that her P.A. was nursing a bad cold that she was trying unsuccessfully to hide. Her face and eyes were all puffed up and flushed from the efforts to suppress her coughing . "I think you're coming down with a cold, Fumiko, and you should really be resting at home and not be here at work," Suzue scolded. "Take the rest of the day off to sleep away that cold! I need you strong and focused next week because it's going to be a killer week with two major campaigns running and at least three more soft launchings."

"Are you sure, Tanaka san? It's true I'm not feeling so good but I can still stay if you need me," Fumiko asked hesitantly. Still, it was clear she badly wanted to go home and rest.

"Of course I can manage — how do you think I coped before I found you? Go on, get out of here this minute! You're spreading your virus around and I don't need that generosity right now! "

"Thank you, Tanaka san, but I'll be in tomorrow as usual," Fumiko said formally, but Suzue knew she was touched by her boss's concern.

Even this little incident reminded her of Mori. It was Mori who had once said, at a workshop Suzue had asked to sit in on, that the golden rule of success was to be fair to your employees, show appreciation where it is due and manage like a mentor not a dictator. But Mori advised that with your corporate enemies and competitors, you must go for their jugular veins, devour rather than be devoured, because in the industry, it was kill or be killed.

Suzue shuddered. God, the man was like a lethal panther, smooth and silky in his movements and demeanor but always waiting in the wings to spring!

But when she rose to a management position, Suzue followed Mori's formula, and although the turnover rate in the industry was generally very high, her teams saw hardly any resignations and had one of the highest productivity figures.

When Suzue was in her final year at university, she asked an adjunct lecturer she'd befriended how she could even get her foot into a "brand name" communications company, given that her grades were not spectacular. "To get anywhere, every newcomer to this industry needs a mentor of some sort to learn the ropes from; hard work and intelligence alone is not enough. If you think you are hard working and smart, there are thousands more people out there smarter than you who are prepared to slog the skin off their backs," the lecturer said, adding that moreover, she was a woman and no one would really want to invest a lot of time and money to train her up.

The lecturer did put her in touch with a few noteworthy contacts but in the end, it was one of her mother's ex-patrons who got her into her first "brand name" company. She suspected her mother had been more than just his drinking companion and often wondered how their story would have continued if he had not died suddenly one day of a heart attack, leaving her mother inconsolable for a long time. Her grandmother insisted that she was mourning over the loss of income from a rich and generous patron but Suzue knew better. She remembered her mother saying once that you might cry for a few minutes or even a few hours for the loss of a customer but nothing more than that.

But Suzue's real mentor was unwittingly Mori Kakuei. Both had their own agendas in their unholy alliance; he was attracted to her bosom and curves and wanted to have a sexy woman hanging onto his arm when he did his wheeling and dealing, and she wanted to observe, learn and absorb everything as quickly as she could, like a sponge.

It was because of all that knowledge she had acquired from Mori that Suzue quickly gained the reputation of entering the industry "old and seasoned" without any of the inexperience and uncertainty of the other entry level executives.

She and Robert had talked about mentorship a few nights earlier and he had asked her whether she ever had one, adding that he couldn't imagine her being mentored by anyone because she was always so self-sufficient and seemed to know everything. Suzue had laughed at that and wondered what Robert would say if she told him her mentoring came in the form of Mori Kakuei — paid sex and sitting in at his business meetings with her ears and eyes wide open, listening and watching while her hand stroked his physical and mental ego. *"That was the kind of mentoring I received. Now, have I got you suitably shocked at last, Mr. Robert Darcey?"* she imagined herself saying.

Then she forgot Mori Kakuei, Robert and everything else as the phone started ringing almost back to back, clients requesting nicely or demanding impatiently, depending on how important they were. Urgent meetings. internal managers clamoring for "just 5 minutes of consultation." the creative department literally hammering on her door for approval deadlines. New York calling, London calling, Singapore calling — she could feel all the telephone lines and waves tangled up into messy knots. God, how did Fumiko handle all that and put in an orderly queue all the people and telephone lines who wanted a piece of her?

By noon, Suzue was beginning to regret letting her P.A. go home but the poor girl was so ill it would have been inhumane to exploit her and make her work. Of course, she could always commandeer one of the girls from the typing pool or her manager's P.A. to help out for the day, but Suzue didn't want anyone but Fumiko to touch what she called her "office shit."

At 1 p.m., the company's internal makeup artist arrived to "prepare" her for a photo shoot and a live interview for a Lifestyle channel. Robert, by coincidence because of his supporting role, was to be featured with her and he arrived on the set looking so debonair in the dark Armani suit she had given him on his birthday, with the lights picking out the golden tints in his hair, that Suzue's heart did a little turn. *"God, that man not only looks gorgeous, he is gorgeous! Any woman in Tokyo would not need a second invitation to move in with him... any woman but me,"* she thought.

Emi had e-mailed her all the way from Africa urging her to give Robert a chance and went as far as to say that Suzue had always been a bit wild and he would bring a measure of stability in her life. Not a lot of stability, or she wouldn't be recognizable as Suzue Tanaka any more, but at least a little to balance her out a bit.

"Even my pillars think I'm nuts, keeping Robert so resolutely at arm's length, but I guess that's what makes us tick like a quartz watch. We're together and yet just apart enough to remain a romantic challenge for each other."

The other pillars had decided to keep Suzue's troubles with Mori Kakuei from Emi who was having a hard enough time dealing with the heart wrenching stories of poverty, sickness and abuse on an almost daily basis, plus her family's almost violent objection to her decision to adopt an African orphan baby and bring her back to Japan. Emi's mother had invited the pillars for lunch at a posh shabu shabu restaurant to request that they try to persuade Emi from going ahead with her adoption plan.

"I haven't been able to sleep ever since Emiko told me about this unacceptable idea of hers," Hiroko Wada said as soon as the usual polite Japanese greetings were over and everyone had taken a seat in a private room the restaurant reserved only for their important clientele. Her hands were twitching slightly on her lap as if she wanted to wring them in frustration. But that would not be elegant and whatever happened, Hiroko Wada had to remain poised and elegant.

She looked, as always, impeccable in a smart Empress Michiko one piece dress complete with a classic strand of pearls round her long elegant neck and hair piled up on top of her head in a chic coil. Hiroko Wada was every inch the aristocratic matriarch of one of Japan's diminishing illustrious families still blessed with old money, class, good breeding and live-in maids.

Suzue actually felt sorry for Emi's mother. She couldn't, for the life of her, picture Hiroko Wada being a grandmother to any one, much less an African child! She suspected even she herself was not fully accepted by the Wadas on account of her curly hair and her "one shade darker than normal" skin, but her career success and industry celebrity status had eventually won them over.

"Try to persuade her to give up the idea — she will be socially destroyed if she encumbers herself with a gaijin child and becomes a single mother! Which man from a good family and background will want her?" Hiroko Wada was lamenting. "I know I should have been firmer and stopped her from becoming a full-time journalist, and then as if that wasn't enough, she was off to Africa and when I thought nothing more could happen, she announces to us that she wants to adopt an African baby and bring her back to Japan! How does she think people are going to look at us?

"In my day, well-bred Japanese girls from good families took up music lessons, ikebana or helped out in the family business till a suitable match was arranged for them! I should have forbidden Emiko from being so serious about her career and handled her more firmly, as my family did with me! But her father insisted I was too traditional and old fashioned and should loosen up a bit. Look where that has led us, with a daughter still unmarried at her age and desperate enough for motherhood to think about adopting a foreign child!"

Mrs. Wada was talking about Emi as if she were an eight-year-old girl instead of a woman nearing 30, and Sachi said as diplomatically as she could, "Times have changed, even for women in Japan. There are some like us who want to make something of our lives, you know, be something in our own right and not live vicariously through a husband. I think Emi just chose that path and no one, not even you, can stop her. I don't think it's about desperation to be a mother but her desire to give a destitute orphan child a home and a family."

"What kind of family?" Hiroko laughed harshly. "People will look askance at them, a single mother without a husband! It's not even respectable and society will not accept them easily. If she goes through with this, Emiko is ruined!"

"I agree that it would probably be wise for Emi to think very carefully about her plan to adopt an African child and I'm speaking as a lawyer here, emotions aside," Tomoko said. "There will be a real problem getting status for the child in Japan which, you know, does not recognize adopted children, even legally adopted ones, so there will be a long legal battle for naturalization and getting a Japanese passport for the child. That alone, is a daunting thought, so I'm going to lay all the cards on the table for Emi to decide whether she really wants to go through with this adoption. That is all we can do and in the end, the decision is still hers."

\*\*\*\*\*

"Penny for your thoughts, my darling!" Robert whispered as he slid into the seat next to hers and stretched out his hand for the official on-camera, co-worker handshake, his lips twitching wickedly at Suzue's look, which said, *"Don't you dare shatter my "cool with the guys" image in front of millions of Japanese viewers. I already have a hard time convincing them that I am Japanese through and through in spite of my wilder than wild curls and dusky skin!"*

Thousands of miles away, in a posh hotel suite facing Central Park, the much celebrated entrepreneur Mori Kakuei sat in front of his laptop watching a video clip of the

Professional Woman of the Year awards ceremony as a poised, smiling Suzue Tanaka strode up the red carpet to receive the award. Why was he so intrigued by this woman anyway? He could have anyone he wanted and Suzue Tanaka might be the kind of tough, spirited woman who really turned him on, but she wasn't the only one. Mori Kakuei had scores of successful women of various nationalities listed in the proverbial "black book" which, in this case, was the blackberry he never went anywhere without. He could call any one of those beautiful women and they would go out with him and more, at the drop of a coin. So why did he want this woman who obviously didn't want him back? She had even refused to give him her private cell phone number but he got it anyway from her agency which was prepared to kiss the feet of such an important client—enough to invade the privacy of one of its directors. Perhaps that was the whole point; it was all because she didn't want him and Mori Kakuei couldn't stand rejection.

*"Look at what I'm doing right now, actually blackmailing her into sleeping with me again! Am I that hard up for female company that I have to resort to blackmail? I'm married to a trophy wife, and at least a dozen women could be considered my regular playmates. And there are the others on the side like Suzue herself used to be, but please do not tell me I'm feeling something for this woman!*

*"Impossible! You, Mori Kakuei, think a woman's most important role in life is to pleasure her man. Remember, you use women to satisfy your carnal appetite so that you are energized to work and manipulate*

*people, and that's how it has always been. You most certainly do not develop feelings for any one woman!"*

He felt better after telling himself his need to possess Suzue Tanaka was because she had rejected him not once but twice, and he was not a man who took rejections kindly. This arrogance was, in fact, how he had built his massive business empire from the ashes of his underprivileged background.

"This is to you, Suzue Tanaka!" Mori said as he flung his wine glass at the TV screen. "Let's see who will outwit who this time!"

# CHAPTER 19

Ten days had passed and still there was no news from Yamano, the private investigator. Although Suzue had tried to stay cool, each passing day brought Mori Kakuei's return to Japan closer and a solution had to be found for her dilema. She hated it when a problem was left hanging, and it was common knowledge that Suzue's tolerance for pending issues was one or two days at most. This time it had stretched for 10 days and worse still, there was nothing she could do about it but wait.

At one point, when she couldn't stand it anymore, Suzue lifted up the phone to call Yamano but Tomoko had cautioned patience. The guy needed time, for God's sake, to rein in a man as slippery as Mori Kakuei, she'd said. It just wouldn't do to pressure him into producing a dossier on Mori when he was not ready to do so.

In the meantime, it was very much business as usual, In fact, earlier in the day, Suzue had even video conferenced with Mori Kakuei over a high-budget campaign her team was working on for one of Big Echo's subsidiary companies. It was strictly a business meeting and to give the veteran entrepreneur credit, he kept it as such. It was professional, impersonal and Suzue found herself actually enjoying brainstorming with him. If there had never been a past between them, Suzue was sure she and Mori would have made very good and productive business sparring partners.

"You have to give it to Mori Kakuei, that whatever he is and has done, he's brilliant and I say this notwithstanding great personal dislike and resentment for the man!" Suzue said as she and the other pillars checked out an Indonesian restaurant in Roppongi for their weekly Friday ladies' night out. "If it wasn't for our past shall we say, "connection," and the fact that he's blackmailing me into sleeping with him, I could really respect and admire this incredibly smart man! "

The pillars had all decided that after a harrowing week at work, they deserved to get an eye-watering, sizzling kick out of eating spicy food at a newly opened Indonesian restaurant that Tomoko had discovered by chance. "Be prepared though," she warned. "This restaurant serves authentic Indonesian padang food, meaning nothing will be Japanised to accommodate local taste buds— so it will be really spicy."

"Well, since we decided that we want to set our mouths on fire, let's go all the way!" Suzue replied. "I hate these half-baked restaurants which serve pathetic Japanised versions of the real thing! My first business trip to Hong Kong was when I tasted real unadulterated Chinese food and after that, I realized how pathetic the Chinese food in Japan is, even in the Yokohama Chinatown restaurants. Plus, we pay a bomb for it!"

"Macho, as always!" Sachi laughed. They were all happy because it was wonderful to see Suzue her feisty self again. "The "real stuff" as you call it can be lethal, so let's hear you sing the same tune when you start eating!"

An hour and three fiery dishes later, Suzue stubbornly refused to succumb to the fireworks in her mouth, throat and stomach, while Sachi and Tomoko had long given up the fight for authenticity and sought refuge in multiple glasses of ice water which couldn't quite put out the fire.

"Oh my God," Sachi gasped. "This is worse than I thought! I think I just swallowed one of those small deadly chillies you're not supposed to eat and it's exploding in my tummy!"

"That's the whole idea, the kick we get from all this turmoil in our bodies," Suzue replied, eyes streaming. "It kind of feels good—it's like being purged of all the toxins in us and coming out of it feeling punished but cleansed!"

"I'm pretty sure there are easier and more comfortable ways of getting detoxed than this!" Tomoko spluttered.

"Oh, don't be such babies you, two!" But even Suzue gave

up when the final dish of curried vegetables arrived and she bit into two of the small chilies Sachi had mentioned earlier. The result of this accidental folly was a fiery explosion and a string of strong words which turned quite a few heads from the nearby tables in their direction.

"My dear God," she panted. "Perhaps I should shove a fistful of these tiny chili devils into the mouth of anyone who is Suzue unfriendly! This should incapacitate them for quite a while!"

"Mori Kakuei for instance," Tomoko suggested, soaking her tongue in a glass of ice water. "My goodness, how do people eat this kind of food on a daily basis?"

"Wait a minute," Sachi said. "I remember a classmate from Malaysia at my university told me once that they take away the tongue burning sensation by eating something sweet, like a dessert afterwards. Let's try and see if it's true." She signaled a waitress and picked out three avocado red bean milk shakes for them, and it was love at first sip.

"My God, this is an amazing drink, dessert, whatever and what do you know, your friend is right! Just three sips and all the fire has been put out!" Tomoko said. "It's incredible, even my tongue has returned to its normal size!"

"This even beats the news I got today that my team will be handling a major sex toy manufacturer's account!" Suzue said. "It's going to be really fun creating the ads for this account; can you imagine, sex toys? I went to their website for the usual product familiarity survey and my goodness, some of the sex toys are mind boggling! Even I blush at the kinkiness and sheer audacity of the creators!"

"Some people have all the luck," Tomoko grumbled. "And to think I only get boring cases involving mergers, acquisitions, hostile takeovers, corporate financing and the like. Even my high profile divorce cases have become polite, you know, standard fare like irreconcilable differences. These days, the divorces of the "Who's Who" couples my firm handles sit politely, straight backed with their hands folded neatly on their laps, mumbling the magic words "irreconcilable differences" when what they really mean is you slept with your secretary, you bastard, "you married me for my money and family name, you son of a bitch," "you slept with the beach boy in Bali, you whore," "you have a shopping and credit card habit I can't take any more," and "how long have you been a homosexual and banging the company driver, you disgusting specimen?

"These days, divorce cases aren't even interesting any more to handle! Trust you, Suzue, to get a sex toy client onto your portfolio!"

They were still laughing when Tomoko's cell phone signaled an incoming text message and her brow creased as she read it.

"It's Yamano. He says he has finished his job and drawn up a full dossier on Mori Kakuei, so he's ready for us to pop by his office this weekend for a discussion," she said at last. Instantly, the relaxed Friday night mood at the table changed to one of excitement and a kind of relief. The anxiety and anticipation that had been hovering over them the whole week was ending, and they were going to meet and get some closure at last.

"This is what I've been waiting to hear all week!" Suzue said. "Whatever I am, I'm not a shirker, and I really want to meet this thing head on and be done with it once and for all. After that, I can focus on being Suzue Tanaka again!"

They decided to meet on Saturday at 11a.m., and having confirmed the appointment by text, Suzue stood up and said, "O.K., that's it. Let's forget about Mori, Yamano, even work for tonight and park ourselves at a karaoke bar to belt our guts out! Are you girls game for some stress-busting therapy?"

"Of course we are," Sachi replied. "Nothing like a good old karaoke session to end this night of surprises!" With scores of karaoke bars lining the main and side streets of Roppongi, they finally decided on one along the main Roppongi dori — simply because it was the biggest, loudest, most outrageously ostentatious. Plus, the lights were a bright electric blue, the pillars' favorite color.

"This place is so full! I don't know why they still need touts to bring in more customers!" Tomoko said as they were taken down a long corridor filled with the same psychedelic blue light as outside which gave them the surreal but pleasantly uplifting feeling of going down a blue tunnel.

"Good grief, is that human?" Sachi grimaced clapping her hands over her ears as a waitress balancing a tray of tall drinks opened the door of one of the rooms and the sound of a female voice, shrieking out a song, floated out.

"Whoever she is, that singer is certainly discharging all her bad energy! I can even feel it spewing all out in that shrill unearthly voice! And look at the name of this place—Blue Moon, of course. How cliché can it get?" Suzue quipped.

The electric blue light cast a kind of euphoria over them, putting them all on a high and that didn't feel unpleasant at all.

"I guess that's why we Japanese started this karaoke craze in the first place—to get away from cramped apartments, without much privacy or room doors that really lock—so that we can let off steam, take over the mike and be a star, or not, for a few hours! It's a wholesome Friday night activity even for the guys with raging hormones," Suzue had explained once, when trying to persuade Robert to actively participate in his first company karaoke bash. "It's a good way to escape reality for those couple of hours or so."

And, of course, during her days escorting some of the most prominent Japanese entrepreneurs, industrialists and top company executives, Suzue had seen more karaoke bars than she cared to admit. Her patrons used the relaxed atmosphere of karaoke bars to squeeze congenial contracts out of their clients and she soon got used to the sight of paper and pen being whipped out in the heat of an enthusiastic karaoke session and signatures scrolled across in mid song! The presence of attractive young women and in-house hostesses certainly helped to negate and melt away the voices of dissent and Suzue remembered thinking men were such suckers, even as she stoked their fires and lined her own pockets in the process.

"I wasn't joking at all when I said at interviews and workshops that my learning process came from very unexpected and unconventional avenues and mentors, quite early in life," Suzue shouted above the din of a couple of really good solo singers. "Some of my most illustrious know-how was gained in karaoke rooms similar to this!"

The Friday night crowd at Blue Moon was a mixture of young office workers, small groups of gentlemen or ladies on their night out ,and the usual handful of sugar daddies trying to keep up with their sweet young things. Notably absent were the corporate high fliers "entertaining" their clients on company expense accounts; they preferred to frequent the higher end karaoke clubs and bars in the posh Ginza area where Suzue used to hang out. Blue Moon and Roppongi karaoke bars were for the younger crowd with shallow pockets and no company expense accounts to latch onto.

The corporate high fliers seemed to think that expense account entertaining was their God given right and should be done in style as befitting their status and all over Ginza, there were restaurants, clubs and bars where prices were set to cater to these "expense accounts" top executives. Suzue abhorred these reckless executives running up exorbitant bills "entertaining" clients, partly because she had played a contributing role in encouraging them to do so in her escort days.

*"Miss Tanaka, you can charge this dinner to company expense so don't you want me to book a table for you at the "Rotanba" in Ginza instead?"*

How many times had Fumiko, her assistant, objected to Suzue's more humble choices for entertaining; she was indignant that her boss was not enjoying the full benefits of her large expense account at some of Tokyo's most expensive restaurants and leaving it all for the other executives who worked less hard and justified their extravagance by the self-imposed rule of "lavish spending plus client satisfaction equals big business."

"My goodness," Tomoko said after they had sent the hovering waitress away with their drink and snack orders and settled down to select their songs. "Do you know what one of those smart aleck, wanna be male lawyers said to me today? He said men can outdo us anytime because they can take clients to massage parlors, hostess bars and well, to call a spade a spade, prostitutes and entertain them with call girls."

"What a disgusting specimen," Sachi replied. "I hope you gave it back to him soundly by saying "You know what, I guess it's just our luck that we too can do something even better which you can't do — and that is, we can actually sleep with our clients and pillow talk them into really generous moods! Can you do that?"

"You bet I did! Shut him up all right — you should have seen the way he just turned red and walked away!"

"Good for you!" Sachi said. "That's what I always tell my

female mentees to do: speak up and don't take a back seat to men all the time!"

"Ok, ladies, that's enough of that gender rhetoric—let's just have fun tonight," Suzue snapped her fingers. "I've found a few songs we can at least do justice to so let's stop talking shop and get on with what we came for—hardcore bad singing!"

# CHAPTER 20

Suzue's heart was thumping so hard it reminded her of the very first time she had ridden what she could only imagine was the only hotel elevator in the world to have chandeliers, right up to the luxury suite of the first mega rich client who had booked her for the night. She had been so nervous that beads of perspiration started to form on her forehead and she tried to blot it out desperately; no man wanted a perspiring woman smelling of sweat, and she was going for broke.

*"How would it feel to be undressing for a stranger and sleeping with him?"*

*"What would we talk about?"*

*"What if he takes away my cell phone and abuses me? No one will hear me even if I scream!"*

Random thoughts, anxious questions swirled in her head, as disorientating as the bright glare of the glittering chandelier lights dancing above. It was a young girl's first intrepid steps into a world where bodies and souls were traded for money and greed; deceit, lust, even contempt were the only acceptable emotions.

Suzue was thinking of that long ago intimidating elevator ride now as she rode up another, more practical grey elevator, to Yamano san's fourth floor extension office. No two elevators could have been more different but it was as if they took her on journeys in opposite directions along the same circular path towards a head-on collision between her present life and the dark sordidness of her past.

"Let's stay calm and see what Yamano has for us," Tomoko

said grimly as the worn metal doors of the elevator opened tiredly, almost directly, into a plain nondescript office with none of the avant garde eccentricity of the private investigator's ground floor premises. "He sounded quite upbeat and positive, though, if that's any consolation."

"Well, I'll be damned!" Sachi whistled. "If this is not the poverty-stricken cousin of Yamano's ground floor offices, I don't know what is!"

They found Yamano sitting at a scuffed wooden table and with his rumpled hair, unshaved stubble and wrinkled clothes, he looked the worse for wear and had obviously stayed up all night.

"You must be wondering why such a stark contrast to the offices downstairs," he said waving his hand vaguely around the ugly, cluttered room they were in. "Well, I am a private investigator so, like me, my office has many faces. Sit down anywhere you want except that black chair over there. That one has moods and no matter how many times I've had it repaired, it still gives way whenever it feels like it! My staff says I should just chop this useless chair up for firewood but if the truth be known, I've grown rather fond of it and am adopting it as my unpredictable lucky mascot."

"I must say you have unusual tastes!" Sachi quipped. "People have dogs, stuffed toys, amulets and the like as lucky mascots, but a chair?"

Yamano laughed as he took a thick brown envelope out from a drawer. Their light bantering had eased the tension somewhat but now it was time to be serious.

"It's all in here," he said taking out a thick sheaf of papers and spreading them on the table. "All the dirt you want on Mr. Mori Kakuei!"

"I can't wait to read it," Suzue said, trying to keep the tremor of excitement and nervousness from her voice "But remember one thing: Mori doesn't care about his personal life because his wife has long accepted his philandering ways, so any dirt about his sexual trysts will not affect him at all. It has to be something which will destroy or at least greatly compromise his business empire — only *that* will bring Mori to his knees!"

"Don't worry; with me, if you want dirt, you have it. I'm not called Yamano the Rat for nothing, you know! Here, take this report, read all 100 pages of it, and then let me know whether it's what you're looking for. But for today, let's just go through this summary of the report that I've drawn up for a quick discussion." The private investigator handed the thick brown envelope to Suzue and a copy of the four-page summary to each of the three pillars.

Suzue's hands were trembling as she started reading the summary: Page after page of dates, places where Mori had broken almost every corporate law to build his empire, shadowy deals, unfair trade, fraud, illegal takeovers, misrepresentation, money laundering, fraudulent share trading, market fixing. Yamano had delivered her all the dirt he promised.

"Wow, I don't know what to say except that you're brilliant, Yamano san!" Suzue breathed. "There's enough material here to put the man behind bars for a long, long time! Mori won't want to mess with me after reading this! Ask our lawyer, Tomoko!"

"This implicates Mori so completely that maybe you have to be a little careful, Suzue," Sachi said. "For something that could destroy him completely and send him to jail, — he might even hire someone to kill you! Remember, a lot is at stake here for him."

"No, I don't think he'll do that," Suzue shook her head firmly. "Mori may be a liar, a schemer, a maestro in manipulations and even a cheat, but he's not a killer."

"How can you be so sure?" Sachi persisted.

"I just am. Remember, I once knew him very well, and whatever shortcomings he has, he's not a violent man," Suzue replied. "Besides, given that I probably would have duplicate copies of this report anyway, it would be far better for Mori to cut a deal with me than have me bumped off! He's a smart man and that is the first thing that will occur to him. You're a genius, Yamano san, and worth every single yen of our agreed fee!"

"It's just part of my job, and with an important corporate client like Ms. Tomoko, I have to do better than my best," Yamano replied briskly, still pan faced, but Suzue could tell he was pleased.

The pillars spent almost the whole night in Suzue's apartment going through the report, stopping only to gasp at the audacity and extent of Mori Kakuei's dalliances on the wrong side of the law.

Halfway through the voluminous report, Suzue stood up

and said, "You know what? I think we've read enough to nail Mori Kakuei and we should call it a night. You've both put your social life and work practically on hold to see me through this and I'll never forget that. I can take it from here so ladies — get out of here and back to your own lives and plans."

"Are you sure you'll be all right?" Tomoko asked. "We can stay the night with you if you need the company."

"No, I'll be fine. We've been cloistered together the past few days and I'm sure you need your space," Suzue replied. "So go on, get out of here!"

After Sachi and Tomoko left, Suzue went over the report again and by the time she reached the last page, she was mentally exhausted. She had expected to feel triumph and victory but in the end, Suzue just felt unclean with the disturbing thought that she and Mori were basically the same. They had used dark, socially unacceptable methods to achieve ambitions that were too powerful and all consuming for their own good. They had shared dark secrets of a salacious past and were now using that against each other. It was really sick.

*****

The phone rang and Suzue saw from the caller ID that it was Robert, whom she had completely forgotten in the Mori blackmail saga of the last few days. Although she actually wanted to be alone that night, Robert's uncomplicated voice was like a breath of fresh air filling up the collapsing oxygen pockets in her lungs.

Their last conversation had gone like this:

"You seem distracted lately, Suzue, and unfocused even at work. That's very unlike you because I've never ever known anything to come between you and your work thus far, so I'm just concerned whether all is well with you."

"Thanks, Robert. I know I haven't been myself recently and yes, something is bothering me. You know how it is — we all come with baggage, and it's just an old baggage I have to deal with. It's irritating and definitely not welcome at this point in my life, but it's not something I can't handle."

"Ok, I know for sure you can handle anything you want or,

in this case, don't want, but if there's anything I can do to help, just let me in. I know you're a tough cookie but sometimes it helps to have someone to lean on."

Suzue told him she needed space and wanted to be alone for a few days and he didn't press her. That was the nicest thing about Robert; he shared her need for space and privacy, was completely independent and believed that two people could be a couple without living together in the same house, city or even country. And, as an added bonus, he was more normal than her and didn't seem to be haunted by any dark secrets. His clean slate, free of encumbrances, had a balancing influence on her.

*****

"This saga has gone on far too long and has to be resolved one way or the other. The whole thing is getting ridiculous and the time to settle it is now," Suzue told herself as she reached for her cell phone and began to type a text message to Mori's personal number. Why was she so afraid of him anyway? The way the dossier went, he should be hiding from her and not the other way around. What was the worst that could happen? The gossip papers could get hold of her story and batter her name around and discuss her on the Channels 4, 8 and 12 morning gossip talk shows for a couple of mornings and eventually, people would forgive her because after all, it was the story of a young misguided girl, desperate to find the money to fund her education. She had harmed and degraded no one but herself. Pit that against a man who had used every arm-twisting, law-evading trick in the book to amass his fortune, gunning down innocent people along the way, and it was anyone's guess which one of them would come out of this mudslinging "gala" event ruined forever. But certainly, their enemies would have a field day!

When she had finished the text message, Suzue pressed "send" and leaned back against her old leather sofa feeling as if a heavy load had been lifted from her shoulders. She had gritted her teeth and sent Mori a warm conciliatory text asking to meet up to discuss his proposal, careful not to give any indication at all how the meeting was actually going to be and what she was going to spring on him.

His reply came almost immediately, a smug "O.K., tomorrow, 7p.m., at the Tower Club Mori Ark Hills, Roppongi. We have a lot to catch up on."

"Oh yes, Mr. Mori, you have no idea just how much baggage we have to catch up on!" Suzue thought grimly as she typed "O.K." and pressed "send" again.

# CHAPTER 21

Suzue Tanaka and Mori Kakuei sat in the elegant lounge of the exclusive Tower Club facing each other. Soft piano lounge music was playing in the background and it should have been wildly romantic, but the obviously well- heeled couple's mood appeared more adversarial than amorous.

*Either I've stumbled on a lover's spat, or on a rich couple's attempts to discuss divorce terms before the matter goes to the lawyers,* thought the bowtied waiter as he took their orders with a discreet "see no evil, hear no evil, speak no evil" expression on his face.

"Well, here we are, after all these years. We're back again together—feels like old times, doesn't it?" Mori said, breaking the tense silence between them at last.

His words sent a chill down Suzue's spine, not so much because of their implications, but because of the strange way he was looking at her. Could it be, God forbid, he was looking at her with feelings? Suzue had been with men long enough to recognize that soft light in their eyes when there were feelings involved. It felt almost wrong to slap him with the inflammatory dossier when he was looking at her like that. Damn that man—how did he make even his victims feel guilty? Perhaps he knew what was coming— maybe he was deliberately doing this to break down her defenses She really wouldn't put it past him at all!

They made general conversation, skirting around the real reason they were meeting, till Suzue couldn't stand it anymore. She was sure now he was deliberately stalling to weaken her, because Mori had never been known to beat around the bush to get anything

**163**

or anyone he wanted. She decided to cut the crap and take the bull by the horns.

"So you've decided to accept my proposal, then?" Mori said suddenly before she could say anything, once again beating her to the punch.

There was that light in his eyes again. Oh God, stop it, Suzue wanted to scream. *You're Mori Kakuei, you're not supposed to be soft or have lights in your eyes. You're supposed to be cocksure of yourself and to take what you want, for God's sake! People like me can handle you if you're your usual arrogant, nasty self — but not with soft lights in your eyes! But you're not getting away with this one. I'm going to crack you before the night is done!*

"I've something to show you, Mori san," Suzue said just as abruptly, pushing a copy of Yamano's report to him. If her heart was hammering out her nervousness, she didn't show any outward sign of it.

"I'll have a look at that later," Mori replied taking the report and laying it aside. "I presume it's a business contract you want me to approve, perhaps to seal our, shall we say, friendship?"

*My God, I believe he thinks I am asking him for business favors in return for sleeping with him!* Suzue seethed. *The audacity of the man to still think of her as a woman who could be bought!* Still, she was relieved because the arrogant and callous Mori Kakuei was back, and he was much easier to deal with that way.

Aloud, Suzue said calmly, "I think you should read it or at least have a glance through it before we proceed further because this could have a big impact on our, shall we say, proposed friendship."

"All right, if you insist," Mori replied smoothly, in the condescending tone of a man who had to placate his woman of the moment.

Suzue waited while he reached for the file and started reading it. Apart from the slight twitching of a jaw muscle, his expression did not change at all. Suzue wondered whether she had brought the right file. *The man is amazing, he must have ice running through his veins!* she thought. *"What man can read such stuff about himself and show no emotion, not even the slightest change of expression?"*

A slight line creased Mori's brows by the time he got half way through the report and somehow that pleased Suzue and made her feel more confident that Yamano's "dirt" was working on its subject.

Fifteen minutes later, Mori put down the report and looked Suzue straight in the eye, his face inscrutable as he said softly, "You did your homework well, Tanaka san, although I must admit that I am a little hurt by all the nasty things people or specifically, *your* people, are saying about me. When you sent me that text, I really thought for a moment that there was something going for us. Pardon me, my mistake!"

It was at that moment that Suzue realized that she had been right about the light in Mori's eyes but after what she had done to him with this expose, he now probably hated her. She would have to press on or be killed by him, professionally, that is. Mori had the unchallengeable reputation of felling his enemies with a thoroughness no one could match when they crossed him, and Suzue did not intend to be on the list of his casualties.

"Come on, Mori san, call a spade a spade — you were blackmailing me to sleep with you," she said. "What do you expect a woman pushed into such a corner to do? You seemed to miss the point that I am no longer your call girl and you insulted me by threatening to expose my past if I didn't sleep with you."

"So what's your game? What do you want to do with these reports — presuming you have evidence of all these allegations," Mori continued as if Suzue had not spoken. His voice was calm, but she could tell by the way his fingers crossed and uncrossed themselves that he was tense and nervous, a habit she had noticed years ago when she watched him and his team manipulate their way through some of their most hostile takeovers and mergers.

Somehow, knowing that Mori was nervous made Suzue feel confident and in control and she went straight for his jugular. She had no desire to destroy him but she was going to have fun stringing him along first and making him cross and uncross his fingers even more.

"Yes, of course I do have evidence — tsk, tsk,tsk, Mori san. Money laundering, tax evasion, insider trading, fraudulent misrepresentation — is there anything you haven't done? You know, don't you, that this can send you to jail till you're old and grey?"

"Ok, cut the crap and tell me what you want. You know

you won't destroy me because whether you like it or not, we were once lovers and as you said yourself—call a spade a spade—I molded you. Deep inside, you know we're alike. We want the same things— power, success, respect and acceptance by society— and that's why we will not destroy each other," Mori replied in a deadly calm and collected voice.

Suzue sighed. Mori was right, of course. He had literally taken the wind out of her sail once again and suddenly she felt flat, the air of triumph at cornering him flowing out of her like the hydrogen escaping from a punctured balloon. Damn the man, he was so sure of her he hadn't even bothered to deny the contents of Yamano's investigative report or threaten her with his formidable legal team and the usual defamation suit.

"Yes, let's get to the point," Suzue said briskly. "Here's the deal. I will trade your silence about my past—which is known only to you—for a non-disclosure of anything in this file about you. I can give you this file as, perhaps, a reminder of what you will face if a single word leaks out about my past. But remember, I have copies so destroying this file wouldn't be a solution. That's everything in a nutshell so shoot, Mori. The ball's in your court now."

Mori hesitated for just a second before replying, "All right, you win this round. We'll keep each other's secrets and as every hypocrital business rival says grudgingly after a hard-fought battle, 'no hard feelings'—but I'm sure you know that."

"Wait, there's something else," Suzue added. " You will not take Big Echo's account from us; that wouldn't be fair because this baggage between us has nothing to do with the company. Do we have a deal?"

Mori did not say anything, he merely nodded. It was clear that he did not like the fact that he had been check mated, and his little conciliatory smile did not reach his eyes. As he called for the bill, Mori said almost somberly, "Do you know, I think we would have made a good team, Tanaka san, you and I. With our combined ambitions, hardness and similar visions, we would have been unstoppable."

His words stifled her and created unthinkable musings that perhaps Mori was right. She needed to get away from those blazing, hypnotic eyes. Suzue gathered her things and got up to go.

# Onna Rising

"Goodbye, Mori san. I don't suppose our paths will cross again, except, maybe, at industry events, and thanks for dinner," she said firmly, and walked out of the restaurant without a backward glance.

Behind the chic glass-topped bar, their bowtied waiter sighed. There would be no happy and romantic make-up sex for this couple, that's for sure, although, for one moment, watching their fire and passion, he was sure the night would have ended on that note.

Suzue took deep gulps of air as she rode the high speed elevator hurtling her down to the lobby. She didn't rush to get out of the building because she knew Mori would be decent enough to let her go without a fuss; it was better for his dignity and ego anyway. He was also smart enough to know he had been checkmated and would honor his word about keeping her past a secret in return for her silence on his own colorful life. Both of them had too much at stake to be playing games. What a pair they were!

She shuddered as she thought about how close she had come to agreeing with Mori that they would have made a powerful team had circumstances been different. It had been just for a split second, but that had been enough to rattle her.

Suzue reached for her cell phone to call Robert. She needed to be reminded that there were still uncomplicated, normal men around who could help stabilize her roller coaster life. Then she changed her mind. It was far better for her to be alone to sleep over this dramatic night and wake up renewed.

Yet it was strange that after her ordeal, the first person she thought of calling was Robert, who didn't even know what was going on, and not Sachi or Tomoko. Suzue shrugged and dismissed it as being the disorientation and temporary insanity brought on by her surreal encounter with Mori Kakuei. Suzue realized on her short subway ride home that her relief at having escaped the Mori mess relatively unscarred, was strangely tempered by a sense of loss.

*It's all his fault,* she thought angrily. *We could have put the past away like mature adults and have been great friends and business compatriots, but no. He had to spoil it all by making this preposterous and indecent proposal, and now it's over between us!*

Theirs had not been a pleasant exchange and when she reached home, Suzue ran a punishingly hot bath to cleanse and remove all the "Mori toxins" from her body. Despite herself, she was smiling as she inched her way into the perfumed, scalding water because she was remembering Robert's face the first time he entered a Japanese bath and almost cried like a baby.

"Jesus, you Japanese are nuts and lunatics!" he panted. "This water is going to boil my crown jewels alive so don't be surprised if I perform below par tonight!" Robert had survived that first mind-popping experience and not only retained his crown jewels intact but actually performed beyond expectations. After a few more dunkings, he had become a "Japanese bath addict." Then there was the "onsen" or hot spring experience that most foreigners would go through at least once during their time in Japan unless they became hooked on this ritual, as happened to Robert.

As Suzue soaked in the steaming water, letting its soothing lavender essence wash all the stress from her body, she thought about Robert and his first onsen experience in Hakone. They had laughed at the Yucata that hung awkwardly around his knees and the sleeves that reached just up to his elbows; it was obvious the ryokan was not prepared to accommodate a gaijin of Robert's 6 foot 5 inches frame! He looked like Kenji, the oversized toy bear of her childhood days, when she dressed him up in a T shirt after it shrunk in the wash.

She wished she could be like Robert—ambitious, driven and yet having a soul. His life was uncomplicated by shadows or a dark past, and he fit everywhere in society; well, perhaps not so much in Japan, where even his foreign registration card called him an "alien." They had quipped about that one day when Robert brought out his foreign ID card and said, "Look at this, Suzue: My 'Alien Registration' card. The Japanese think we gaijin are all aliens! Nice!"

"Well, with that great height of yours, you *are* an alien, to most people outside of Tokyo anyway! Remember the time I took you to that small village in the North? I don't think anyone in that village had ever seen a gaijin before let alone one as tall as you! I'm sure you terrified a lot of people that day!"

"Yes, I was quite the local celebrity! You know, Suzue, I

am amazed at the contradictory faces that Japan and Japanese people present to the world. I mean, Japan must be one of the few countries where traditional kimono clad men and women can board the subway, stroll down the street or dine at restaurants in high-tech, ultra modern mega cities like Tokyo, looking like they stepped right out of the Meiji era, and no one bats an eyelid! I'm just thinking how much attention we could attract if we wandered the streets of London in Victorian clothes!"

Suzue soaked in the water for a long time, random thoughts and memories crowding her mind. The lulling effect of those swirling thoughts must have sent her to sleep because the next thing she knew, she was almost immersed in water that had turned stone cold. Suzue shuddered as she remembered her grandmother's stories of how overworked and exhausted people drowned in two feet of bath water simply because they fell asleep while taking a bath! Good grief, she certainly wasn't ready to die yet, not when she had just check-mated one of the most powerful entrepreneurs of modern Japan! She also got wind, somehow, that she might be slated to become the next MD in the boardroom. Finally, she might, just *might*, have found a man who fit quite nicely into her ideals for a sound relationship – independence, privacy, lots of space from each other and a shared animal passion for each other's body in ways that some of her other boyfriends had found too wild and tacky. Suzue chuckled as she remembered one of them admitting that he couldn't keep up with her because he was all worn out!

The luminous dials of her digital clock showed 11 p.m. and Suzue shuddered again. God, she had fallen asleep for a solid thirty minutes, or perhaps more, in a deep Japanese style bath tub filled with water! What were the odds she could have drowned in lavender essence? The growling of her stomach reminded Suzue that she had barely touched her dinner, a magnificent gourmet concoction made by some of the finest chefs in Tokyo. That was something she rarely did, coming from a home with few luxuries – there was definitely no gourmet food when she was growing up – and now her grandmother's rhetoric of "waste not, want not" rang in her ears.

*What a waste!* Suzue thought as she opened her fridge and found nothing but a carton of milk, a couple of eggs, wine and some salad greens, the result of a particular aversion to shopping for food in the supermarkets. *Not even enough scraps to feed a chicken.* She grimaced and made a mental note to be more conscientious about her supermarket responsibilities as she took out the two eggs and cracked them into a pan to make a simple omelet.

"A plain omelet, slightly stale bread and a half bottle of wine have never tasted so good,"she told Tomoko during an impulse midnight return call.

"You're impossible and disgusting tonight on two counts," Tomoko replied. "For one thing, Sachi and I have been frantic over you the whole night, and I was just about to make my 20th call and not a squeak from you till now? And secondly, how many times have I told you to move your fat ass down to the supermarket and get yourself some decent food? Tokyo has some of the finest supermarkets in the world and you have what, two eggs and a carton of milk in your fridge?"

"O.K., O.K., I promise! Don't scold, Tomoko, you're terrifying when you do that," Suzue implored, holding the phone away from her ear. God, the woman could shriek when something pissed her off! "Anyway, I have great news about the Tanaka versus Mori case. We won, Tomoko, we won! And I say "we" because I couldn't have done this without you and Sachi. After I served Yamano's dirt report on him, Mori agreed to back off indefinitely *plus* I got him to confirm that he will not remove Big Echo's account from us! That's how good for us and how damaging for Mori the report was! Now, have I put a smile on your face and am I forgiven for having a stark naked fridge?"

There was a hiss at the other end of the line then Tomoko whistled, "Omedeto, congratulations, Suzue, we did it! O.K., for that you are forgiven all your recent transgressions, and, by the way, I was just trying to cover up my anxiety for you with my earlier lambasting of your fridge! Sachi and I have been worried sick the whole day and all that bad energy had to come out somehow!

"And I thought, hell, this woman must have called Robert first and forgotten about us! I must skin her alive!"

"Oh my God, do you think I would do that—call a guy first, over and above my pillars?" Suzue lied, tongue in cheek because Tomoko was right—Robert *had* been the first she was going to call before she realized he didn't even know what was going on! "But the truth is that I was so exhausted and distressed after the whole thing was over that I fell asleep in the bath tub until half an hour ago!"

She almost bit her tongue with guilt when Tomoko continued, "But heck, even if you did call him first, it's fine, I was just kidding! We all know how it is with us girls—always being there for each other when we hit rock bottom, but not necessarily the first to be called when things are resolved! Poor long-suffering girl friends—but that's what makes us resilient against all the storms we have to face; having each other to whine to and detox ourselves with to ride another storm!"

"Aw, come on, Tomoko chan, that's so sweet but yes, it's been a rough ride. Not to mention the worry that I might lose our company a mega client like Big Echo and then wouldn't be able to meet the target I set for myself for this year," Suzue replied. "You know how it is—the minute we women slip, someone is always ready to jump in and kick us out. You know something, Tomoko? I will never let go of this position I have achieved! I'll fight tooth and nail anyone who tries to usurp me, and that's why I didn't have any qualms about eliminating Mori Kakuei if he hadn't agreed to back off. I decided that if I had to go down, I'd take the omnipotent Mori along with me! "

"Good, Suzue, I'm glad to hear that! Since you became more involved with Robert, I thought you'd gone soft and was losing your shine as your industry's golden girl," Tomoko said, obviously relieved.

"Are you kidding me? Me, gone soft?" Suzue protested. "Over my dead body! I never understood those highly qualified and trained women in positions of responsibility who quit their jobs without a qualm as soon as they marry and have children, thereafter fading into apron-clad, shopping cart wheeling okusan tachi! I can never be that because I live and breathe corporate suits and an Iphone wielding lifestyle!

"Oh, something just occurred to me. Is Michael with you and did I interrupt anything by calling so late?" Suzue wondered.

"No, he's not here," Tomoko replied in an edgy voice. "We had a bit of a tiff a couple of days ago and I sent him back to his

**171**

place to sulk on his own time, not mine. You know, Suzue, I"m beginning to see the wisdom of your insistence that a relationship be enriched by lots of space and periodic overhauls!"

"Vindicated at last!" Suzue laughed. "God, Tomoko, it's good to be able to laugh like this again!"

# CHAPTER 22

"Tanaka san, we've won, we've won!" It was one of those cold, grey, drizzly mornings and the rush hour on the famous Tokyo subway Yamanote had been awful, but the sun literally shone out of Fumiko's beaming face as she danced into Suzue's office, waving a piece of paper.

"Calm down, Fumiko, you're making me dizzy with all that prancing! First of all, tell me what we've won and then we'll see whether it's worth celebrating," Suzue said to her enthusiastic personal assistant.

"Tanaka san, we've won that snooty high fashion account we have been working so hard to pitch for, isn't that fantastic?" Fumiko replied and her eyes were shining. "You said that would be a very difficult account to win but we did it!"

When Fumiko first joined her team to replace Mayuri, her trusted PA of almost a decade whose husband had relocated to Los Angeles, Suzue had been dubious about the diffident young woman who appeared to have a major self-esteem problem. "I don't have time for babysitting newbies," Suzue had grumbled to the pillars. "I need someone already broken in and who knows what I want." But Fumiko came highly recommended by Mayuri, so Suzue decided to give the new PA a chance. "I know right now Fumiko Aoyama looks as if she will crumble if you say 'boo' to her, but trust me, Suzue, with a bit of patience, and you training her to adapt to your style, Fumiko will be a very loyal and efficient PA," Mayuri promised."I've known her since middle school and believe me, you won't regret your decision to take her in."

"All right, if you say so, I'm pretty sure Fumiko Aoyama will be almost as good as you. I say almost because no one can ever replace you, Mayuri," Suzue sighed. "You've been quite a PA, sticking right with me through thick and thin—through your first marriage, a first child, divorce, remarriage and your second child! It's been quite a ride for both of us, Mayuri, and I'll probably never again find a woman like you in Japan! Oh, what will I do without you?"

"You will do what you've always done—manage very well, with Fumiko manning the fortress for you," Mayuri replied soothingly.

And she had been right. After a few stumbles, Fumiko went on to become almost every bit as good as Mayuri—if a little less assertive and forthcoming—but her loyalty and meticulous aversion to any form of error more than made up for that. On top of that, Fumiko took her job very seriously and, unlike Mayuri, without a husband to cater to and accident-prone children at home to give her domestic emergencies, she really enjoyed working long hours. In fact, it was her boss who often had to send her packing!

Suzue made it clear right from the start that she didn't want, as her PA, a robot who responded to push buttons and voice commands, but a hands on person who could take the initiative when it was needed and remove the burden of administrative nitty gritties from her shoulders. Suzue had never liked the traditional Japanese corporate culture of hierarchy which did not encourage juniors to ask questions or express their opinions. Right or wrong, the boss or superior always had to have the last say and even if you knew he was wrong or that there was a better way of doing things, you had to shut up. Suzue didn't subscribe to or encourage this rhetoric at all, and her subordinates called her Suzue informally, instead of the deferential Tanaka san that was the norm in Japanese corporate culture. This made them feel very much a team, especially as they were encouraged to voice opinions across hierarchal lines.

"Do you know how many new talents and fresh ideas from the young blood of this industry our outdated corporate culture is missing out on?" was Suzue's justification for her unconventional style of staff management.

Suzue had always worked her team on the basis of

consultative brainstorming and she encouraged the young executives to speak up, ask questions and be thirsty to learn. Not all in the company's top level management were happy with the mess she was creating in their traditional pyramid of hierarchy and power, but even they had to admit grudgingly that her team had the greatest productivity figures, the most outstanding business results and the lowest staff turnover rate in a volatile and ever-changing industry. So there was something the "Tanaka woman" as they called her, had to be doing that was right.

"I want you to speak up when you see me at the edge of a pit about to fall in! Don't jump in with me just because I'm the boss—push me back!" she told a horrified Fumiko early in their relationship, when the PA was still clinging to the traditional Japanese pyramid style of management.

"You mean, like point out your mistakes to you and give you my opinions?" Fumiko asked, not quite believing what she was hearing.

"Yes! If you have something good and constructive to share with me, speak up!" Suzue replied and Fumiko nodded, not quite sure she would be able to meet this tall order. But five years on, Fumiko ran Suzue's life at work on oiled wheels and had blossomed from the self-effacing girl whose favorite phrase seemed to be "I'm so sorry" to a moderately confident individual who had stopped apologizing at the drop of a coin, had gotten rid of her shuffling gait and was not afraid to speak her mind.

"I molded that girl," Suzue boasted to Robert. "Banned her from starting most of her sentences with 'I'm sorry' and look at her now—she even walks with a bold stride! And I heard the other day that she was baring her teeth at a disrespectful supplier to protect our territory!

"That's just it, Robert san, I feel so good when I'm instrumental in empowering another woman to believe in her own ability. And, contrary to what most people think, every time one woman is empowered, that's a step towards making women in Japan feel good about themselves."

"You're a great mentor, Suzue," Robert replied. "I've seen you mentoring the interns and young executives straight from university and you're doing a fantastic job at that for someone with, may I say, very few domesticated and nurturing bones in her otherwise gorgeous body!

"But it's not only your gorgeous body I'm in love with, Suzue," he added. "It's your heart. You're very tough on the outside but your heart, which I have this gut feeling has seen pain and been scarred, is more compassionate and pure than all those people who regularly criticize and judge you simply because you are a very successful woman and not a man.

"I've just found out about the pro bono work you and Tomoko are doing to provide assistance and counseling for foreign workers and illegal immigrants who are stranded in Japan without the means to pay for legal representation. You aren't just donating money from a distance, but actually going down to the centers to physically help out," Robert continued. "I guess you didn't want to tell me this part of your work and your "busy" weekends because you thought I would think of you as a softie! Sometimes I think you're too hard on yourself, Suzue, I don't know why. But nevertheless I admire and love *all* of you — hard-boiled, soft-boiled, well-done, rare, medium rare, whatever! I just wish you would put down your guard a little with me!"

"Oh, Robert, you make me sound like a piece of meat or an egg, but that's the nicest thing anyone has ever said about me. I do have some issues in my life and someday when I'm ready, I'd really like to share them with you. But till then, let's just enjoy what we have and don't think so much," Suzue replied. As soon as the words were out, though, she saw the disappointment in Robert's face and she could have bitten her tongue off.

Oh God, what was wrong with her? Why couldn't she express the emotions she had developed for him instead of hiding behind that cool, non-committal front she always put up— even for Robert? She could tell he was hurt by her rejection and who could blame him? It took a lot for a very private person like Robert to open up his heart and soul to anyone, and this was what he got.

Then she hardened herself. What was it Mori had once told her? Nice girls don't get the penthouse, so go ahead—be a bitch! And what had she always told herself? That she would not be pressured by any man, not even Robert, to say or do anything till she was ready to do so. That was, after all, the foundation on which their relationship was built; destroy it and the whole structure would come tumbling down and she'd be back to square one and her expiration date rhetoric. No, she shouldn't compromise her own needs and space for a man because that was not how she was, and a relationship based on compromising her very core convictions and lifestyle would never be sustainable.

As Suzue herself once said, "Why should a woman always be the one to compromise herself, her own needs, her career and her life in a relationship? Look around you — a woman is always doing the giving — she'll give up her career, give up all the things she once loved, in some cases even give up her friends so she can be on call to the family 24/7."

But Robert proved himself difficult to shake off a few days later when the subject of her mother and grandmother's visit to Tokyo came up.

"You must miss them a lot because I can see how happy you are that they're coming to see you," he said. "Do you want to introduce me to them?"

"No, definitely not," Suzue shook her head firmly. "It's not the right time. Remember something, Robert; my family is not too fond of the idea of gaijin boyfriends, lovers, partners or potential husbands seeing as how my father, a gaijin, walked off and left my mother with a half Japanese ainoko and so many whispering neighbors that they had to leave their beloved Kyushu and move to another part of Japan for so many years.

"Of course, no two gaijin are the same — and knowing you, Robert, if I ever got pregnant with your child, far from walking away, you'd probably want to move into my womb with the child to take care of him or her! But that's not how they will see you and knowing that I am with a gaijin will freak them out so, no. Maybe at some point in the future but not right now.

"And please don't kick up a fuss about this and blackmail me with 'if I don't introduce you to my family, it means I'm ashamed of you,' because if you do this, I'm going to have to let you go. I cannot have a man who pressures me into doing something against my better judgment because I'd lose myself." Suzue closed her eyes and waited.

To her relief, Robert laid his hand gently on her thigh and

replied "It's all right; I can see where you're coming from and you must introduce me only when and if you feel they will be comfortable with it."

"Ok, you passed the test so we stay on board," Suzue mumbled, not even aware she had spoken aloud till Robert asked, "What test?"

"Nothing at all, I was just thinking aloud," Suzue replied. "Hey, thanks for being such a sport. You make it so easy to love you!"

"Then go ahead, love me!" Robert suggested. His eyes were twinkling but Suzue knew he was dead serious.

To diffuse this awkward moment, she laughed lightly and said, ruffling his hair, "Don't you flutter those drop-dead gorgeous eyelashes at me, especially since you know damn well what a lethal effect they have on women!"

The moment passed and Robert replied in like manner. "By the way, I love your disgusting line about me moving into your womb with our hypothetical baby and you as our neighbor! One big happy family!"

# CHAPTER 23

"I'm going home early today because my mother and grandmother are here from Kyushu," Suzue announced to Fumiko, feeling almost guilty to leave while they were in the midst of frenzied preparations for a campaign. But she deserved at least one early night because she had been working late every day and had neglected her family who were staying at her home.

Although her mother and grandmother had assured her that they were perfectly happy and comfortable lazing around the apartment and watching the city go by from the windows, Suzue knew that they had come all the way to Tokyo to see her because they missed her. She was sure they longed to sit round the dining table, the whole family together again, cradling cups of hot green tea and sipping miso shiru soup. Instead of that, they had got an empty apartment and no Suzue till late at night when she stumbled in, took a bath and collapsed on the bed. They hadn't even had the time to talk to her except at the breakfast table before she grabbed her coat and rushed out of the door.

"Just check whether I have any conference calls to attend to that can't wait till tomorrow," she instructed Fumiko, still reluctant to leave her office early in this busy campaign period.

"Go home, Tanaka san! You've been practically sleeping in the office the last two nights and it really isn't fair to your family. After all, they don't come to Tokyo everyday, and as the PA you always taught to speak her mind, I'm asking you to go home. I'll stay on and handle anything that comes in," Fumiko replied.

"Nag, nag, nag," Suzue laughed. "I don't think I taught you to do that and it's not even in your job description! But thanks,

**179**

Fumiko chan; I really need someone to tell me off once in a while. I forget to take care of myself sometimes. Ok, I'm off then—and if anything crops up, just buzz me on my cell phone.

"Oh, one last thing. Mr. Darcey has agreed to cover a few clients for me," Suzue said trying to sound as casual as possible, although the shrewd Fumiko probably already knew about her special relationship with Robert Darcey. "I can't imagine, though, which client would like an oversized gaijin from the digital team towering over them, so try to match him with those clients who are used to interacting with foreigners."

"Just go, Tanaka san and don't worry so much! I've got everything covered, including Darcey san." There was the hint of a smirk in Fumiko's voice and Suzue smiled as she gathered up her things and charged out of the door. Her PA had even developed a saucy sense of humor, a far cry from her early days of low self-esteem and irritating "I'm so sorry" opening liners. Fumiko was a perfect example of a woman who had been mentored into realizing her own self worth and the right to live life the way she wanted.

She'd come a long way in her personal life as well. When Fumiko first joined Suzue's team, she was in a tumultuous relationship with a "salary man" from one of Japan's "big four" corporations. This man treated her like a doormat and stripped her of her self-esteem layer by layer with his constant criticism of everything from the way she walked to her lack of knowledge about the topics he was interested in. Fumiko had to distance herself from her friends, ate only at restaurants he liked, watched his favorite movies, and so forth. In fact, everything was about him and what made him happy; she was not in the equation at all.

"He's a jerk! Just dump him, move on and have a life!" Suzue prodded, exasperated at her PA's lack of courage to walk away from a relationship that was compromising her dignity and self respect.

Although Fumiko hung on for a few more months, she was observing how her boss gained the respect and grudging admiration of the men she wooed relentlessly for their business without losing her dignity, and the ones she cut down to size if they crossed her.

One day, after a long weekend break, Fumiko walked into the office, her trademark long sleek jet black hair cut into a short sassy bob and tinted dark auburn. She looked as if she had been in a cat fight and came out of it the winner. And although Suzue could guess what had transpired over the weekend, she waited for her PA to unload it all on her.

"I took your advice, Tanaka san, and I broke up with him over the weekend," Fumiko blurted out at last. "After working for you and seeing how you manage your life with complete freedom, I couldn't stand being controlled like that anymore. As you told me just a couple of weeks ago, no woman has to live this way with so much unhappiness and fear because of the constant surveillance and control of a man. You were right, Tanaka san; it's far better to be single and free than to be caged up in an unequal relationship where the scales are tilted, as always, against the woman!

"My God, it feels so good to be rid of this heaviness and perpetual dread that I will say or do something to trigger His Majesty's displeasure! It's amazing to wake up in the morning and know that whether my day will be — good or bad — depends on me, myself, and not on some selfish jerk I wasted six years of my life with!"

"I'm so glad my message finally got through to you," Suzue let her PA rattle out her pent up emotions before replying. "And yet there are so many women in Japan who still believe it's better to have a bad husband or partner than to be single. It's all that pressure society puts on women to marry or be stigmatized with being left on the shelf and growing old, alone and unwanted. It just kills me to listen to young women with complete economic independence talking like that! Fairy tales and romantic garbage that women feed each other from the time they are young; it's pathetic!"

Suzue was thinking of this conversation as her train hurtled homeward and she knew she had been right not to start the practice of explaining everything to Robert and having to justify her decisions to him. Spoiling him like that would have gone against the grain of her identity and would never have been sustainable. If he wanted her, he would just have to accept her need to be free.

The minute she opened her apartment door, Suzue was greeted by an unfamiliar but wonderful aroma — that of real home-cooked food from the kitchen, and she groaned appreciatively. God, how long had it been since she ventured into the kitchen to turn out a meal that didn't come from a restaurant? She really had to acquire some domestic skills because as things stood, even Robert was far better than her in the domestic and kitchen department! He had jokingly commented a few nights ago that Suzue had destroyed his cozy vision of Japanese girls, to which she had replied, tongue in cheek, that if he had noticed her skin tone and hair texture, he would have realized by now that she was not "your typical Japanese maiden!"

Her mother and grandmother were cutting up vegetables at the kitchen table in companionable silence while a pot of Suzue's favorite pork curry brewed on the stove. It was a tranquil domestic scene that added warmth and life to her newly renovated chrome and glass kitchen, which had been bare and cold with minimal usage most of the time.

"I don't know why you have such a beautiful and well-equipped kitchen when you don't want to do any cooking in it," Tomoko had complained when Suzue first remodeled her kitchen several months earlier.

"That's the point; the kitchen is so classy after the renovation that I don't feel comfortable doing heavy cooking and messing it up!" Suzue rationalized, tongue in cheek.

"You're nuts," Sachi replied. "And we're going to the supermarket right now to buy food to cook up a storm tonight so that this kitchen can be broken in at last!"

But by the time they got back from the supermarket after a long day at work, the trio were so tired that they unanimously voted to ring for pizzas and Suzue's kitchen remained in its pistine state. The subject of the virginal kitchen never came up again.

"Suzue chan, you're back early!" Baba, as she called her grandmother, was obviously pleased to be able to have a dinner with her granddaughter at last. Suzue gave the older woman a hug. Dear Baba, no matter how old or how many awards she won, Suzue would always be her "little gap- toothed Suzue chan"! Sometimes, Baba's unfailing trust in her pricked Suzue's conscience and she wondered what her Baba would feel or think if she knew the kind of things her adored granddaughter had done to get where she was.

Dinner that night was wonderful, the small dining table overflowing with food, and in the room, much laughter and pride from the stories Suzue regaled her mother and Baba with about her clients, her work and her escapades with the pillars.

After the dishes were cleared away, the three women brought their hot green tea over to the western style sitting room because Baba loved the feel of the smooth, cool leather sofa Suzue had recently added to her eclectic collection of two English wing chairs and a French-inspired chaise lounge. Baba was admiring her huge flat screen plasma TV and Suzue switched on the cable to show her the foreign channels.

"Watching all these foreign news networks helps me improve my English," Suzue was saying as she turned on CNN International, her favorite American news network. Some U.S. senate member was giving a speech, a Black man in military uniform, and Suzue was just about to switch back to the Japanese channels when she noticed her mother's face. It had turned chalk white and her eyes were glued to the TV as if she could not bear to look away. Then with a strangled cry, she got up and ran out of the room moaning, "Switch off the TV, please switch it off!"

Alarmed, Suzue was about to run after her mother when she felt Baba's hand on her shoulders, pulling her back.

"Let her go," the older lady said sharply. "Your mother just needs some time alone and after a good cry she'll be all right."

"But why is she crying, Baba? I don't understand. The TV was just showing a U.S. senator giving a speech — there's nothing sad, tragic or even unusual about that! I don't think Mother is even remotely interested in politics to be moved so much by a speech given by some foreign politician in a language she barely understands!"

Her grandmother did not reply but her eyes, too, were glued to the man on the TV screen and they were shining with tears. A cold shiver ran down Suzue's spine as she followed Baba's eyes and really looked at the face on the screen for the first time. The curly hair, the skin tone and those eyes. Why did he look disturbingly familiar, as if they had met at some point? A thought flashed through her mind, a chilling thought that Suzue dismissed immediately as being ludicrous and hallucinatory.

"No, it's impossible! Don't even think of something so ridiculous! For some reason, we're all hallucinating tonight!"

**183**

And yet, why was this stranger from a country thousands of miles away, who was just another face on a TV screen, affecting her mother so much? There could only be one reason, and it was an unthinkable one.

"I picked up the language while I was serving at the US military base in Japan in the 1970s….." the man was saying.

Suzue's heart began to thump so fast and loud she thought it would give way as the words "serving in the US military base in Japan in the 1970s" roared in her ears.

Her mother and this man…..she and this man. There was a very big question mark that had to be answered, the one which had plagued her for as long as she could remember, and only one person could answer that question—the woman who had given birth to her. And Suzue wanted those answers tonight.

For a moment, Suzue hesitated. Her mother had seemed very distraught and perhaps now was not the time to push her. Then she hardened herself. God, what about her, Suzue? She had lived with this stigma of being an ainoko long enough. All the smirks and pitiful looks from her friends and teachers at school and the men who leered at her sexy curls and big breasts, the chest that she tried so hard to suppress during her sensitive teeanage years. She'd wanted to be flat like the other Japanese girls.

Did anyone care about how she felt in all this or what she had to go through and what it had made her into? It was about time her mother faced her responsibility to tell an innocent child who her father was, and if he had anything to do with the man called Roger Carlista they had just seen on TV, she had the right to know.

Suzue got up and walked determinedly to the guest room where her mother had fled and knocked on the door, softly but firmly.

"Mother, okasan, can I come in?" she called out and without waiting for an answer, pushed open the door and stepped into the room.

Rumiko was sitting at the edge of the bed just staring into space, but she automatically shifted a little to make space for Suzue as if she had been expecting her daughter to come in and confront her.

"Mother, I think we need to talk," Suzue said as gently as she could, despite her raging thoughts and thumping heart, because she was going to nail her elusive biological father at last. "When that American army turned Senate guy appeared on TV, the way you reacted struck a chord in me. All kinds of thoughts started racing through my mind, but I pushed them away till I heard him say that he served with the US military in Japan in the 1970s. Then all the pieces started coming together. Mother, is that man who I think he is?"

Rumiko met her daughter's flaming eyes that held hers relentlessly and answered simply. "Yes, Roger Carlista is your father, Suzue."

Although she had expected that answer, to hear it actually affirmed by her mother stunned Suzue and she felt as if she had been shot in the head and declared clinically dead. For the first time in her life, she opened her mouth but nothing came out.

"Suzue, say something," her mother pleaded. "I know I should have told you before but I just couldn't bring myself to do it. Because of my selfishness, for decades I left you hanging in limbo, wondering where you came from and who your father was. I'm so sorry! You have the right to be angry with me and I'm prepared to take it."

Rumiko started to cry—raw, anguished sobs of pain at the burden she had made her daughter carry for so many years, and that snapped Suzue out of her momentary blackout.

"No, mother, I'm not angry with you—not a lot, anyway. After all, this Roger Carlista is nothing to me, just a stranger who happened to be my biological father. It's him I should be angry with because he walked away from us and left you with the burden of bringing up his love child as a single unwed mum in Japan," Suzue replied.

"Can I tell you something else? But you must promise me that you will not explode."

"All right, Mother, I promise. So tell me."

"Don't hate your father so much, Suzue. He didn't really walk away from us…"

"What the hell, mother! Don't make excuses for a man who doesn't deserve it!" Suzue interrupted. "If he didn't walk away, where was he when I was born and when I was a child and longed for a father like the other kids and when I was an awkward teenager and needed a father figure in my life — where was he? Oh yes — and where is he now?"

"Let me finish, Suzue, please? Well, in the third year of our relationship, Roger was sent back home to the United States because he had finished his term and couldn't stay on in Japan. He pleaded with me to go back with him and get married there but I was too scared to leave Japan. Also, being an only child, I couldn't leave your grandmother to fend for herself, almost 10,000 miles away.

"So he went back by himself and we made all the promises that young lovers do but it was hard in those days to keep in constant touch with only the post — or what you young people these days call snail mail — and the occasional phone call.

"A month after he left, I discovered, to my horror, that I was pregnant, and my life just turned upside down. I was frightened, alone and carrying the illegitimate child of a gaijin. Who could I turn to for help? I considered writing to your father to tell him of my condition but in the end your grandmother became suspicious of my constant morning sickness and weight gain and I couldn't keep it from her anymore.

"I remember the day I confessed everything to her. She almost went to pieces and when she recovered, your grandmother made me promise to keep my pregnancy from your father and never contact him again. She was understandably worried that your father would insist I moved to America and get married if he knew I was pregnant and she would lose me unless she did the unthinkable — which was to leave Japan and came along. In the years that followed, I often wondered if I had not made that promise to your grandmother and informed your father about my condition whether our lives would have been different.

"So you see, Suzue, your father didn't really walk away from you. He never knew you existed!"

Suzue didn't even know how she maintained her cool sufficiently to assure her mother she was fine with the mega family skeleton in the closet that had just been revealed. But after her mother and grandmother had gone to bed, Suzue sat in front of her computer for a long time before determinedly accessing Google search and typing in the words "Roger Carlista."

He was a prominent man and there were pages of

information about Roger Carlista, and one page in particular caught Suzue's attention. His personal bio stated that he had been married for 28 years to the daughter of a well-known industrialist, and the couple had two children, a son who was 26 and a daughter who was 24 years old. There was even a family picture of the Carlistas and Suzue enlarged it and stared for a long while at the smiling faces of the man who had fathered her out of wedlock and his official family.

She understood at last where she'd gotten her curly hair, dusky skin and large eyes with the prominent double eyelids, a look that an increasing number of Japanese girls were flocking to their plastic surgeons to acquire. Her mystery father had a face and name at last and he was not even an anonymous face in the crowd but a prominent person whom she could trace and track on any search engine. In some ways that was not a plus because there would always be the temptation to track Roger Carlista in the news, thus making it difficult to forget him and push him out of her life.

Suzue sighed. Her early night off and the family dinner that had promised so much bonding and catching up had turned into a nightmare of epic proportions. Well, she had always longed to put a face and a name to her biological father, and her wish had been granted tonight. But it came with a very high price tag.

# CHAPTER 24

"I'm sorry you had to find out this way," Sachi said a few days later after Suzue had finished recounting the dramatic events of the night she had discovered her biological father's identity.

The pillars had gathered at a new Italian restaurant in trendy Omote Sando to celebrate Sachi's 36th birthday with wine and good Italian food. The queue was long, because the restaurant was new and well-reviewed, but that had been worth it because the food was superb.

"We're officially old," Tomoko declared as they raised their glasses for a toast. "Remember those days when birthdays would be celebrated with pub crawling and dirty dancing in "metallic" discos till the early hours of the morning and then staggering into the first train to go home—bleary eyed and makeup running? Just look at us now, a trio of obasan tachi—old ladies—sedately drinking wine and gulping down Italian food! What happened to our perpetual dieting and picking on finger food and comparing stick thin arms?"

"Hang on, Tomo, I take great objection to your branding us as obasan tachi!" Sachi protested. "I'd much rather think of us as three successful, sophisticated ladies who have acquired a taste for fine food and living and best of all—can afford it!"

Sachi and Tomoko had been so busy ribbing each other that they hadn't noticed that Suzue was unusually quiet and her usually caustic tongue didn't seem to be working. But it was only when they were waiting for their dessert that Suzue brought out her Iphone and passed it around.

"What do you think of this man on my Iphone?" she had asked.

"Distinguished and acceptably good looking, but nothing extraordinary that catches the eye," Sachi replied, passing the phone to Tomoko.

"I like his salt and pepper hair and smile but his eyes look kind of sad," Tomoko commented, peering intensely at the grainy picture. It had been a long day at work and her contacts were drying up and blurring her vision so she couldn't see very clearly.

"What if I tell you that this man is my biological father?"

"What?" Sachi and Tomoko burst out almost simultaneously. "If this is a joke, it's not funny!" Tomoko added.

"That's what I said too, till I heard it from the very person who should know — my mother," Suzue replied.

"But how, when and where? You know, of course, he's an American who lives 10,000 miles from Japan?" Tomoko asked, peering at the face on Suzue's Iphone and the caption beneath it with greater interest and intensity.

"Well, how? The usual way. They met, fell in love, had unprotected sex and an accident I guess. Where? When he was posted on the US military base in Japan. When? In the 1970s... " Suzue replied and proceeded to tell them about the surreal experience of turning on the TV and being told that a stranger on the screen was her father and that his blood flowed in her veins.

"Oh my God, I don't know what to say! You've shocked and awed me into incoherence," Sachi said. "But whether you agree or not right now, Suzue, this is the best birthday present you have given me today. The identity of your missing father has cast a bigger shadow than you will admit on your life. I hope that at least this will give you some peace and closure to the nagging questions surrounding your identity and roots."

"Yes and no — because now you have the problem of deciding whether you want to contact your father, given he doesn't know you exist at all," Tomoko said. "Are you going to contact him, Suzue? Fortunately or unfortunately, he's a public figure and it will be very easy to find him."

"Frankly, I really haven't decided what to do," Suzue replied. "Of course, the immediate impulse is to take a plane to the United States and "claim" my father, but you know, I was just looking at a family picture of him, his wife and their two children and they look so happy. They seem like a loving and wholesome family, and I find it hard to burst that bubble of happiness and completeness that my own family never had. I rationalize that one family has already been destroyed, and there's no need to destroy another. Then I get angry and ask myself why I would care so much about a person who destroyed my mother's life and made mine a difficult and stigmatized one. In a sense, finding out who he is closed one can of worms but opened up another, so it's really a no-win situation."

"But, Suzue, to be fair, you're forgetting one thing: He never knew about you and still doesn't know about you, so it's unfair to insist he walked away from you," Tomoko said. "Maybe you should discreetly try to contact him without disrupting his family life. After all, you just seek recognition of your parentage and don't want anything else from him. You're a very successful woman in your own right, Suzue, and anyone would be proud to be your father!"

"I wouldn't be too sure about that!" Suzue replied. "Imagine a guy with everything he has — an up-and-coming political career, a sterling reputation, decades of illustrious service in the military behind him, a picture-perfect family... well, as far as I can see anyway... to suddenly have an illegitimate daughter sprung on him — how do you expect this guy to react? Welcome his illegitimate daughter with open arms and declare her to the whole world? I don't think so. And that's what I'm afraid of, Tomoko — rejection. I'm afraid of being the skeleton in someone's closet and bringing bad news and bad publicity to him."

"Well, it's a risk, Suzue," Tomoko said. "And I've never known you to be afraid of taking risks! That's what made you in the first place!"

"Yes," Sachi agreed. "Remember the Walker and Nobuto accounts? No agency would touch them because they believed Walker was so beaten up it would never rear its head again and Naruto was too small to be worth even a sniff. But you saw the potential and took a calculated risk on them and you made them turn around and grow. Now everyone is fighting for their business but they will never go to anyone but you. It's even in their "constitution" — that the business will stay with your agency as long as you remain on the board of directors. It's your branding, Suzue — you're an astute risk taker with the golden Midas touch! "

"Thank you, arigato, for your never failing confidence in me, but you're forgetting something here, Sachi. There is no emotional quotient involved in dealings with clients like Walker or Nobuto except, perhaps, the triumphant feeling of proving everyone else wrong. But here, we're talking about a parent and child reconnection package which is guaranteed to come with deep, overwhelming emotions that will be harder to handle or forget especially if things turn out badly," Suzue replied.

"Yes, of course, I do see where you're coming from but then again, have you considered that it may be unfair to let this man, Roger Carlista, die without ever knowing that he had another daughter?" Tomoko persisted, refusing to let Suzue go without facing all of the facts and realities.

Exasperated, Suzue took out her iPhone again and said, "Before you both get too carried away with this sentimental rhetoric, take another good look at Roger Carlista's picture. Do you honestly think he remembers his time in Japan with my mother, much less think about whether that time produced any consequences? When he was talking about his stint with the US forces in Japan, his face did not show any emotions at all. It was as if he was talking about a business posting and that was it!"

"Well, that is the public face he shows," Sachi said. "Who knows what feelings and memories lay behind that face? I'm a firm believer of the saying that "behind every face is a story." Some lives and some stories are more dramatic than others but we all have stories which we hide behind our public faces."

"I give up on you two," Suzue sighed, exasperated. "Both of you are not making this easier! Come on, show me some spirit here! Tell me I have nothing in common with this man except our genetic material, and now that I have put a face and an identity to the missing link in my life, let it go. Tell me that, girls, because *that* is what I want to hear!"

"No, Suzue," Tomoko shook her head. "It's complicated, that's for sure, but you know very well that is not what you want to hear! You want to have the assurance that if you go look for your father, you will not be rejected. More than anything else in the world, you want to go up to him and say 'Hi, I'm your daughter from your Japanese lover, Rumiko Tanaka from your US military base days in Japan—remember her?'

"But you're afraid to take the risk in case you see a look of horror, disbelief, fear or rejection on his face. That would put a nail on the coffin of your own fledgling belief that, among a thousand bad and selfish men, there are at least a couple of good ones."

"The hell you are right, Tomoko," Suzue shouted, lowering her voice only when she realized their fellow diners were becoming involved in their heated discussion. "I want to go up to Roger Carlista and tear out whatever little hair he has and force him to remember Rumiko, whose life he ruined because when he made his input during his "stint" in Japan, he never looked back to check whether there was any consequental output! I want him to know the years of embarrassment and social stigma he put my mother and me through; my battle against rejection only stopped when I became too successful to be ignored and rejected. And most of all, I want to yell at him and tell him that next time you want to do a "stint" in Japan, Daddy, wear a proper condom! My God, how I want to kill that man!"

"No, you don't want to kill him," Sachi said quietly. "More than anything else, you want to love him and have him accept you with open arms and make up for all the lost years of not being in your life. You don't need a famous or rich father, you just want a father! That's what you really want."

"It would be easier to acknowledge him if Roger Carlista weren't such a prominent man and an up and coming political figure. He can't afford to have a scandal, and his opponents would love to get their hands on something to blow out of proportion and discredit him," Tomoko added. "Can you imagine how the women, in particular, in his strait-laced religious community with holier-than-thou family values will judge Roger Carlista if any of this becomes public?"

"Yes, and given that he was never told about me and therefore didn't intentionally abandon me, I should not be the one to destroy his life and his political career. So perhaps I should just learn to live with a vicarious father that I know and keep in touch with through TV appearances. It'll be hard to see him on TV and feel nothing; maybe I should just unsubscribe CNN International and stick to Japanese news networks so at least I will never have Roger Carlista suddenly appearing any time he wants, to mess up my day or night as the case may be."

"That seems to be the most practical decision but we all know that sometimes the head says one thing but the heart says another. Even the toughest person sometimes can't resist the pull of the heart. And what about Robert? Do you intend to tell him or keep him out again like you did with the Mori saga?" As usual, Tomoko was the one to ask the sticky questions that Suzue would rather keep under wraps.

"Thanks for reminding me that Robert is another complication in my life," she sighed. "My head tells me I should just let him go and return to my days of uninvolved affairs and expiration dates—but my heart tells me I don't want to let him go. Men—whether they be your father, your brother or your boyfriend— always spell trouble! I should know better!"

A burst of the classic "Happy Birthday" song from the next table reminded the pillars that they had been celebrating Sachi's birthday before Suzue's shocking announcement eclipsed everything else.

"Oh gosh, I'm sorry, Sachi," Suzue said. "I've been casting such a long shadow over what was supposed to have been a merry night of eating and drinking to celebrate your birthday with you. Tell you what, let's forget Roger Carlista, that wretched man and move on to one of those mad, bad Roppongi bars. Maybe we'll do something wicked like chatting up a guy or two, raising their expectations, you know, below the waist, and then giving them chaste good night kisses before walking off. They'll be so pissed off, I'm sure our backs will be smoking like hell fires as we walk off! That should be fun, like when we first started pub crawling every weekend till we got freaking sick of it!"

"The Roppongi bars—best panacea for pain! As they say "Have problems, hit the bars!" Tomoko laughed. "Come on, let's go."

# CHAPTER 25

For a whole week after her mother and grandmother went back to Kyushu, Suzue didn't have time to think of anything but work; not even of her newfound father, Roger Carlista. She was glad for the distraction provided by working on a major pitch for a new financial services account, one that the Board of Directors had approved for her team with a generous budget.

The next three weeks saw Suzue working alongside her team for an insane number of hours. Tempers would flare, many lunches and dinners would be missed or eaten at bizarre times and some nights, she would make them all sleep at the office. Suzue was sure that by the time they finished the project she would be so hated that someone would murder her if if he or she could get away with it. She only let up on "night duty" when Ken, the well-known hen-pecked member of her team, pleaded that his wife was threatening divorce if he slept another night at the office.

"That guy is so hen-pecked I would probably be doing him a favor if his wife divorces him!" Suzue complained to Robert on a rare night eating out together. It had been so crazy at work that they hadn't been able to do anything more than grab a sandwich, and it was a real blessing that Robert was in the same line and understood the crazy hours during the peak of a major pitch.

"I'm probably the most hated person to my team right now, and if they believed in voodoo, they would have made a voodoo doll in my image and stuck needles right into my heart!"

"Vivid imagination as usual — that's my Suzue," Roger laughed, happy that they were finally alone.

"It doesn't worry me at all, all this fire and steam spouting out of everyone's nostrils, it's normal," Suzue replied. "As soon as the pitch is over and in particular, when we are awarded the account, you'll see all this angst against me just melting away in the heady euphoria of success and sense of achievement. Happens all the time, as sure as the sun rises and sets each day!"

It was a beautiful night of twinkling city lights with just a hint of frost in the air, and it was only natural that the two overworked but intimacy-starved young professionals would snuggle up as they headed towards Robert's apartment after dinner. "You don't want to go to my place tonight," Suzue said as they were tossing a coin on whose apartment it would be. "It's in a holy mess and would definitely not set the right romantic mood for a night of very indecent exposure!"

"Are you kidding? An untidy apartment wouldn't stop me and after a hiatus of, what, three weeks from any form of intimacy with you — I would take you right here on the sidewalk if it wasn't against the law!" Robert replied.

Suzue gave him one of her special punches — the ones that she had learned in self defense classes and that really hurt — but she was smiling and really happy for the first time in a long while. She loved the way Robert was completely open about his feelings and desire for her and the way he appreciated her voracious sexual appetite with a passion and intensity that made her feel strangely loved. In fact, with Robert, she could behave like a complete slut and yet not feel like one and she discovered that night that the longer they abstained from physical intimacy, the greater and more intense their eventual reunion.

"You know, Robert, the way we made love tonight was so intense and so, you know, desperate with all the raw desire of three weeks' abstinence, it has set me thinking that maybe we should do this more often — take longer breaks from each other," Suzue said. "I know it's unconventional and a departure from the "couple thing" but who says we have to do the same things everybody else does?"

"I totally agree with you on this one because I don't think we can achieve this depth and level of exquisite pleasure and passion if we are at it almost every day!" Robert agreed. "I remember my mother telling me that after some time, my father went from a challenging and creative manual mode to auto pushing all the right buttons mode and eventually, he even started pushing all the wrong buttons! It was at that point that she told him to stop pushing *any* buttons and just leave her alone!"

Robert's droll analogy of his father's fall from sexual grace made Suzue laugh and she only sobered when she was reminded of her own father and the big question that had been plaguing her of whether she should tell Robert about Roger Carlista or keep him out again.

"It makes me think that someday if I do have to go back to U.K., we could still manage to email, chat and skype our relationship across the great divide and, whenever we meet, there would be no need to push any buttons — they would start flashing and buzzing all on their own! Maybe long distance is the answer to the question of how we can keep our passion alive and burning bright ten, twenty years from now!"

For the last couple of weeks, there had been rumblings in the U.K. for him to return to the London office where he was very much needed to beef up the digital department and oversee the Tokyo digital team he had revamped from London. Just 18 months ago, Robert would have jumped at the idea of transferring back to London but then Suzue had come into his life and, all right, he had to admit it, Japan had gotten into his system as so many of his work mates and friends who had experienced stints in Japan had warned him it would.

Mike Barnaby, his friend from grammar school days, was a classic example. When Mike first came to Japan, he hated everything from the raw fish and disgusting fermented soy beans they called "food," to the Japanese way of saying "No" when they meant "Yes." He felt like a huge lumbering oaf beside his impeccably mannered, well-dressed, soft-spoken and bowing Japanese counterparts. Everything and everyone baffled him and the inability to communicate made him feel isolated and he had to run for cover to the "know all" "seen all" "done all" expatriate community he disliked.

The list of complaints went on in Japan-bashing emails sent to Robert regularly, almost always culminating in the "I can't wait to get back to the U.K." rhetoric. But in Mike's second year in Japan, his emails became fewer and his list of complaints had subtly changed to glowing accounts of trips to fascinating mountain resorts and his droll first experience of stripping naked in a Japanese onsen or hot spring and being the center of the surreptitious side glances of his Japanese fellow "bathers." All of a sudden, things, places, people and even food that had been irritating became quaint, stimulating and "zenfully" refreshing.

Robert waited for the inevitable female name to creep in and it did in the form of Mayumi, a "friend" from a subsidiary company he had met on a year-end company skiing trip. Within months, Mayumi helped Mike change his views about Japan and the Japanese people. When his company ordered his rotation to the United States, Mike did the unthinkable. He resigned and set up an English language school in Mayumi's hometown of Omiya which tapped into young Japanese men and women's thirst to learn English, even if they refused to speak it. Eventually, the school turned into a thriving chain of four schools in the region.

The following year, Mike proposed to Mayumi and Robert combined attending his friend's wedding with a preliminary "inspection" of Tokyo, where he was due to be transferred in a matter of months.

When he arrived in Japan, Robert not only had the "cultural shock" faced by most first timers to the country, he was also dumbstruck by the transformation of his childhood friend. The erstwhile, diehard English gentleman who swore by casual dressing was actually speaking passable Japanese and bowing correctly to him!

"I know this isn't much of a greeting but look at your clothes, old bloke," Robert couldn't help saying. "You're actually wearing a tie and a long sleeve proper shirt like the Japanese salary men we used to watch on TV and laugh about!"

"The price I have to pay for going into the language school business here; I have to dress real proper because my pool of students are salary men and women looking to learn what is popularly known here as 'business English,'" Mike replied a little sheepishly. "But on my days off with Mayumi, we dress real scruffy!"

"A Japanese girl dressing scruffily? You're kidding of

course!" Robert replied. "Remember how we use to call them little Audrey Hepburns with their tiny waists and sun dresses?"

If Robert thought that was all Mike had become, he was in for a shock and he could only watch in amazement as his sworn English-patriot friend ate unagi, Japanese eel, sashimi, raw fish and even natto, the gluey fermented beans Robert had called simply "yuck." And Mike ate it with chopsticks as if he had been doing that all his life!

Had one single woman called Mayumi done all this to Mike? And she was just your average Japanese girl, all five foot one inch of soft-spoken sweetness with a porcelain skin that any skincare promoter would die to have. "But all that softness and graciousness, it's just gift wrap for a tiny woman of steel and amazing business sense. Mayumi is one of the reasons why what started as just one school has grown so big," Mike explained. "She's incredible, 50 kg of positive energy and endurability wrapped up in that demure package! I can't explain it but it's just a Japanese thing! And it's not only the women — look at the men too! Little dynamos, an average 5' 2" or 5' 3", the amazing brains behind the technology that produces all those brand name products and cars used the world over!"

"Michael Barnaby is smitten and a woman has got the better of you after all!"

"Yes and no," Michael replied. "I'm crazy about Mayumi and all that but I meant it when I said Japan grows on you after a couple of I-can't-wait-to-get-out-of-this-place years. Although interest in a woman is the main reason for staying on in a lot of cases, I've also known guys who sink their roots in here simply because Japan has gotten under their skin and they don't want to leave."

Robert sighed as he thought of Michael's amazing integration into Japan and his own possible return to London. He felt Suzue's fingers running through his hair, still damp from the sweat of their earlier passion and she said, "I might have something to tell you if you promise not to be shocked or even if you are, if you do a very good job of hiding it."

"I'm good at taking shocks from you," Robert quipped. "You're always full of surprises and the unpredictable and that's what I find so special about you. Spend a night with my little minx, Suzue Tanaka, get hit by a sandbag and leave the next morning insanely happy and as in love as ever! How is that possible, but it is with you! Come on, hit me with it and let's see if I survive this new sandbag!"

"Ok, don't say I didn't warn you!" Suzue replied and although she was smiling, the smile didn't quite reach her eyes and Robert sobered up, sensing that Suzue's "sandbag" this time was important.

"Robert, I found my father and he's living in the United States."

"Did you say you found your father? I don't understand. I thought you said your father died when you were a baby."

"I lied about it, Robert," Suzue replied simply, typically offering no apology for lying. "It just seemed less complicated at the time to say he's dead instead of going into the whole rigmarole of explaining that he was an officer with the U.S. forces in Japan and got into what I hope was, at least, a love affair with my mother which produced me. It was easier to think of him as dead and tell everyone that. After all, I thought that chapter of my life was closed and after donating his sperm to my mother, the scumbag had jumped ship and would never resurface again!"

"Oh my God, I never knew, Suzue," Robert replied and his voice was filled with the intense emotions he felt for her. "Of all the sandbags you have ever thrown at me, this is the hardest. But amidst the pain of knowing how you must have suffered in silence all these years, is a little glimmer of hope because you said you "found" your father?"

"Yes, I did but there's more. You know, I spent my entire life, till now, hating my "no show" father and that hatred intensified as I grew up and saw my mother and grandmother struggling to bring me up. There was societal stigma, financial constraints as well as the silent pain of my mother for the price she had to pay for falling in love. Then there was my own pain of growing up without a father and being an ainoko. My dusky skin and curly hair set me apart from the other Japanese kids and always put me on the edge of the circle of acceptance, looking in. No matter how hard I tried, I could never fit in with that glaring "foreign" stamp on my body, and it made me really bitter!

"I grew up tough, fighting with kids who called me an "ainoko" and then having to hide from my mother and grandmother the cuts, bruises and the occasional nose bleeds from such scuffles because I didn't want my mother, in particular, to cry again for bringing me into this world, different and stigmatized.

"My mother was always feeling bad about causing me so much pain in my childhood and sensitive teen years, and I watched her pay a very heavy price all her life for loving a man unconditionally. Although the subject was taboo and never discussed, it did cast a very heavy and dark shadow over the whole house and sometimes I would just try to make myself feel better by making up stories about my father. One time, it would be that he died saving my pregnant mother from danger, another time it would be a car accident or falling over a cliff, anything, just to make myself feel better. But it was always there, the fish bone which gets stuck in your throat and refuses to go down, no matter how many glasses of water you drink to flush it out.

"I think it greatly affected my feelings for and about men and the existence of love. As if this was not enough, everything was further exacerbated when I was 12 years old and discovered that my mother worked in a hostess club in Ginza, entertaining rich men, to put food on our table and make sure that I had everything the other kids at school had. That, Robert, is where I got all my angst and expiration dates from. I was really quite a messed up kid!"

Again, it was on the tip of Suzue's tongue to tell Robert about her own hostessing and escort agency days but she stopped herself. One sandbag at a time was enough because a man could only take so many sandbags a day!

She felt his arms around her holding her tight but he didn't say anything, sensing that she needed to talk everything out of her system but didn't necessarily need any comments, and Suzue was moved by his silent support. She felt her own heart constrict and for a moment, she closed her eyes, feeling the comforting warmth of his body seeping into her, slowly unknotting all the tense muscles and tight emotions of a trying time.

Swallowing hard, Suzue continued determinedly but there

was a catch in her voice. She made no excuse for the intensity of her emotions; after all, it was not every day that a woman discovered her long-lost biological father and found the courage to talk about him!

"Three weeks ago, when my mother and grandmother were down here, we were just horsing around one night and I happened to turn on the cable news on my TV. Imagine how I felt when my mother, for no apparent reason, suddenly broke down over a news conference. I looked very closely at that stranger on TV, and I saw myself in his face, the eyes, the nose, that hair… Robert, my blood just turned ice cold and froze.

"I have always hated to see my mother cry but I was determined to get it out of her this time. I felt she owed it to me to understand that I needed closure to the question of who is my father. I had a double whammy that night when she socked it to me that my father was that prominent politician on TV and that he had never abandoned us. In fact, he tried to take my mother back to the U.S., but she had refused to leave Japan and he never knew about her pregnancy or of my existence.

"At that moment, I was just so overwhelmed with emotions I didn't know where to turn or what to say. What exactly did I feel about the way my mother had taken our lives into her own hands and decided on our destinies without giving my father a choice? I should have been angry but I couldn't because I knew she had done what she thought was best for us. She was much younger than I am now, with a widowed mother to care for and the father of her child was over 10,000 miles away and she didn't even know how to find him. My God, Robert, she must have felt so alone and terrified, so she did the best she could. How could I be angry with her?"

Robert's arms around her tightened and she felt his breath as he whispered against her hair, "If you were not Suzue Tanaka, I would ask how did you manage to keep all this to yourself for so long? But you are Suzue, so I won't ask that question but just tell you how much I admire and respect you for your incredible spirit and strength."

"Thanks for saying that, my darling, but my experiences so early in life have also made me hard and cynical. Perhaps you can understand better now why I find it so hard to trust and to love. But that same hardness and cynicism have also made me so resilient to all the hard knocks in life that every time I fell or someone pushed me down, I got up again, angrier and stronger than before. It has kept me going through all the years I was finding my own place in Japan."

Suzue sighed as she ran her fingers down Robert's lean muscular thighs, "I've had other experiences you really don't want to know about. I'm really complicated and messed up and I have bizarre ideas about relationships so maybe you really shouldn't love me because I would most certainly complicate your life."

"I don't have a crystal ball so I really don't know what kind of future we will have, but you're all I want and you should know by now that I'm not afraid of complications and have quite a few bizarre habits and needs myself. Don't you see, we're like my mother's cracked pot and cracked lid, a perfect fit together!"

Suzue smiled despite herself. Robert was just impossible! He would always come up with droll analogies to make her laugh and smile even in the most dire situations. Cracked pot and cracked lid indeed! But she had to admit that it was a very apt analogy for both of them.

"I hope, Suzue, that knowing your father didn't abandon you as such—he simply never knew about you— will help heal some of the scars that have shaped your life, for better or for worse," Robert continued. "There's no pressure or deadline; just love me if and when you can and in any way you want."

Suzue sighed deeply. Where would she ever find a man like Robert again? And yet why was she so tight-fisted about giving love and sharing her feelings with him? She wished he wouldn't make her feel guilty by loving her so much! God, Robert was just so darn good, and she didn't know how to handle her feelings for good men.

All the men she had ever known had been as selfish and egocentric as she herself was with them. Her father, who hadn't taken the trouble to find out if he had left any baggage back in Japan but had simply moved on with his life and forgotten her mother. Her first boyfriend, who had wanted mostly sex from her. Then there was Mori and the other men of her escort days who didn't expect her or any of the women they paid for to have feelings or needs, they were just commodities. Then there were the string of part-time lovers she had dallied with, to de-stress, as she climbed on a very fast track up the corporate ladder. They had simply taken from each other what they needed and gave nothing in return. That had suited Suzue fine and it was a breeze to handle such egocentric men and take what she wanted from them. Last but not least, there were the condescending men at work who treated her as a joke and no threat because she was a woman — until she showed them what substance she was made of as she sailed past them up the ladder of promotions.

But then Robert had come along and for the first time in her life, a man gave her something and didn't even expect anything in return. God knew she didn't want to lose this man and the way he made her feel really good about herself, rough diamond, angst and all. But she was having a problem getting out of a lifetime of being in survival mode. And trust was not on the agenda.

"So are you going to contact your father? And if I may give my two-cents worth, I just feel that he should know that he has a daughter in Japan. In the same situation I would definitely want to know," Robert's voice cut into her thoughts and she was glad he had steered them away from a difficult and sensitive topic even though it was to another equally complicated area.

"I'm just not focusing on that right now. Maybe I will at some point in the future but you know, Robert, my father is Roger Carlista, a United States Senator. I happened to find a family picture of this Roger Carlista and his family on Google images and they look so happy together I almost feel I should just let it go and leave them alone. It's like, what's the point of stirring a hornet's nest and getting so many people hurt and stung?" Suzue replied.

That night, Suzue stayed over at Robert's apartment and they alternated between sensual love making and moments propped up on their pillows just talking quietly. The next day was Black Monday (the dreaded first day of the work week). Though Suzue broke with her tradition of always sleeping by 10.30 p.m. the night before Black Monday, the next morning she woke up energized nonetheless because her mind and body were at peace.

"Perhaps we should do this sleepover on Sunday nights more often," she quipped as they started to dress for the day.

"Strangely, I feel fresher than after those 10:30 p.m. curfews I've been imposing on myself all these years! You must be good for me, Robert Darcey!"

# CHAPTER 26

It was the first time the normally even-tempered Sachi had raised her voice at her assistant over a minor hitch in their week-long fashion show arrangements and the girl had run off crying.

"Why are all these young girls so sensitive these days? They have egos a mile high and skin eggshell thin!" she complained, exasperated, to Tomoko who had called to introduce a client interested in her fashion label. "Look at Momo chan; she wants to be a fashion buyer one day. How is she ever going to survive the sharks crowding the sea of this industry if she buckles every time I raise my voice? I've tried to toughen her up but I guess I'm not as good or effective a mentor as Suzue. Look at how she has shaken up her PA, Fumiko!"

"Maybe it's because, unlike Suzue who is known to have a sharp tongue and is happy to use it at the drop of a hat, you are normally so kind to Momo so it's harder for her to take it when you become this irritable," Tomoko replied. "Anyway, you don't sound too good yourself, Sachi. I've known you long enough to spot the 'something's bothering me' vibes you are giving out today. If anything is up and you want to share, just unload on me, O.K.? Being a lawyer, I'm a good listener. It's my job, after all!"

"It's my parents again," Sachi sighed. "Recently, they've upped the pressure on me to marry and start a family. The hilarious part about this is that before, the nagging was for me to 'marry a man who is prepared to take our family surname because you are the only child and there's no one else to carry on the Ishikawa surname' — but now, it's 'just get married as long as he's educated and has a good job.' He doesn't even have to come from a good family anymore! Can you believe it, Tomoko? I'm up for grabs!"

"Yes, I can understand how that can depress any self-respecting woman, especially one as self-sufficient and successful as you," Tomoko replied. "You just have to let it all fall on deaf ears and stay away till they get tired of it. That's what I did to my mother, till she gave up on me as totally unmarriageable and moved on to her current campaign of nagging me to save for my old age! If she finds out that I'm occasionally living with a Japanese-American "gaijin" outside of holy matrimony, she'll freak out! Perhaps that's what you should do, Sachi; just ignore them till they get sick of it. They have to stop at some point!"

"You don't know my parents, especially my mother; she never gives up! My cousin just quipped that even when I'm 60 years old, if she's still talking and walking, she'll have 60 to 65-year-old widowers and divorcees lined up for me!

"And now on top of all that, my dad has terminal stomach cancer and it's his wish to see me married before he passes on. I guess that's why my mother has upped the pressure tenfold! I don't know how Japanese parents think that putting pressure on their kids to marry will achieve a result; it's not like you can just go out to the streets or a "spouse store" to get a husband with a lifetime warranty of, if not happiness — because that would be too much to ask — at least, compatibility. And yesterday, my mother suggested using an omiai to introduce some "suitable" guy to me! All this on top of one of my most important fashion shows this year! So tell me, doesn't a woman under such pressure have the right to snap at her assistant?

"It's not that my parents have ever prevented me from having a career or anything like that; in fact, without my father's quite substantial financial contribution, I would never have been able to start this fashion house. But it's almost like my mother, especially, is telling me 'We've indulged your dream to be a fashion designer, now go get married!"

"It's not that I'm dead set against marriage or anything like that but my fashion house is just taking off and going places and marriage, kids and domestic problems will just hold me back. You know what it's like in Japan, there's just so little childcare support for career women because I guess women are expected to give up working to be stay home wives and mothers. Honestly, how many young women with a focus on their careers want to get married and have children? And the government rumbles on and on about the falling birth rate in Japan and does very little to address the real problem here!"

"If it's any consolation to you, the guys get it from their families as well," Tomoko replied. "My cousin is 35 and since he turned 30, his family has been subtly parading girls before him. But you know what? He's totally gay, always has been, and he's been with a partner for five years! He's had to live with this lie because his family will never accept it. In fact, I think they'd rather him dead than gay! Sometimes I just feel so sorry for his parents; all that effort to source out suitable girls for him for nothing!"

"Some consolation that is!" Sachi grimaced. "Perhaps I should go along with this omiai thing just to shut my mother up. I could agree to see some of the guys 'on display' and then reject every one of them till even the omiai gives up on me."

"Yes, Sachi, turn this obsession of your mother's into an interesting chess game—just have a spot of fun with these people!" Tomoko replied. "I used to think this Japanese matchmaking thing happening right here in the 21st century was disgusting, predatory, meat-market nonsense that should have stayed in the Meiji era. But, come to think of it, it's just like any of the online dating agencies flooding the internet. Some of the most respectable people use it to find potential friends and marriage partners, that's all."

\*\*\*\*\*

But whatever domestic woes she had, Sachi didn't let it affect her work and that season, she wowed the fashion world with her collection and a new label she had added to her young fashion empire. At the end of the season, Sachi swept up at least two 'young designers' awards and made so many waves that even snooty veteran fashion houses wanted to know who she was.

"My goodness, I'm so proud of Sachi and she looks just ravishing tonight," Suzue said as both she and Tomoko sat in special front-row seats at the biggest fashion bash of the year, watching the normally publicity-averse Sachi receive her awards and make a short speech with the confidence of a veteran public speaker. Of the pillars, Sachi had been the least successful, not because she was any less talented, but because her industry was just so competitive, and Suzue and Tomoko were glad all her persistence and hard work had finally paid off in this "made it at last" recognition of her talent.

"And to think her parents want her to give up or at least compromise all this hard-earned limelight by getting married and having kids, with very little solution in sight on how to manage both bringing up kids and a full-time, highly competitive career," Tomoko whispered back loudly, trying to make herself heard above the roar of applause.

The catwalk came alive with spotlights again and the models started sashaying down its red carpet, showing off Sachi's creations on their long, lean bodies and banishing all thoughts or discussions of husbands, babies, marriages and omiais as Tomoko and Suzue sat on the edges of their chairs, completely fascinated by this evidence of their friend's awesome talent.

"My goodness, Sachi, compared to the glamour of your industry—although I love it and wouldn't give it up for all the world—my job is just dirt and grit!" Tomoko complained much later when the three had adjourned to a nearby bar for drinks after the show. Sachi knew she probably should have attended the post-show party to network and suck up to all the right people, but in the end, she decided to seek the restful company of the pillars instead, declaring that she just couldn't face another night of superficial "smile to dazzle and kill." Fashion and creating fashion was in her blood and would never go away, but there was very little sincerity or even kindness in the people who made the industry tick. Instead, there was always this shoving and pushing to be noticed by the right people, to stay in the limelight and be on top of everyone else. Nevertheless it was the hard, brittle world that Sachi loved, a platform to launch and showcase her talent.

"You were sensational tonight, Sachi," Tomoko said. "Did you see how the international big names and Who's Who of the fashion world were simply captivated by your collection? You should be at the bash hobnobbing with them and not here, chainsmoking with just the old girls!"

"Oh, it's fine. There will be another bigger and even more

glittering affair tomorrow night, and I'll go to that one," Sachi replied. "One 'bash' per fashion show is all I can take or my facial muscles will be frozen into a perpetual smile!"

"You have a very special talent and you must never give that up, no matter how much pressure your family gives you to go get married and shore up our nation's plummeting birthrate," Suzue said. "Someday soon, we want to see your name and clothes on giant billboards, marquee-like displays and high-class fashion magazine covers, not only in Japan but the world over. I'll create an ad for you that will make you blush and everyone else sit up!"

"Coming from you, I can well believe that!" Sachi laughed, softening the lines of stress on her face. "I've kept almost every single one of your ads and they all make statements that are hard to ignore. Remember the one you did for the mega sex toy company?"

"Yes, I don't know how I had the cheek to come out with that one! I heard it was banned or at least debated in some countries, but you know what? It is generating so many sales they keep pestering me to come up with more daring ideas – as if I were a sex toy guru! On the plus side, they have doubled our fees and extended our account indefinitely, so I'm not complaining!"

"What do you think of our die-hard omiai matchmaking system, Suzue?" Sachi asked this unrelated question suddenly as they each lit up to their eighth cigarette, even Tomoko, who was usually a very light, occasional smoker.

"Well, you know my take on the marriage institution generally, and the omiai system in Japan is serious business to get couples hitched up for marriage. There's not much wriggle room for those who just want to meet people for friendship, dating, even casual sex like those internet dating sites," Suzue replied. "It's customer service, basically, serving up human marriageable meat as the main course. But it did serve its purpose, in the past, because there was no way men and women could meet freely and find each other for love. And these days, it still serves a purpose because many young people are too busy to go through the tiresome, time consuming meet, date and court ritual towards marriage."

"Two of my girlfriends got married through an omiai," Tomoko said, her face a little red from the heavy smoking she was not used to but was determined to conquer, at least for the night. "I followed them through the whole process and thankfully escaped totally unscathed to go on to law school! The whole thing was quite artfully and graciously done, you know, softly persuasive without seeming to put any pressure at all! But everyone concerned knows just how much unspoken pressure there really was! Our PR people can certainly learn a thing or two from those little old matchmaking ladies!"

"Anyway, why this sudden interest in omiais?" Suzue asked Sachi. "Don't tell me your mother's infamous 'mating instinct' is rearing its head again?"

Sachi nodded, blowing out cigarette smoke in angry swirls. Her clothes and demeanor was totally at odds with the traditional world of matchmaking and the kimono clad, deceptively demure matchmakers that were trying to claim her.

"I like the way you put it, Suzue. Unfortunately, yes, my mother is starting her mating call again!" Sachi sighed. "In fact, this long weekend, she's arranging for an omiai to come to the house. Of course, I can put my foot down and say no, and although she may rant and use all kinds of psychological blackmail to make me feel bad, there's nothing much she could do about it. But I've decided to let her carry on just to humor her because she's had a really rough time dealing with my father's cancer, and maybe she just needs a diversion from hospitals, blood tests and the pall of sickness and death."

"It might be fun though, stringing a few guys along and taking the illustrious omiai with them," Suzue suggested. "After all, you don't have to touch the merchandise or go beyond the first date. I wouldn't have minded sending an omiai or two on a wild goose chase, but fortunately or unfortunately, I was never omiai material. Any self-respecting family with a well-groomed son to promote has only to look at my bio to turn tail and run!"

Suzue paused before continuing. "I would imagine my bio would go like this: 'Suzue Tanaka, father unknown, of mixed racial origin and unique appearance. Please, someone, anyone, give her a chance!'"

"You're impossible and wicked, Suzue," Tomoko laughed. "With a bio like that, you would put any omiai out of business. All you need are these three phrases: "father unknown," "mixed racial origin," and "unique appearance" to send parents and bridegroom hopefuls running for cover!"

"All right, it's decided then," Sachi said when their laughter had subsided. "I'll spend this long weekend giving some omiai a good run for her money and return to Tokyo next Monday, triumphant and unscathed. After that, I don't think my mother will be in a hurry to ram another matchmaker down my throat again!"

# CHAPTER 27

As the sleek shinkansen train pulled out of Tokyo station, Sachi breathed a sigh of relief and settled back in the comfortable seat for the three-hour ride to her hometown of Matsumoto. It was a precious long weekend and the crowds of holiday makers cramming the mammoth Tokyo station had been hair-tearing crazy. Although Japanese commuters were usually very considerate and orderly, good manners went out the door and it was every man for himself during the weekday rush hours and the holiday season crush, especially for those commuters without reserved seats.

Normally, on her trips back home, Sachi envisioned the fresh mountain air and small town peace and calm even before she stepped on the train. But not this time; she was not looking forward to the trip home because of what Suzue called her mother's obsessive "mating instincts." Couldn't her parents understand that the budding fashion house was her life and her baby and she just couldn't cope with anything or anyone right now? It was so unfair that a woman in Japan always had to make this hard choice between career and marriage and starting a family while men could just get married and continue with their work, literally unencumbered. On the contrary, they gained wives to take care of their needs, from sexual right down to menial domestic chores, and to bear them children that they didn't even have to take care of.

It was not that Japanese husbands treated their wives badly or controlled them in any way; in fact, her mother wore the pants in the house as was quite the norm in most Japanese families. Ever since she could remember, her mother controlled almost everything in the house from the family kitty to what her father ate or wore! He became totally dependent on her and everyday he simply wore the clothes, even underwear, that she laid out for him in the morning!

"I guess to your mother, this is a good life — being queen of her home and lording it over the whole family. She just can't understand why a woman would want to go out and slave like the men! It's her way of protecting her daughter from the harsh world outside," Tomoko had once said.

"That may be so but I will never give up the work I love so much for even a marriage made in heaven, if such a thing exists at all," Sachi had replied . "If I ever do consider marriage, I've got to see what is in there for *me* — otherwise my mother can bark all she wants!"

Sachi was thinking of this conversation as she watched the much loved Mount Fuji peeping precociously out of a few wispy clouds dancing around her. Cameras snapped and flashed as scores of Japanese holiday travelers in her coach tried to capture the image of their beloved Fuji san from the fast train. No matter how many times they viewed or passed Mount Fuji, the same holiday travelers would snap away. It was almost an automatic response to the grace and beauty of Japan's most famous mountain.

Poor Suzue. Her life had been so tough with her family situation, the men who had used her and the doors that had closed on her because of her "unique appearance," and now there was the specter of her father coming back to haunt her and Robert Darcey staying in her life beyond the expiration date. Both situations demanded decisions and could potentially mess up a life Suzue had so carefully carved for herself.

Sachi remembered Suzue's famous quote about her journey to the top which she liked to repeat as if it were therapeutic: "Every time I received a hard knock or someone closed a door in my face in my formative years, I got angrier and it was that anger that drove me on. You know how it is; when you are in so much pain that your body and mind go numb and someone can cut you with a knife and you don't feel anything, even though you are gushing blood. I used to liken it to my mother's rhetoric about childbirth — that the pain is so great and numbing that a woman doesn't even feel anything much when her vagina is cut to enlarge it for the baby to come out. It's this oblivion to pain that makes me so strong. I will stop at nothing and no one to get what I want out of a life that has never given me anything for free."

Compared to Suzue, Sachi felt that her life had been relatively easy, and this current deadlock with her mother was nothing more than a hit on the knuckles that could be quite easily resolved because dating was something that was within her control and manipulation. But the minute she came out of the exit of Matsumoto station and Sachi saw her mother at the wicket, scanning the crowd of exiting passengers anxiously for her daughter, all her irritation for her family melted away. Her father had braved the crowds to come to the station too, against medical advice to stay away from crowded places during his cancer treatment. He stood quietly behind his wife, his eyes anxiously searching. His clothes hung loosely on a once robust frame and Sachi realized how sick he really was.

God, how long had it been since her last visit back to Matsumoto; it had to have been at least half a year! She had almost forgotten how clean the air was and how pleasant the smell of the abundant greenery and fields of orange trees with their luscious sun ripened fruit during the season.

After her small 2DK bachelor girl's pad in land-starved Tokyo, her parents' two-story bungalow house with its five bedrooms and a small garden seemed palatial.

"This house has so much space compared to my tiny, forty-five square meters apartment in Tokyo! Now, this is what I call a real home!" As soon as she had said this, Sachi could have bitten her tongue off because she had just given her mother enough rope to hang her.

"Then why don't you give up your job in Tokyo and return here? You will be able to have an even bigger house than this and I'm sure you can easily find a job," was her mother's immediate response.

"I'm in the high couture and fashion business, Mother, and Tokyo is the fashion nerve center of Japan," Sachi replied patiently. "Do you see a market for high fashion here?"

"Well, people in these parts like to dress up too. You could start a boutique here," her mother persisted. "Am I not right, Otoh san?"

Her husband nodded. In his condition, he would agree to anything just to avoid an argument with his wife.

*Poor father*, Sachi thought. *He hasn't had much of a life either. Maybe for husbands, too, marriage spells the end of a carefree life of drinking and messing up their own rooms and of having long-suffering mothers pick up after them. Maybe for men too, getting married is like entering into a gilded cage of having every need taken care of, in exchange for a loss of — ironically for the sole bread winner of most families — financial independence and having to develop sudden hearing loss against the drone of female nagging and whining.*

*"Take out the thrash!"*

*"Walk the dog!"*

*"It's your turn to take Sachi to the jyuku!"*

*"Ofuro, Otosan, and don't smoke in the living room!"*

These were childhood memories of her mother's voice.

*Grim exchange*, Sachi thought as she skillfully steered the conversation away from sensitive subjects by distracting her mother with the many presents she had brought back for her, in particular, a beautiful Hermes bag bought on a recent fashion show trip to Paris.

Sachi was allowed a complete day of rest, delicious home cooked meals of all her favorite dishes and even a night out in the local izakaya drinking beer, sake and wiping off plate after plate of izakaya fare made from the freshest vegetables and seafood from the region.

The following day, her mother broached the all-important subject of the omiai calling in the afternoon to see the family and have an informal chat.

"Just a social visit, Sachi, nothing really serious. You'll agree to see her, won't you? At least save me some face by doing that!" her mother pleaded, scanning Sachi's tight-lipped face anxiously.

"Like real it's a social visit; second day at home and the chess game has begun! I can feel my biological clock beating like a drum, not ticking!" she texted Suzue and Tomoko grimly.

But aloud, Sachi said calmly, "You know my sentiments on this subject, Mother, but, I'll sit in at your omiai meeting just to make you happy since you've already arranged it and I don't want to embarrass you. But that's the only reason why I'm agreeing."

Sachi told herself that perhaps the experience of a centuries-old Japanese tradition might even give her some ideas for her next fashion show. After all, the inspiration for her award-winning creations this year had come from watching dancing to Indian classical music at the opulent wedding of one of her Indian models.

As expected, the afternoon with the omiai turned out to be a painfully polite event with much bowing and scraping and layers of unnecessary protocol to wade through simply to secure a matchmaking deal.

"It's turning out to be a pain in the neck; too much dressing on the salad," Sachi texted Suzue. "You know what? I've no patience for these little old ladies and will jump ship the minute I can, without my mother losing her precious face, that is."

At some point, one of the little old ladies in an impeccably correct kimono with hair piled high on top of her head in a chignon, took out two photographs and laid them discreetly on the table, at an angle where Sachi could see the face on the photos without appearing to be looking too eagerly.

They were pictures of a youngish man with an arresting face. Not drop dead gorgeous or anything like that, but a face that was intelligent and engaging and for some strange reason, it caught Sachi's attention although she tried hard not to show it. Goodness, what made a personable young man like that go to an omiai to find a partner? Perhaps he was secretly gay?

"This is Jun Sawada Jun, a banker, from a very respectable background. You know the Sawada family, the owners of Sawada Tofu?" the omiai, Mrs. Miyamoto, was saying as she looked directly at Sachi. "I've shown him your photo and your bio and he's interested in meeting you tomorrow for an informal dinner.

"You can think it over and give me an answer by tomorrow morning," Mrs. Miyamoto continued in that hushed voice of hers, as if she were a funeral director talking to a bereaved family. Very cleverly, she did not push the matches but gave her clients space to think. To give the omiai due credit, the whole meeting ended so graciously Sachi found herself promising to give her answer by the following morning and it was only later that she realized she had been insidiously drawn into the matchmaking web.

"Me, Sachi, a fashion designer of no mean reputation, being

tricked by a small town matchmaker to consider going on what is actually a blind date?" she lamented to Suzue that night. "This is getting ridiculous, and the sooner I get back to Tokyo, the better for my sanity!

"And what gave my mother the right to give them my photos and bio without asking me? I should murder her for this!"

"I actually find it kind of exciting, going on a 'supervised' date at our age!" Suzue laughed. "Loosen up a bit, Sachi. Just have a spot of fun with this Sawada Jun and anyway, it's one way of passing away a night in a small town. Do you have anything else better to do by way of entertainment?"

In the end, Sachi caved in to her mother's pleas to just go and make a new friend, and, if nothing more, perhaps they could even get cheap tofu in the future!

It was no big deal to Sachi; after all, she met so many people in the course of her work, this man was just another person she had to meet, that was all. The only thing she insisted on was that the meeting be casual and informal, without the omiai hovering around. To press her point that it was just a casual meeting of a new friend and not a potential husband she had to impress, for the dinner with Sawada Jun, Sachi donned a pair of old jeans and a T-shirt that had seen better times, much to her mother's horror.

"At least put on a nice dress! Don't turn up looking scruffy like this, even if you're not interested in this whole thing," she scolded, but Sachi ignored her and went in her jeans and T-shirt anyway.

The place this Sawada Jun had selected for their first "date" was a bit of a surprise. It was a Mexican restaurant called "La Cantina" which turned out to be a rustic wooden log cabin with two huge cactus standing like sentries on each side of the entrance. Sachi didn't even know there was a Mexican restaurant in her sleepy hometown, let alone one as eccentric as this La Cantina place.

It was not a restaurant the kind of man who would use an omiai to find a wife would choose for a first meeting and Sachi had to admit that she was more than a little curious about this Sawada Jun.

As she pushed open the heavy wooden door, the sound of a husky voice crooning out Spanish love songs greeted her and Sachi looked around for a possible Sawada Jun among the crowd of diners already filling the restaurant. She had refused to conform to the omiai practice of being present at the first meeting to introduce the couple formally to each other because that would be too contrived. "Ridiculous! I refuse to be chaperoned as if I am a woman of the Meiji era," she had said firmly. "Do you know how many men I meet in the course of my work? To me, this Sawada Jun is just one more man, that's all, and having someone to introduce us "formally" is so contrived it's like selling a product!

Sachi laughed now as she tried to imagine a kimono- clad matchmaker in a place like La Cantina with Latin music and the guitar instead of samisen as a backdrop. Perhaps this Sawada Jun had chosen the restaurant to sabotage the omiai and derail her!

She sat down at a round, marble-topped table and ordered a beer, thoroughly enjoying the music and the atmosphere so much that she hoped Sawada Jun would not show up and she would be spared the chore of making polite conversation with a stranger. "I'm supposed to be on holiday and it's really too much of a bother to be polite and pleasing to anyone," Sachi groaned as she downed her second San Miguel beer.

Captivated by a Latin number the singing duo was belting out, Sachi had completely forgotten why she was in the La Cantina when a shadow blocked the light at her table and she looked up to see a flash of white teeth gleaming down at her.

"Hi. You must be Sachi Ishikawa?" the man said

"Yes, I am. Why do you ask?" Sachi replied sharply. She never liked to be approached by strange men, especially at a restaurant or bar, because she believed a woman had the right to dine or drink alone without unsolicited men bothering her.

"Because I'm Jun Sawada and you asked to meet me," the man replied.

"I asked to meet you?" Sachi asked and her voice was cutting. "I was told that you wanted to meet me real bad after seeing my photos which, by the way, were shown to you without my knowledge or permission."

God, the arrogance and cheek of this man! Who did he think he was, strutting up to her like that and accusing her of forcing this meeting?

# Onna Rising

"Ok, let's try this again," the man called Jun Sawada said. "My name is Jun. I'm thirty-three years old, single and this meeting is the result of a desperate attempt by my mother to get me married off. I can see that you are also caught in the same or at least similar bind and neither of us want to be here. In fact, we can't wait to get out of this place and lie to our determined mothers that we met and hated each other on sight and then move on with our careers and carefree single lives. Does that sound much better?

"And now, shall we spend the next thirty minutes or so being civil to each other, make small conversation and then split? You can start by inviting me to sit in that empty chair opposite you, for example."

"What the hell...?" Sachi stopped herself in time before a slew of "invented by Suzue" unladylike words tumbled out. This man was impossible, too arrogant for his own good, but she refused to be rattled by him, if that was what he was trying to do.

Sachi gritted her teeth and gestured none too gently to the empty chair.

"Be my guest," she said. "You're right. I was dragged here kicking and biting against my will and right now I'm forced to sit here and talk to you because they've chained me to the chair. Get one thing straight, Jun Sawada or whatever your name is: I'm a very successful woman entrepreneur in the business of high fashion and I absolutely do not need to get married. And now I will give you twenty minutes of my time, tops.

"So what shall we talk about? The weather? Hmmm...it's night and pitch black outside so I don't know whether it's cloudy or sunny!" Sachi continued sarcastically.

Jun Sawada took a closer look at the woman he had blamed for spoiling his evening. Not bad looking but my, what a sharp tongue!

"Look at us," he said. "Two intelligent professionals in our own fields meeting under the umbrella of one of Japan's oldest traditional procreation negotiators, the omiai! You should be sitting in a tatami room demurely sipping ocha and showing me what a good wife with ample domestic skills you will make and I should be painfully polite and correct. Instead we are in a noisy Mexican restaurant, downing beer and using very strong language on each other! Now, doesn't that call for at least friendship and exchange of name cards to network and stay in touch?"

"Our matchmaker will freak out that instead of horning my domestic and wifely skills at you, we are brandishing our business cards at each other!" Sachi laughed despite herself and relaxed. Jun Sawada seemed a nice enough person and not on the prowl for a wife so maybe they could just be friends.

The evening passed pleasantly. Sachi's twenty minutes eventually extended to three hours, and when they parted, it was with promises to stay in touch when they both returned to Tokyo.

When she returned home, her mother was waiting for her and Sachi noticed how much she had aged with the stress and worry over her father's illness. She decided to humor the older lady with the airy comment that the meeting had gone quite well and Jun was a likable person which was true, anyway.

But Sachi put her foot down when her mother tried to impose a deadline to decide on whether she would marry Jun Sawada on the assumption that he proposed.

"The omiai has to be, you know, remunerated if this is successful so it will be unfair to drag this out for too long," her mother explained.

Sachi was bristling inside but there was no need to add to her mother's worries by telling her she and Jun had ended up networking more than working up a mood for holy matrimony so she replied diplomatically, "These things need time, you know, mother, but if we're destined for each other, we'll get there."

Fortunately, her mother knew when to stop and left it at that, but she probably went to the nearby Shinto shrine to pray hard that Cupid's arrow would finally pierce through her daughter's age-hardened and invincible heart with the name of Jun Sawada!

The next day, Sachi boarded the train back to Tokyo with mixed feelings. She was dying to get back to her apartment where no one badgered her to get married and to the fashion house she lived for, but a part of her was uncomfortable about leaving behind her aged parents to fend for themselves. Their tearful eyes and brave smiles bothered her long after the train pulled out of Matsumoto station and she had transferred to the shinkansen to hurtle at breakneck speed back to Tokyo.

# Onna Rising

Sachi sighed. Why did it always have to be like this—the conflict between duty and tradition on one side and forward thinking and a 21st century lifestyle on the other? And inevitably, it was always the women who felt guilty about following their visions.

# CHAPTER 28

Narita Airport Terminal 1 was jam packed with holiday travelers either taking off to exotic destinations or returning from them, tanned and lugging surfboards. Suzue sighed. She was long overdue for a holiday, but work schedules had been so tight lately that it had been impossible to fit in even a few days to de-stress.

She made a mental note to book a short getaway to Guam with Robert the following week. To hell with work; she would pencil out a few days. He had seemed a little down recently and the getaway would do him good. Suzue knew something was bothering him but she didn't press; Robert would share whatever it was when he was ready to do so. That was the kind of relationship she had demanded of him so she had to give him the same respect and space, but being a woman and instinctively wanting to know everything—it was hard to contain herself!

Someone gripped her hard on the shoulder and she turned round, almost colliding into Tomoko, with Sachi in tow.

"My goodness, Tomoko, you grip like a man!" Suzue said. "That really hurt! You must be a real tyrant in bed!"

"So I am told!" Tomoko replied in kind. "I can't believe Emi is actually arriving in under an hour's time. God, how long has it been since we last saw her?"

"About a year, I think," Sachi said. "The last time I Facebooked her, I told her if she didn't come home soon, we'd forget all about her! I was kidding of course but she seems to have taken it seriously and the next thing I knew, she said she was heading home!" It was a weekday and they had all rushed to the airport straight from their offices, still dressed in corporate suits and stilettos.

"I almost didn't make it," Tomoko said, her face still flushed from running. "It's been quite a day! Let's see: Acrimonious name calling in a high-profile property division matter involving individuals you will definitely know if I name them; a very nasty takeover bid; two attempts to sabotage my professionalism; another attempt to hijack one of my clients by a smooth-talking stinker of a brother-in-law and wait, there's a last one for the road! Just as I was packing up my laptop to leave, a very high-value client whose feet I must kiss in the scheme of things, called and kept me engaged for almost twenty minutes. It was only after the fifth plea of "I have to go to the airport to pick up my grandmother who is arriving any moment in a wheelchair" that she let me go with profuse apologies and goodbyes that took up another five minutes and set me thinking that perhaps I should have said stretcher instead of wheelchair!" Tomoko paused. " So how were your days, both of you?"

"The usual murderous day!" Suzue replied. "Killer deadlines, ongoing run-ins with our media agency and, as a grand finale, we fired a client who never took "no," "impossible," or "unsustainable," as answers to his demands."

"For me, it was a less than glamorous day of near fashion disasters, temperamental models and lackluster photo shoots. Also, my best makeup artist threatened to resign on me because of a spate with his girlfriend in creative — occupational hazards of a not so glamorous industry back stage, you might say," Sachi said. "But then, what would the fashion industry be without an adrenalin charge, emotional highs and lows and the occasional super bitches, right? "

"We'll probably fall flat on our faces if we chart up static graphs on any given day! But you know what, no matter how much we growl about our work and those absolutely nasty days where nothing goes right, we wouldn't give it up for all the world!" said Tomoko

"Absolutely, but today was one of those hair tearing days when I got very close to asking myself, is my mother right to want me out of this man-eating, carnivorous world so that I can ride on the back of someone like Jun Sawada?" Sachi replied.

"Oh, speaking of that, how has your Jun Sawada been? Has he asked for your hand in marriage yet?" Suzue asked with a straight face, but her eyes were twinkling.

"Since when did you become so romantically cliché inclined? Believing in happily ever after — shame on you, Suzue san!" Sachi retorted. "But seriously, the ironic thing about this whole affair is that we got together through an omiai and the reason why we are still friends and very definitely in touch is because each knows that marriage proposals are not in the agenda! I wonder whether the omiai is paid for sealing a friendship or has it got to be marriage, as in signing on the dotted line? I daren't ask my mother lest I open up a whole floodgate of verbal diarrhea! She probably wants to skin me right now!"

The flight data on the huge arrivals board flickered, announcing the landing of Emi's plane and they moved forward to the exit area to wait for her to disembark. Emi hadn't wanted to tell her parents the date of her return to Japan, explaining that she needed some space and her pillars' strength and energy to shore her up before she returned to her home in Mejiro to face a barrage of questions about her life choices.

"I'm really excited to meet the little girl, Sumi, she has adopted and I presume will be bringing back to Japan with her," Tomoko said, almost hopping from one stiletto to the other, both from excitement and the real pain of standing so much on those killer heels because she had forgotten to bring her flats.

"We all are excited, but when I asked her whether she was bringing Sumi back, she didn't seem to want to talk about it, beyond saying that she was trying to make arrangements," Sachi said. "She seemed kind of sad so I didn't want to press it, but I hope she managed to get a long- term visa for the child to come to Japan."

"Well, we'll find out soon," Tomoko said, straining her eyes to look through the frosted glass of the exit doors. "I did advise her to get a tourist visa for Sumi first and once in Japan, apply for the long term visa. It'll be harder for them to reject her application once the child is physically in Japan."

"I don't know how she's going to cope though, without parental support to look after the little girl, unless she gives up her job or manages to find a daycare center for Sumi. Even then, she will still have to juggle work and rushing to the daycare center and you know, TV work keeps long, erratic hours," Suzue said.

The three women were so engrossed in their discussion they didn't notice Emi rushing out of the exit until she was almost upon them. It was a tearful but happy reunion and it was only later that they noticed how thin she had become and how her skin, always so porcelain fair and clear, was now tanned and blotchy.

"I know, I know, I look a sight," Emi said. "It's all that sun and field work that just ruined my skin. My mother will throw a fit when she sees me, but two weeks of after-sun whitening treatment and cool weather will make my skin snap back again."

"Sun burned, roasted, overdone, whatever, we're just glad to have you back, Emi," Sachi said. "Come on, let's go to ABC Baggage Sending Service and have your luggage sent to my place because you can stay with me till you return to Mejiro. You know, I just love this system of door to door baggage delivery and collection from and to the airport in Japan. It's so freaking convenient; every time I go through airports in London, New York, Los Angeles and so on, I'm always screaming, why don't they have a baggage delivery service so people like me don't have to lug big suitcases all the way downtown by train!"

It was only after they had deposited Emi's two suitcases with the delivery service that they noticed she had returned alone.

"Oh my goodness, I just realized the little girl, Sumi, is not here. You left her behind, didn't you?" Tomoko asked in her usual direct and point blank manner.

"Please don't judge me too harshly for this, but I had to leave her behind in the end," Emi replied. "Rest assured that I put her with a good family who loves children and she will never want for anything and receive the best education in the region that money can buy, I will make sure of that. I know it doesn't look very good but I don't feel guilty about it because Sumi is in a much better place than if I had left her with her mother who would almost certainly sell her off into child prostitution. I shudder even now as I think of that possibility happening to Sumi and although I had to leave her behind, I know I rescued her from a fate worse than death itself.

"You understand, don't you? It was too difficult to try and

**225**

bring her back to Japan with me. The visa, all the obstacles they would put in the way of my officially adopting her — I am told it could take years and years to get a passport for her, if she was granted citizenship at all. Plus my parents have told me they will disown me if I bring a gaijin child into the family and I'd be on my own to struggle as a single mum.

"But the main deciding point was when I asked myself this very important question: Would Sumi be really happy in Japan, where she would always stay outside the circle looking in because she is so different? I remember you telling me, Suzue, what you had to go through, growing up, and you're just a fraction of how different Sumi would be among the Japanese children.

"The truth is, after considering everything, I just couldn't cope, so I gave up! I'm sorry if I failed as a mother even before I began but I'm not as strong or resilient as all of you. And when I saw Sumi so happy, bright-eyed and at home with the family who will care for her, I knew that I had made the right decision. Why remove her from an environment and people where she will grow up confident and proud of who she is and how she looks and bring her back to Japan where she will look different, feel different and never be accepted — even by her mother's family.

"I am half angry with my mother for not giving me any support and at myself for being too weak to fight societal pressure," Emi continued. "In the end, I caved in to stern calls from the forces that be, to conform. On reflection, do you think I did wrong to give up little Sumi so easily?"

"No, Emi, I don't think so," Suzue replied. "You were right when you said earlier that you don't have it in you to fight this and it wouldn't have been a half-baked battle but a fully fledged war, from your family to society and even the authorities. You would have had to fight both clean and dirty, because there is no full-fledged, all out war that doesn't have a little dirt, and you're not cut out for that, Emi. I'm not criticizing you or anything like that, but you were born and raised genteelly, so to speak. Fighting this kind of ongoing battle for what could be years, just to get Sumi the right to stay on in Japan, wouldn't have been sustainable.

"And, what's more, from a very emotional angle and how Sumi herself would fare in Japan, I agree with what you said earlier:

Perhaps Sumi will be happier where she is because she belongs and is fully accepted in her own right and in her own skin. I've been there, Emi and I know what it's like growing up different and craving for acceptance all the time. I've seen my mother struggle, being a single mum, and having to protect herself and me with a 'see no evil, hear no evil, speak no evil' armor to survive.

"My mother is a tough Kyushu woman but even she barely made it," Suzue continued. "So all things considered, you made the right decision, Emi."

"I absolutely agree," Sachi said. "But remember, even though you had to leave her behind in the end, you managed to rescue her from a potentially terrible life and put her with a family who will give her a childhood and an education that will help her be all she can be."

"Thanks; I feel so much better already," Emi replied. "But this is not the end. I'll still go and see her from time to time and provide financially for her. I grew to love her the few months I spent with her, and for that brief moment I was a mother, something I never thought I would be able to handle. But you know what I discovered? Even the most hardened of us still has maternal instincts deep in us — yes, even you, Suzue. Can you believe it? I changed diapers for the first time in my life and I even sang lullabies to get her to sleep!

"I've always led a protected life, and in Africa, I had the chance to toughen up and protect someone else for a change, and it felt really good. I keep thinking of Sumi, whether she's O.K. and whether she's missing me, you know, that kind of stuff. Well, there's one person who will be very happy about this — my mother! And to be honest, after all the things she said about Sumi when I sent her the pictures, I don't feel like making her happy at all!"

"Stay with us for a while till you're ready to go back, and this time you might want to consider getting your own place," Tomoko said. "Just imagine having your own apartment and being able to have Sumi over during school holidays when she's a bit older!"

"Yes, it's time I get my own place, although this will ignite another fire with my parents — but you know, somehow, that doesn't bother me so much anymore. I think I've come into being my own person at last," Emi replied. "Anyway, can you imagine an African child running around my parents' home?"

"Not in a million years!" Sachi replied. "Your mother has made your house so air-tight Japanese — from the sculptured matsu trees in the garden to the kotatsu table and gold-coated hanging tapestries — that anything non-Japanese would stick out like a sore thumb!"

"Oh my goodness; I'd almost forgotten how cool and fresh the air is in Japan at this time of the year and how much I've missed it!" Emi said, breathing deeply as they finally emerged from the Meguro subway station for the short walk to Sachi's apartment.

It was a beautiful night with a crescent moon hanging in a sky that was for once so clear it even allowed a few stars to come out and dazzle, right there, in Tokyo itself.

# CHAPTER 29

Call it her sixth sense, but Suzue always knew when there were going to be upheavals in her life even before they happened. As April moved into May and she had that restless, uneasy feeling again, Suzue shrugged it off as "pre- promotion evaluation nerves," and plunged into a whole new spate of presentations, strategic planning, boardroom sparring, workshops and the part of her work that she was beginning to like, mentoring a couple of new interns, fresh from university and rearing to learn, as she herself had been, years ago.

She and Robert had spent a lovely week in Okinawa, Japan's southernmost island, soaking in the Ryuku history and culture and the late spring sun on some of Japan's most beautiful beaches, miles of white sand and sub tropical vegetation against a spectacular coastline. They had shuddered as they thought of the black, murky sands of some of the beaches around Honshu island, compliments of Japan's many volcanoes.

"I can't believe this is part of Japan except when I hear the people in the streets speaking Japanese," Robert said. "Look at the temples, splashes of red everywhere and kind of cluttered, unlike the preference for sober natural wood colors and zen minimalism in the mainland. It feels more Chinese than Japanese, like it's in a world of its own, standing a little apart from the rest of Japan!"

"An ingénue, like me," Suzue laughed. "I don't know if you've noticed this, but even the Okinawan people themselves look different. They have bigger eyes and a very slight tan to their skin – although that could be attributed, I guess, to the amount of

**229**

subtropical sunshine exposure they get here."

They explored the shops, hand in hand, along Kokusai Dori or International Street in Naha, and Suzue was reminded of the complications in her life only when they came across the American servicemen in uniform thronging the streets in the evenings, alone, in groups or with local girlfriends drinking at the many "Welcome U.S. servicemen" bars and pubs. They reminded her of her father, young and in uniform as he would have been, holding hands with her mother, like the mixed couples they saw shopping, dining together or just strolling down colorful, vibrant Kokusai Dori.

Had her parents been like that, holding hands, laughing and trying to communicate in bad English and Japanese? Had love conquered everything in the end, the language problem, the culture divide, even the tight morals of a smalltown girl who must have loved so desperately to throw all caution to the wind and take a leap of faith to follow her heart. How had she felt when she was eventually left to fend for herself, pregnant out of wedlock, unemployable, knowing that she had broken her mother's heart and compromised her own future?

For as long as Suzue could remember, her mother had only two ambitions for her: Economic independence and education. It was a bone of contention, this clash of values between her mother and her grandmother, whose priority was to have Suzue married off to a good man and settled down to a respectable life as soon as possible — probably due to seeing her own daughter end up a single mum to an ainoko, working in a Ginza hostess club and completely unmarriageable.

Robert's hand tightened on hers and he shouted above the buzz of traffic on the busy Kokusai Dori, "Penny for your thoughts, Suzue!"

"Oh, nothing sinister, just that watching those US servicemen in uniform reminded me a little of my father and I kind of visualised my parents like those mixed couples over there, that's all," Suzue replied. "You know, Robert san, I don't think I can remember my mother really laughing, that kind of laughter that comes from the heart, the soul, and from inside. I used to make excuses for her, telling myself that she probably was so tired of superficial laughter and pampering spoiled, rich men at work, that at home she only wanted to be her real unsmiling self! I don't know if that makes sense to you."

"Of course it does, and I hope I can meet your mother someday. She's a remarkable woman in that she took risks and accepted the challenge of raising you – a challenge that few Japanese women of her era would have dared face," Robert replied. "You might say she gambled her life on love and failed – but I wouldn't say that at all because she produced you – another unique and remarkable woman who lives by her own rules and on her own terms. I guess that's why I respect you so much, Suzue."

"Thanks, Robert. You really make my day by saying all that because on an average day, I'm not generally well-liked. Some women find me too forward and insensitive because I speak my mind and "talk straight," and I make those who want things to stay as they are uncomfortable by trying to upset the God-given role of women in this country. Then I go piss off the men because I encourage women to emerge as an equal player in what the men consider their domain. Look at the fast food joints which openly advertise wages for women to be 800 yen an hour while men get 1,000 yen an hour for exactly the same job!

"Even my own family thinks I am nuts when I tell them I might enter politics in later life so I can give women a much bigger voice in the decision-making machinery of this country! My grandmother is terrified that no man will touch me because I'm so strong-headed and too successful – can you believe that?"

"Well, your grandmother doesn't have to worry because there is at least one man who will always be more than willing to touch you, and you're looking at him," Robert replied with more than a twinkle in his eyes.

"If I tell her that, she will freak out and go running to her shinto temple to ask what she has done in her past life to deserve yet another gaijin infiltration into her family!"

Suzue smiled as she thought of this conversation while on the colorful Kokusai Dori of Naha. Dear Robert; Japan had gotten so much under his skin sometimes he forgot he was a gaijin! He was the only one who didn't view her growing interest in politics as bizarre. Even her pillars were skeptical, and she suspected they went along with it just to humor her, fully expecting this to be a passing fantasy.

Since the Okinawan trip, Suzue had become much calmer and less troubled because she had made the decision not to establish contact with her father and effectively close that chapter of her life. After all, she had fulfilled her dream of establishing the identity of her biological father; it was time to move on and continue with her life, without looking back.

One uplifting event was that her agency won a big account involving a military supplies company and Suzue, who had been cultivating the deal for months, was credited for this big boost to her team's target for the year.

"With the big bucks this account will bring in, I can actually relax for the rest of the year, but you know a workaholic like me isn't going to do that," she told Robert over a cup of coffee in the company's cafeteria. "But perhaps it'll give me more time to spend on my workshops, mentoring my two interns and my growing movement to empower underprivileged women. Oh yes, and shadow a politician I want to learn from. Last, but not least, I'll have more time for spicing up my life in the romance department!"

"Since I am the beneficiary of the last item on your "to do" list, I'm certainly not complaining!" Robert whispered into her ear as they drained the last of their coffee and prepared to return to work.

A few days later, Suzue addressed her team. "A delegation from the U.S. is coming next week to speak at a workshop we are conducting in connection with this mega military supplies account because it involves a consortium of American military supplies giants. This will be a high- powered group, including a couple of very influential military figures and we really have to manage this event better than perfect," she said, brandishing a fax message that had just come in. "I want everyone on this team to be focused and give 110% to this project. Anyone who is not prepared to do that is free to decline the challenge and opt out now."

In the end, no one opted out, not even the pregnant coordinator whom Suzue put on light duties, because they respected her so much. Suzue was no couch director team leader; she got down on her hands and knees to work alongside them and if they had to work through the night, so did Suzue. She did not conform to the conventional Japanese management style of seniority and hierarchy. Instead she developed her own consultative style, which encouraged queries and suggestions from subordinates, and believed that anyone who had an idea should be given a voice. When all was said and done, a significant number of her more successful ad campaigns had blossomed from the ideas and voices of her young executives and a couple of times, even from the interns.

Ironically, Suzue herself had never been given a voice voluntarily and no one listened to her till she became so successful they couldn't ignore her. Although she was still considered a rebel and a misfit, what Suzue Tanaka said or did made an impact, and even those who hated her could not afford to brush her aside any more.

Suzue was at a meeting when Fumiko placed the program details and the list of speakers on her desk, so she did not review the little booklet till the next morning.

Robert had stayed over the previous night and Suzue was still euphoric from their powerful night of uninhibited love-making as she idly flipped open the program booklet and scanned the list of speakers.

A name leaped out from the list and almost blinded her. The words blurred and danced in front of her eyes. Suzue's blood turned to ice and she shivered as a voice screamed over and over again in her head, "No, this is not possible; someone must be playing a cruel joke on me!"

But it was there, stark black letters on the white paper of the little program booklet. Roger Carlista was listed as one of the main speakers.

Roger Carlista, there was no mistaking the name. Perhaps it was another Roger Carlista? Not in a million years, her voice of reason told her. Carlista wasn't a mass manufactured surname at all!

"Are you all right, Tanaka san?" Fumiko's concerned voice cut through Suzue's frozen mind and brought her back to the practical matters at hand. "You look kind of cheesy!"

She saw Fumiko give her a strange look and she snapped

back to her usual self, strong and totally in control. God forbid that Fumiko should think she had gotten herself pregnant! How well they all knew that speculative look when a female colleague looked "cheesy!"

"I'm fine — maybe a little out of sorts because I haven't had breakfast yet," Suzue replied. "Perhaps a cup of coffee and a muffin from the pantry would wake me up considerably!"

"Yes, of course, Tanaka san. My mother always said breakfast is the most important meal of the day and if you skip it, the rest of the day won't be the same!" Fumiko fussed as she bustled off to get Suzue her second breakfast of the day, giving her boss at least a little time to compose herself.

So, by the hand of Destiny, no less, her father was going to be one of the major speakers in her upcoming workshop and she could either avoid him by nominating someone else to be the forerunner while she worked from behind, or she could go ahead with her original plan and stay in the forefront — which meant inevitable interaction with her father.

"God, what are the odds that this would happen, given we are 10,000 miles and at least one ocean apart?" Suzue groaned that night, pushing aside even her favorite toro sushi at a sushi bar where the pillars had organized a cozy little "Welcome back" dinner for Emi. "Sorry I'm not very good company tonight, but I'm just annoyed at the way my past keeps coming back to haunt me! Just when I had come to terms with never being able to acknowledge my father and had achieved a certain measure of peace, here he comes waltzing back into my life where it affects me most — my work!

"Look, perhaps I should just go off because I'm spoiling your fun, moaning away like this!"

"Walk away from us now, walk away forever," Tomoko replied. "When have we ever let anyone of us slink off to suffer alone when there's a problem, especially a problem as big as yours right now? Look, Suzue, it's O.K. to moan. Bang your head against the wall if it makes you feel better and cry as much as you want with us. Go on, wallow in self-pity! We'll humor you and maybe we can find a solution together for you."

"Thanks, Tomoko. I really need your lawyer's mind and

logic to rein in my emotions and make a cool decision that's in the best interest of my work and this campaign that my team has slogged over for weeks! It's not only about me here, it's also about my whole team. They expect a strong, focused team leader, not a quivering emotional wreck, to see them through what will be a week of enough stress and anxiety as it is. "

"Absolutely," Sachi agreed. "So if you feel you won't be able to handle working so closely with this Roger Carlista, you should consider getting someone else to be the lead."

"I know, but no—I've made up my mind. I'm doing this, no matter what! If I could separate my emotions from my goals when I was working the social escort circuit with its constant, consented physical violation, I can face my father and still go on with my work," Suzue replied. "Facing my father has got to be much easier than sleeping with different men night in and night out! You know, the only thing I got from being a social escort, apart from financial returns, was telling myself that in later life, whatever obstacles I faced, nothing would be as bad as the things I had to do as a social escort. If I could handle that, I could handle anything—and you know what? I did! So I can handle this. I should not be the one to run and hide!

"Anyway, Carlista's here only for two days, and I don't have to meet him if I don't want to, but at least I get to see him in the flesh. And when it's all over, I will just put this behind me and probably never see him again."

The ringing of Emi's cell phone provided a welcome diversion. It was her mother with the usual plea to come home as soon as possible, and to be sure to use lots of sunblock to protect her skin.

"She still doesn't know I'm back in Japan. I had a bad moment last night when she asked why the line seemed unusually clear; thank God I put the ring tone of my cell phone to music so she won't be able to tell my location from the ring tone!" Emi said. "I'm reporting for work next week so I'll have to be officially back from Africa. But this week staying here with you, Sachi, has shown me that I really need to move out and have my own apartment, just to have some privacy and a life!"

"Let's drink to those of us with old scores to settle and new challenges to take on. We're strong, energetic and invincible and we'll be all right!" Tomoko declared, and the sound of glass tinkling against glass was beautiful and reassuring.

# CHAPTER 30

Suzue was glad Robert had been selected from the digital team to help with the digital aspects of the project because somehow, his reassuring presence helped to strengthen her resolve to face her father squarely and not let her emotions compromise her usual sterling performance.

"I haven't decided yet. I guess it really depends on the situation and on whether I want to acknowledge him after accessing what kind of person he is," Suzue replied when Robert asked her whether she intended to identify herself to Roger Carlista during his two-day stay in Japan. "Trust me: To meet my biological father in this bizarre way after years of fantasizing about the moment and, certainly, confronting him at a high-profile business symposium, is hardly a touching fairy tale ending! Story of my life, of course!"

"It's you, Suzue. Nothing about you and what you do is normal or ordinary; that's why you sit in the boardroom and head your own dynamic team. Men may make fun of you or begrudge you your position, but they can't ignore you! Plus — you get the corner room, so to speak!" Robert replied.

"I'm sure I make a very good punching bag for the boys when they're standing in a row, doing their thing in the bathroom! One of my ex-boyfriends told me about this, but it merely amused me and I tell myself it's better to be talked about than to be forgotten!

"Oh, and lest I forget, thanks for making me feel so special, Robert. So far, you've been the only guy worth hanging on to beyond the expiration date!" They had this random conversation as they stood backstage waiting for the cue to start the symposium. Suzue was still smiling as she took her place in front of the mike and, to a round of applause, declared the symposium open. She was a natural at public speaking and no one would have guessed the thoughts in her head as her eyes scanned the audience, knowing that her father was out there, watching her.

Suzue went through the speech she had prepared, rattling out figures, targets, objectives and market projections. She followed that with a short question-and answer session, all the while remaining totally in control. Robert, watching from backstage, was amazed. God, she was one cool chick! It wasn't everyday a woman discovered that the biological father she had been wondering about her whole life was actually a speaker at a very public symposium that she had been largely responsible for putting together . But looking at Suzue Tanaka, no one could have imagined the raw emotions raging inside her.

She had returned to her seat in the front row when Roger Carlista stepped up to deliver his own speech, and Suzue's whole world stood still. Father and daughter faced each other across a small podium, two strangers from different sides of the world thrown together by a one-in-a-million chance.

She had seen him on TV before so she knew what to expect; but what shook her was the fact that he was right there in the flesh, a few meters from her, and she could touch him if she wanted to. In the end, it was anger that helped Suzue contain her emotions and carry on. This man had ruined the lives of her family and had given her nothing but a lonely childhood; how dare he stand there, supremely confident, respected and successful, and look through her as if she didn't exist?

No, perhaps he shouldn't have such a peaceful life and she should make him sit up and notice her. Before she could stop herself, Suzue stood up and fired a question at Roger Carlista. She felt herself shuddering as he turned and looked at her. Suzue didn't even know what she had asked but it must have been an intelligent question because Roger Carlista's answer seemed to please his audience. God, could nothing mar this man's public perfection?

When he took her question, she fancied he looked at her a little longer than one normally would a total stranger and she shivered. They looked so much alike—surely he saw something of himself in that stranger?

# Onna Rising

The moment passed and Suzue put aside her personal drama to give her full attention to the workshop that followed. It was a roaring success and she had just flopped onto a chair to take a short break when she felt someone tapping her on the arm.

"That was a very good workshop, Ms. Tanaka," a familiar voice said and she spun around to come face to face with Roger Carlista.

"Thank you," she replied coolly although her heart was thumping. Even at his age, he was a good looking man with a firm muscular figure and the same dusky skin as hers; it was anybody's guess how much better looking he had been as a young man and it was little wonder her mother hadn't been able to resist his advances. "It's part of what I've been doing for years, so I'm used to this kind of work."

On an impulse that she knew she would later regret, Suzue added, "If you have a moment, let me buy you a cup of coffee." Roger Carlista readily accepted and as they headed to a nearby Starbucks, she felt him looking at her, puzzled and a little disorientated.

"Pardon me, it must be the jetlag and time difference that are playing tricks on me," he said, as they sat down with their steaming mugs of coffee. "But I feel I know you from somewhere."

Suzue did not answer for a moment. This man must be blind if he could not see the striking resemblance between them! God, they even shared the habit of involuntary rubbing their left jaw with a forefinger. It was uncanny!

It made Suzue burn with the sudden desire to hurt Roger Carlista and make life difficult for him.

"Perhaps you do," Suzue blurted out quickly before she could change her mind. "I've heard that you were stationed in Japan many years ago. Perhaps I remind you of someone you used to know in Japan?"

It was a cruel dig but Suzue didn't care. He deserved it after callously walking away from her mother and never looking back. It was because of him that she never could trust any man and had gone through life using and discarding them as her mother had been discarded. God, she should hate this man with all the scratching, clawing and biting fury of a woman scorned, but somehow she could not, fool that she was.

**239**

"Yes. I did a stint in Japan and while there, I was in a relationship with a Japanese woman named Rumiko Tanaka," Roger Carlista said and his voice was distant, as if he was far away. "She was the gentlest and most beautiful woman I ever dated and when I was transferred back to the U.S., I pleaded with her to marry and move back to America with me. But she was so afraid to leave Japan that she refused and nothing could make her change her mind. When it was time for me to ship out, I had to go without her.

"Tanaka," he continued. "I know it's a common surname in Japan but it's odd that you're also Tanaka and I don't know how to say this, but you don't look Japanese. In fact, it's really bizarre and a ridiculous thought, but we even have the same skin tone and dare I say it, have some resemblance. I saw this the minute you asked me that question and I got a good look at you. That's why I came to look for you after the symposium. You conducted an awesome workshop and all, but I think I just needed to take a closer look at you."

"Ok, I'll be brutally honest with you, Roger Carlista. Rumiko Tanaka is my mother and I leave everything else to your imagination," Suzue said. Instantly, she saw a spasm shoot across Roger Carlista's face, contorting it, as if he was in pain. It was out at last and there was no need for polite inuendos.

"Are you my daughter? If you are, why is it Rumiko never toldl me about you?" Roger Carlista cried out.

There was a long silence, till Suzue couldn't stand it anymore and she replied in a rush, "I had always wondered who my father was till one day, about six months ago, when my mother and grandmother came to Tokyo to visit me and we were watching CNN. You appeared at some news briefing and my mother just broke down. It was then she confessed to me that you were my father and that you never knew about me because she discovered she was pregnant only after you left for the U.S. I don't think there's any need to do a DNA test; just by looking at us, it's pretty obvious we share the same genetic material. There, you have it—the whole story of the baggage you left behind in Japan all those years ago."

For a long while Roger Carlista didn't say anything but his hands gripped the edge of the table till the knuckles showed white. He was breathing so heavily that Suzue was afraid he would have a heart attack. After all, although he looked good and fit, Roger Carlista had to be well over 60 years old and had just received news that was shocking enough to knock a younger man flat.

"I never knew about you," he said at last. "But when I looked at you this morning at the symposium, even from that distance, something jolted me. And although the moment passed, the haunting memories of the past did not and I was compelled to seek you out—especially when I found out that your surname was Tanaka. I can't even think how this could have happened!"

"The usual way, I imagine!" Suzue couldn't resist replying. She was surprised at how calm she felt as she sat across from her father, watching the emotions race across his face. It was strange that although she didn't hate him, Suzue was glad that the discovery of her existence was causing him pain.

"I know everything about you, Roger, as I'd rather call you. Like that you are married with two children," Suzue continued. "After I discovered you were my father, I searched your profile, but I want you to know that this meeting is totally fortuitous. You see, I had decided that having identified my father was enough to bring closure to a disturbing chapter of my life and that there was no need to cause ripples in your family by trying to meet you. After all, I've never had a father so I don't need one any more, not at this stage of my life, anyway.

"I suppose I can understand that you didn't know about my existence since my mother kept it from you, but what bothered me was that you could just walk away from her and never look back—not even once—to find out if she was all right. After all, you shared a life together for almost four years before you shipped out!"

"I don't blame you for being resentful about that," Roger Carlista admitted. "It looks bad of me and perhaps it is, because I chose the easy way out. I didn't fight for your mother. When she refused to come away with me, I just let go and returned to my life in the U.S. and believe me, although I never forgot her, I just didn't have the will to complicate my life with a transatlantic and cross-cultural relationship. And today, I'm humbled by this, for want of a better word, "fallout" from a four-year relationship with a beautiful woman I should never have left."

"Well, Roger, you did leave her and now you have another

Rei Kimura

picture-perfect family who has nothing to do with all this baggage from your past so this is as far as we can go," Suzue replied. "I'm a very successful professional, as you can see, and I've provided well for my mother so we don't need anything from you. I just needed closure for the open-ended question that had been bugging me ever since someone asked me "Who is your father?" Today, I found that closure, so we can move on from here and perhaps treasure this moment in time when our paths crossed."

"Yes…and no. You're very different from your mother, Suzue. You're harder, less forgiving, with an amazing ability to control your emotions. But for some people, there's this eternal battle between the heart and the head," Roger Carlista said. "I've never wanted to visit Japan because I was afraid I'd be tempted to look for your mother, and being married and no longer a free man, I didn't have any right to do that. So can you imagine how I felt when the plane landed in Tokyo and all the memories came rushing back? Yes, even a hard-core military man like me can still remember and feel.

"And for the record, picture-perfect is as far as it gets with my wife and me. There's none of the warmth I shared with your mother, and now that I've met you, it's going to be even harder to get back to my life without longing for it once again."

"No, Roger, no! Please leave my mother alone if you're not free to offer her the committed happiness she deserves a second time around," Suzue responded quickly but firmly, even though her voice was quivering. "She has found a certain measure of peace in her life and it would kill her to be tossed around again, so, please, go back to the U.S. and forget us. You did it before so you can do it again. And even if your marriage is not a happy one, you made your choice so please don't get my mother involved and destabilize her life again, if you really care for her."

In the end, Suzue and Roger Carlista spent two hours over cup after cup of coffee which they ordered but allowed to grow cold without touching because they were too caught up in what Suzue decided would be the first and last time she and her father would meet. She felt she owed it to Roger Carlista to give him a few hours of herself and, for her part, she wanted to get as much as possible of this man who had fathered her and and who she would

242

probably never see again. These few hours would have to last them a lifetime.

The insistent ringing of her cell phone signaled the end of their time together; the second part of the workshop had resumed and Fumiko was looking frantically for her. The relaxed atmosphere changed abruptly and Suzue stood up and extended her hand to Roger Carlista.

"I hate long, emotional good-byes but you probably don't know that," she said, almost biting her tongue off as soon as she said that. God, why couldn't she stop digging at him?

"Goodbye, Suzue. This has been the most touching moment of my life, and it's very unlikely that I will ever forget you and your mother although you have ordered me to do so, in no uncertain terms," Roger Carlista said, and although he tried to make light of the moment, his voice was unsteady. "I'm glad to see you so confident and tough; that's the foreign side of you, but I'm sure you've realized it by now. Here's my card, in case you ever need anything from me. The ball's in your court. Sayonara, Suzue chan, as I would have called you had we been given time together when you were growing up.

"By the way, you speak amazing English and we could have communicated wonderfully if things had been different, but it was never meant to be."

"Goodbye, otoh san," Suzue said, using the word "father" for the first and last time.

Then, without another word, she took his card and walked off, never once looking back. She was determined not to be drawn into emotional goodbyes and empty promises to meet again that she didn't intend to keep, so cut and dry was best.

The next day, after Roger Carlista had left Japan, for some strange reason Suzue felt melancholic, as if a part of her went in that plane with him.

"Damn the man!" she told Robert. "Waltzing into my life like that and weakening me with all these unwelcome new feelings! I still remember the touch of his hand as he held mine for just a second before he left—it was my only physical contact with the man who fathered me. He will be hard to exorcise but I'm damn well going to try!"

# CHAPTER 31

Suzue took almost two weeks to recover from her unexpected encounter with her father, a long time for someone like her who usually "got over hard knocks and emotional baggage at the speed of light," as Tomoko put it.

It wasn't only Roger Carlista who was putting a dent in her life; a friend in Human Resources had hinted at Robert's very possible transfer back to the London office to head their newly set-up digital marketing department, and that had really upset her. Suzue knew she would miss him terribly if he left Japan—after all, living in separate apartments and essentially giving each other as much space as needed was not the same as living in different countries, thousands of miles apart.

"I've heard from HR that Robert might be sent back to London," Suzue said as she chewed on a piece of celery stick over a business lunch with Tomoko. She wished she was crunching up Robert's face, instead. "But he hasn't said anything to me; he's probably worried about how this could affect or even end our relationship."

"And will it? End your relationship I mean," Tomoko asked. "It's one thing to maintain a degree of space from each other in the same city, and quite another thing to do that from two different cities thousands of miles apart."

"I've been doing some hard thinking ever since HR told me about the potential move, and I feel I'll be O.K. with it," Suzue replied. "Somewhere along the way, I've actually developed feelings for him and we have the most passionate physical relationship —

with the added bonus that we totally connect mentally and professionally as well.

"We've made our own rules about giving each other space and not moving in together, but you know what? Even so, we're beginning to enter the stable rut phase of "your place" or "mine." We're beginning to lose that heady, drunken excitement of those first two years, and before it plunges into first, routine sex, then duty sex, a little long distancing might not be so bad. It might build us up to a hungry, desperate appetite for passion and intimacy every time we meet," Suzue said. "I don't know—does what I just said make sense?"

"It might not to a lot of people, especially for those who just want a stable life and marriage with hopes of growing old together, and there's nothing wrong with that, but coming from you, this departure from the norm makes a whole lot of sense!" Tomoko replied. "But I can see where you're coming from, Suzue. If it were not for the fact that Michael is away a lot, we'd probably have split up by now! I'm a lawyer and intend to be one like, forever, and he's no lameduck himself, so that is a formula for friction if we're glued together for any uninterrupted length of time. I don't see why I have to put up with that."

"Robert is a darling and hates confrontation, so it's very easy for us to slip into a routine relationship. Of course I know that being apart has its own problems, like the temptation to stray and the fact that one or the other party might not quite be sitting around patiently waiting for the next reunion. But I want to take that risk and know that I can let go when and if my game of chance falls through.

" My mother and grandmother have called me crazy, wondering why can't I be normal, like other women. They cry in despair, but I can't help the way I like to live, taking risks and being on the edge," Suzue said. "That's why I love this industry—it's ever changing, fast, terse and on edge, all contra the stability it's said most women look for!

"There's a lot of wisdom in the saying 'Men: you can't live with them and you can't live without them' so the best compromise for me is to live with them, but

with intervals long enough to miss and want them so that

the fire of passion is not allowed to go out. But it's not for everyone, especially the faint-hearted!"

"But you know, as I grow older and hopefully wiser, I realize that we have been hard and unfair to the other women out there who only want to get married and raise a family. I mean, the world doesn't revolve around us, and without those women to prop up the birthrate, the institution of marriage and family, there wouldn't be a sustainable society in Japan!

"In fact, a few days ago, I thought of what it would be like if every woman in Japan was like me — with little intention of having children and totally disrespectful of the institution of marriage and unable to provide a stable family life for the next generation of Japanese — and it wasn't a good picture at all!"

"I totally agree with you, Suzue. The thing is to strike a balance between the two extremes so that for every ten women who do, you know, "the good work," there are at least two like us who are around to flex our muscles and say, 'hey, don't push us around!'" Tomoko replied."We're the most alike amongst the pillars, Suzue, but you can get away with more things than me. When your lifestyle and ideals don't go over well in Japan, people just make excuses for you and shrug it off with 'Oh, she's a gaijin, that's why!' — and you capitalize on that shamelessly, when it suits you! No such luck for me with my stamp of 'Born, bred and made in Japan from 100% pure Japanese genetic material!'"

"Thanks for reminding me of my 50% non-Japanese 'genetic material' who, by the way, had the cheek to send me an email yesterday, despite strict orders to stay away!" Suzue said. "He must have used his charm or 'gaijin chyoi' to wrestle my personal email address from my PA or HR! Speaking of HR, if Robert doesn't say anything by tonight, I'm going to tackle him about his imminent transfer back to the U.K. and let him know that although it was a shock at first, I'm cool with it."

As it happened, Suzue didn't have to tackle Robert about his leaving Japan; he brought it up himself over dinner that night.

"I already know," Suzue replied. "I've got friends in HR so I've known about this for over a week now. I was just waiting for you to bring it up."

"As you predicted, Japan's got under my skin and of

course, I don't want to leave you, so I tried to reject the transfer. But the powers-that-be insisted I am the only man who can set up and develop this new digital arm in London, so a polite request became an order. One consolation though is that they've promised to let me return to a Japan posting in two or three years' time," Robert sighed. "But till then, what happens to us?"

"It doesn't have to end, you know," Suzue replied. "I'm cool with us long distancing, provided there is daily contact by email, chat, phone or whatever. And it'll be fun and exciting planning trips to meet up in London, here or any part of the world we fancy! Recently, I've become lazy, so this will be the impetus to push me out of Japan to travel and see more of the world again. But I can't do this alone; you must want it too, Robert, and feel that it's right for you, because living in separate apartments in the same city is different from living in different countries and meeting four or five times a year."

"To be very honest, my request to stay on in Japan was turned down quite suddenly in the end so I haven't had time to collect my thoughts, but off hand, although I've said before that I'm fine with long distance relationships, I don't know how this will actually work out," Robert replied. "Of course I could lie to you and say I'm totally all right with it, but you know, you're not the kind of person that one can lie to and get away with it. I don't want to lose you but I honestly can't say I can do this long distance thing without trying it out first. To ask you to leave the work you love and sweated your guts out to build up and come away to London with me is out of the question, and I wouldn't even dream of asking, so I guess we'll have to see how things work out."

Suzue was stunned by the impact Robert's words had on her; it was as if someone had driven a chopstick through her heart and left it there. God forbid, was this the pain women from time immemorial had felt over matters of the heart, the kind of pain that she had scoffed at and swore would never happen to her? She stifled a crazy impulse to tell him she was tired of her high-powered job and wanted to take a break anyway, and perhaps follow him to London, because both of them knew that within a month of doing that, she would be bored stiff.

"I guess you're right, we have to really be in a long distance relationship before we can say with certainty whether it works for us," Suzue said instead. "So let's have our say in six months' time, not now."

"It'll be very hard to leave you and I don't know how you can be so calm about it," Robert replied. "Does nothing ever faze you, Suzue? Look at me, I'm this big strapping man and I'm the one with tears in my eyes!"

Suzue didn't trust herself to speak but she willed Robert to look deep into her eyes and see all the pain and sadness in her heart and he did.

Without a word, he paid the bill and they left the restaurant to walk all the way back from Harajuku to Shibuya. They didn't need to say anything; the intimacy of their arms wrapped around each other as they walked spoke volumes of their feelings and the sadness of not knowing whether they could make their relationship last through long distancing. Suzue knew she could but she wasn't sure about Robert any more. One thing she was sure about was that if they didn't make it, she was tough enough to get up and move on.

*One of the perks of growing up fighting and struggling with issues,* she thought wryly. *Thank you, Roger Carlista, the father of my dreams!*

The next day Suzue knew she would be herself again, but just for the night she wanted to let her guard down and cry a little. It was ironic how she had sworn never to let a man affect her and here she was, emotionally rocked by two men in a row, Roger Carlista and Robert Darcey. They made her uncomfortable because she was used to men as objects of physical interest and not objects of emotional distress and yet she would not have missed this new experience for all the world. It was raw, it was painful, but it was life!

*This is payback time,* she thought grimly. *I've been using guys far too long and never suffered a day for it, even when I hurt them — and now these two guys are making mincemeat of my emotions! But I will survive, as I always have!*

Three weeks later, Suzue was at Narita airport again, watching another man fly out of her life. Robert held her with all the intensity and passion of his feelings for her, not caring who was staring at them in the crowded airport. He spilled out his guts telling Suzue how much he loved her and waited to hear the same words from her but she just couldn't bring herself to say it. It was only when he had given her one final kiss and walked into the security area that Suzue felt the words of love coming, tumbling over each other, as if embarrassed to be released.

She ran after him, mouthing the words, but he could no longer hear her. At some point, she might write those words in an email but she had lost the chance to say them to him in person before he left Japan. Suzue bit her lips hard to stifle the cry of frustration that was threatening to explode right there, in the middle of the crowded departure area. She remembered how, the night before, she had kissed Robert till her lips ached with the knowledge that the kiss had to last him till the next time they met, and now he already seemed so far away, even before the plane left Tokyo airspace.

"I'm going to miss you so much," she whispered as she stood at the observation deck watching his plane take off. "How dare you leave me like this, Robert Darcey!"

Her apartment seemed dark and forlorn when she returned and Suzue switched on every light she could find. There was a lump in her throat as she entered her bedroom and saw the sheets still rumpled from their passionate love making that morning. Had it been only a few hours ago?

After clearing up the remains of their breakfast, Suzue turned to the only respite for her emptiness and pain, her laptop and work. As she opened up her personal email, one particular message caught her eye. It was from Roger Carlista.

She opened it up and read it once, then read it again. She sat there for a long time thinking. Then Suzue made up her mind and clicked "Reply."

# CHAPTER 32

"Today I'm not going to check my personal email a hundred times or go on MSN to see if he's online another hundred times or sift through my tons of text messages to see if there's one from him till my fingers protest my lack of pride and dignity at being manipulated by modern technology in the name of Robert Darcey," Suzue declared to her pillars and her bruised and battered pride. "Today I'm going to get back Suzue Tanaka and perhaps encourage that new Australian guy who has been eyeing me from day one."

"Yes, Suzue, go for it—or rather, go for him," Tomoko replied. "After all, as the saying goes, the best way to put out one fire is to light another."

"Can you believe it? One email to tell me he arrived safely and after that, nothing! Isn't that so typical of a man? There's no point and it's definitely counterproductive to develop any feelings for them; my expiration date concept was much better!" Suzue said.

"But remember one thing—you've always been treating Robert with this cool nonchalance, at least on the outside, as if you didn't care. He was always the one expressing his feelings, so how the hell would he know what you feel about him?" Sachi said.

Sachi's words reminded Suzue of their parting at Narita airport. He had waited for her to say words of love back to him, but she had not done so till it was too late. Perhaps Sachi was right; it was the last straw and he had just given up on her.

"I was so sure about both of you and that you had finally found your match, Suzue," Tomoko sighed. "Maybe he's sick…. or even dead?"

"Thanks for giving me the chance to gloat over his death," Suzue replied wryly. "But no, if he were dead, the whole office would be buzzing with news about that! So I'm afraid he's alive and kicking, but he just doesn't want to contact me. I can think of a few reasons why, but I'm not going to go into it.

"I realize from what happened that most women, no matter how smart, how successful and how tough, have gone through this rough patch of waiting for a phone call, an email, a text, anything from her man of the moment— and I say 'moment' because at the end of the day, I still believe that emotions, feelings, love, whatever, are only for as long as they last. Some go on forever, along a rocky or reasonably smooth road, some bomb out after a while. I thought that, because I'm so cynical and tough about men—especially in the romance department—I would escape this. But look at me; over the last few weeks, I've been moping around like a weeping willow tree! It's disgusting but I can't help it!

"But now, enough of that; I've a business and campaigns to run. It was a beautiful roam in the park, while it lasted. The only thing that leaves a bad taste in my mouth is that history is repeating itself, only this time, thank goodness, it's the 21st century and I'm hardly the femme fatale of my mother's era! Doesn't that feel good?"

"Yes, it surely does, but you know, Suzue—dare I say this, but falling in love with Robert has changed you, made you a softer and more tolerant person," Sachi said. "You used to be a pure spitfire female version of macho! Don't get me wrong, you're still a force to be reckoned with at work and still so darn good no one wants to cross you, but on a personal level, you've become more human, less judgmental and harsh about weaknesses in others, and that's not a bad thing at all!

"Even the tone of your workshops has changed. You used to be all out to get the guys, and that made some women uncomfortable because hey, a lot of them out there still believe in love, marriage, relationships, children and families. And no matter how much you fight against it, women have always, whether openly or secretly, desired the perfect relationship. That's why, after a bad fall, they still get up to try again and again!

"Now, in your workshops, you tell women that they can

want all those things and still be smart, successful and be all they can. That is what a lot of them want to hear. They want to learn how to achieve a work/life balance and be as successful as you are. You're the skirt in the boardroom that a lot of talented and well-educated young women want to emulate, and this new you gets the message across much better and more effectively than your old 'fight till you drop dead' stance," Sachi continued. "Remember that time you asked me to speak at one of your workshops and I told your bunch of aspiring women professionals and mentees that they could wear skirts, stilettos, and make up galore and still be awesome and successful in their own rights? You were mad at me for days because I went further and said they could be the Suzue Tanakas of Japan and still be feminine, since the whole idea was to be women wearing skirts and be successful and not to be women having to wear the pants and trying to be masculine and swear like a man in order to succeed. The message is to succeed as women not as women pretending to be men!"

"Thanks for that long speech extolling my virtues! But I assure you there's still a lot of spitfire left in this old girl yet!" Suzue laughed. "And to think I was wondering why my workshop audience has swelled to almost full house recently! You're right, of course, Sachi. I was this cynical, bitter, twisted person who forgot not every woman has shared the same experiences as me and so it would be unfair to impose my rhetoric of man-bashing and two-year expiration dates on them — although I still very firmly believe that men need a beating on a professional level!"

"Well, I think that some of the fault lies in the women themselves as well," Emi said. "You can't expect a company, for instance, to spend tons of money training a woman to be top executive material when, if at the end of the day, all she wants is to quit after getting married and become a full time home-maker. What happens then? All that training goes to waste.

"I've seen it happen. A female colleague of mine, very smart and very highly educated, was slated to head our current affairs department and the company spent a lot of money on her training, including overseas stints. Then, one year into her post, she gets married and resigns! Even I felt the pain of all that training and resources gone to waste! Although I fully support equal professional rights for women, in this case, I can actually empathize with the company and their rationale that they would have been better off investing their resources on training a man."

"Absolutely!" Suzue agreed. "You know, through all the emotional shenanigans of the last few months, I have come to realize that it's women in Japan who have to change their mindset before they can shout and scream about society and employers not giving them equal opportunities and responsibilities. My workshops in the past haven't really been delivering the right message because I was using them to work out my own issues against the men who I imagined had 'wronged' me—my deserter father and men like Mori, who used me.

"I conveniently forgot that I used them too because I fleeced large sums of money off Mori and the men of my social escort days to finance the best education that money could buy. I advocated a women-versus-men rhetoric, with minimal trust and aggression all the way, without realizing a barking dog with no bite carries very little weight and can be ridiculed and brushed aside as rabid!

"And then I stop to think: What makes people take all my quirkiness and my non-conformist, loud-mouthed bluntness? I'm even the wrong gender! It's not for love of me, for God's sake! It's because I'm good and I'm totally committed to my work. They can hate me all they want but they can't ignore the fact that I have carried away some of the most coveted industry awards and a lot of the most blue blooded corporations in Japan pay to buy my ideas. I am very firmly seated in the boardroom of my company because my high net worth clients want me there!

"I've learned and changed the style of my workshops, and I urge women to make themselves so indispensable that they cannot be ignored or sidetracked. Above all, don't take the back seat anymore, go for the front seat! And always remember when you seek and gain recognition, there are responsibilities that go with it. You cannot walk away from those responsibilities, even if you make the decision to get married, be in a relationship, have children, whatever."

"You have become a good mentor lately, Suzue. Look at all those ambitious young graduate women who go to your workshops, disillusioned because all they can get are temp or going nowhere jobs, and they come away after a few sessions totally renewed and armed with referrals to your vast network of potential employers, some of whom no doubt owe you a favor or two! Do you know how many women you've helped land good jobs?"

"Remember Mayuri from creative and her incredible ad creations?" Suzue said. "I hired her when no one would give her a serious job with prospects. I saw the talent in her and the same burning desire to make it that I had, so I gave her a chance. Three years on, she is the most outstanding creative director on my team and true to her word — a marriage and a baby later — she is still with me, putting in as much as she did before! This is what I want to see happening to women in Japan!

"But, hey, let's stop talking about me! As my grandma once said, 'always remember that the world doesn't revolve around you alone,' — words of wisdom I constantly try to drum into the heads of this modern "me" generation! What has been happening to all of you?" Suzue said. "I've been so absorbed in my work and the Roger Carlista/Robert Darcey dramas that I haven't spent enough time catching up with you guys."

"Well, work has never been better. We're taking our next line to Milan this year and when all that excitement and euphoria dies down, the killer work will start. There will be the usual hair-tearing despair, bursts of sunshine tempered with tantrums, frayed nerves and the coffee machines will be whirring nonstop — but you know what, it's the kiss of life for me," Sachi said. "O.K, O.K., I know you all want to know what's up with Jun and me. Remember Jun, the omiai guy? You probably know this already, but we've been staying in touch and seeing each other, not because we want to add success stories to the wretched omiai system, but simply because we have similar visions and feel comfortable with each other. We're good in bed when the mood seizes us but we have absolutely no plans to hitch up. In fact, the other day, we had a talk and decided that the best way to beat boredom and losing the spark is marry late, and I mean real late, like into our 40s. That way, we wouldn't have much time left to get bored with each other!"

"Good thinking! Imagine, if you marry in your twenties as most Japanese women are still doing, by the time you reach your 40s, you would have been together doing the same things day in and out for 20 years! The age of 40 is when it's said women peak sexually, you'd come home to a husband or a husband comes home to you and doesn't even notice if you go out with him with curlers in your hair. He'd consider marital bliss to be a bottle of whisky or a can of beer and flopping on your precious sofa to snore away any illusions of romance and passionately ever after!"

"Well said, Sachi, I couldn't agree more although this trend is not helping Japan's appalling birth rate," Tomoko added. "My gynaecologist was going into a whole rant the other day about how selfish women have become to let their eggs shrivel away before deciding to try half-heartedly for a baby. I thought I had better agree because he had my legs in stirrups and an awesome instrument up my intimate part! Then he did an ultrasonic examination of my ovaries and grumbled that I had so few good eggs left!"

"Is yours considered a successful match in the omiai scheme of things? Or has it got to be a piece of paper signed and sealed, complete with temple wedding ceremonial rites?" Suzue asked Sachi when their laughter had died down.

"I haven't the faintest idea," Sachi replied. "But if the paper has to be signed and sealed, given our belief that marriage for us, if ever, would have to wait till we are in the 40s, our poor omiai will have to wait a long, long time to consider it a done deal! Jun was commenting the other day that when we return to our hometown, we both might have to go into hiding!"

"What about you, Tomoko? Will Michael be making an honest woman of you?" Suzue quipped, knowing her question would irk the "male superiority" allergic Tomoko.

"You must mean if I have decided to make an honest man of Michael?" Tomoko retorted, predictably peeved. "No, we've decided to leave the 'knots untied' so that we'll have to continue pleasing each other and not get into a marital rut, but we're not averse to making honest people out of each other when the time is right. Strange though this may sound, we want children. And my parents are so desperate for grandchildren they are prepared to take the burden of child caring off us so that I can continue to practice law as vigorously as ever. As things stand, they will welcome any grandchild — whether born in or out of wedlock — so that's encouraging to our breeding plans!"

"You should have seen my poor, one hundred percent pure

traditional Japanese mother cringe when she promised me her child-caring services if I could just get my baby machines cranking! When all was said and done, she actually attributed the departure from her hitherto diehard belief in the marriage, then children, to having to play her part to prop up our nation's plunging birthrate! My poor mother! The world and society, even in Japan, is changing too fast for her!"

"What about you, Emi?"

"Everything has been amazing! My stories on Africa appealed to the powers that be so much they are doing a three-part documentary and I've negotiated for myself to have the presenter and narrator's role," Emi replied. "You're so right about women being afraid to step forward, to be the first to raise her hand. That was me before, but now I refuse to take a backseat. They wanted to put some guy as presenter and narrator but I told them there'd be no African stories unless I'm slated to present the stories myself."

"Wait, there is more! Do you know my mother started to do volunteer work with two of her equally bored and aimless 'high tea' friends and, as with any new project, she immediately went into overdrive! This current obsession has hijacked her attention from me so there wasn't much of a fuss when I moved out last week. It's heaven to have my own space and apartment; I can even think about having Sumi over to stay during school breaks! I feel so renewed and empowered by my own financial and emotional independence! This is called coming into your own and being true to yourself!"

An hour later, the four women parted and Suzue took the familiar walk from Harajuku to Shibuya. It was a route she and Robert had often taken and reminded her of his ongoing silence and how much it was hurting her. Perhaps she should just swallow her pride and call him; it was something she would have to think about over the next few days. The fresh night air revived her flagging spirits and Suzue felt better than she had the last few weeks.

*God, why am I moaning and groaning over a man who is keeping me at arm's length? Why on earth am I even waiting for him? Even Emi has become emotionally independent!* she thought, just as her Iphone buzzed. She had a message.

Suzue touched Inbox on the screen automatically and her

heart began to race. Robert Darcey had just sent her an email.

"My darling, is your offer of a long distance relationship still available?" it said.

This time Suzue didn't wait till it was too late. She hit the reply button with one word: "Yes!"

# About The Author

Rei Kimura is a lawyer with a passion for writing about unique events and personalities. She has adopted an interesting style of creating stories around true events and the lives of real people in a number of her books, believing that is the best way of making hidden historical events and people come alive for 21st century readers.

With this objective in mind, Rei has touched on historical events like the horrific sinking of the Awa Maru and the Kamikaze pilots of World War II and woven them into touching stories of the people who lived and died through these events.

Then there are stories of courage, love and rejection beautifully portrayed in "Butterfly In the Wind" a story of the concubine of Townsend Harris, first American consul to Japan, set against the colorful and turbulent era of the Black Ships. This book has touched the hearts of many and been translated into languages from Spanish, Polish, Russian, Dutch to Thai, Hindi, Indonesian, Marathi.

Rei's writing also touches on interesting issues like that raised in "Japanese Magnolia" a book based on the true story of two men, a samurai and a peasant who dared to cross two forbidden areas in feudal Japan, that of homosexuality and a class society "so sharply defined it cut like a knife."

Other controversial stories she has written include "Japanese Rose" a book which asked the question was there ever a Japanese female kamikaze pilot in the Second World War?

But it's not all history and culture, she also writes on contemporary events like "Aum Shinrikyo-Japan's Unholy Sect" an expose of the 1995 sarin gas attack on the Tokyo subway. Occasionally, her love for animals and sense of humor surfaces in this very heartwarming and delightful story of a rogue Pomeranian dog, "My Name is Eric," a complete departure from Rei's normal story lines but nevertheless, a refreshing one!

Kimura considers her writing as part of the perennial quest for truth, challenge and fulfillment. Her books have been translated into various Asian and European languages and widely read all over the world.

Apart from being a lawyer, Rei Kimura is also a qualified freelance journalist and is associated with the Australian News Syndicate.

*****

Thank you for reading Onna Rising. If you liked this book – or any other of our releases –, please consider rating this book at the online retailer of your choice. Your ratings and reviews are appreciated by the author and will help other readers find new favorites.

Visit www.demarchepublishing.com for more interesting titles.

# Onna Rising

CPSIA information can be obtained at www.ICGtesting.com
Printed in the USA
LVOW13s1528240314

378711LV00001B/266/P